HOME REFRIGERATION AND AIR CONDITIONING

by Edwin P. Anderson

THEODORE AUDEL & CO.
a division of
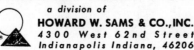
HOWARD W. SAMS & CO., INC.
4300 West 62nd Street
Indianapolis Indiana, 46206

Foreword

In writing this book, the purpose throughout has been to prepare a helpful service guide that offers useful information covering all phases of modern household mechanical refrigeration and air conditioning. The text covers specialized tools used in servicing refrigeration and air conditioning equipment, plus trouble charts for diagnosis of common everyday troubles.

Although the general design and control methods used in modern equipment resemble, in many respects, those previously employed, numerous improvements have been made. These improvements have resulted in more efficient and compact units that require less space and maintenance. Thus, for example, the hermetically sealed motor compressor has replaced the so-called open or belt-driven type of condensing unit. Also, the capillary tube is used for refrigerant control, in most cases, instead of the expansion valve, because of the simplicity and freedom from operational troubles.

The material in this book has been carefully organized so as to give you a practical understanding of the construction, operation, and servicing of modern electric and gas refrigerators and

Foreword

air conditioners. Before you can successfully diagnose and remedy any trouble, you must be familiar with the theory of refrigeration and air conditioning and have a good working knowledge of the purpose, design, and operation of all parts.

EDWIN P. ANDERSON

Contents

Contents

Contents

Cooling capacity—refrigeration cycle—capacity requirements—installation method—electrical components—thermostats—control switch—compressor and motor—refrigerant system—trouble chart

CHAPTER 1

Fundamentals of Refrigeration

As far back as history records the activities of the human race, we find that one of the greatest concerns of mankind has been the preservation of foods. In the earlier periods this amounted solely to preservation of grains which were harvested in times of plenty and were stored for use during periods of drought. However, as man learned the values of the various meats and vegetables as foods, he also became interested in their preservation.

The earliest attempts at preserving foods consisted of storing them in caves where the temperature remained lower than the outside air. Other methods of preserving meats, fish, fruits, and vegetables consisted of drying, smoking, dehydrating, pickling, and cooking. Some of these methods are employed today even among the most advanced peoples. The disadvantages of these methods lie in the loss of natural freshness, moisture, and flavor, as well as a considerable loss of the nutritive value of the foods.

Refrigeration, in the true sense of the word, was first employed by the Romans, Greeks, and Egyptians, who cooled water and wines in crude vessels made of porous material which extracted a small amount of heat by evaporation. The first methods of cooling foods for preservation consisted of either placing the foods in vessels immersed in streams of cool water or storing them in holes in the ground.

The ice box came into use early in the nineteenth century. Natural ice was used. The melting of the ice absorbed some of the heat of the foods and reduced the temperature considerably inside the box. This represented a marked degree of improvement over former and more crude methods of preserving foods.

The next important development in household refrigeration was the introduction of manufactured ice. From 1830 to 1870 considerable progress was made in the development of machines for producing artificial ice commercially. The use of these machines made pure ice available in even the warmest of climates, and in dependable quantities. At about the same time, some improvements in the construction of household refrigerators were made. More attention was given to better construction, sanitary linings, and better insulations. This made it possible to maintain refrigerator temperatures from 20 to 30 degrees below room temperature and preserve foods for a considerable length of time. The domestic or household refrigerating machine has been under development for many years. However, since 1923 this type of machine has been manufactured in large quantities and has proven a commercial success. Today, this type of machine is no longer considered a luxury, but is regarded as a necessity by all people of our age. The increasing volume of sales in mechanical refrigerating equipment has greatly reduced the market for manufactured ice.

APPLICATIONS OF REFRIGERATION

Food preservation is the largest application of mechanical refrigeration today. Without modern refrigerating machinery the packing house industry, the transportation of perishable foods, and the preparation of many other edibles would not only be difficult, but in many cases almost impossible. Refrigeration has not only saved quantities of meat, fish, eggs, milk, and cream from spoilage, it has also played an important part in the diet revision of the world. No longer are the inhabitants of one hemisphere, country or locality dependent upon local foods, but many draw upon the entire world as a source. This has made possible great developments in agriculture and livestock raising in countries far distant from potential markets. It has permitted the utilization of the great productivity of the tropics in supplying fruits and foods for other parts of the world.

Nearly all of the industries involved in the preparation of foods and drinks make extensive use of artificial ice or mechanical refrigeration. The dairy industry, for example finds that for precooling milk and cream, and in the manufacture of butter and ice cream, refrigeration is indispensable. In many industries, the cooling and conditioning of air is an important phase of the manufacturing process. Among these processes may be mentioned the manufacture of photographic films, explosives, the machine production of cigars and cigarettes, candy and chewing gum, and rayon. They are important users of refrigeration, not only because of their size, but also because of their dependence on conditioned air for successful operation.

The cooling of liquids plays an important part in the mechanical and chemical industries. Oil-tempering baths are kept at constant low temperatures through refrigeration, and in the jackets of nitrators and mixing machines for the celluloid, smokeless powder, and rubber industries, cooled brines are used to keep the mixtures at the correct temperatures. In the chemical industry, the use of refrigeration for drying air and gases and for the purification of solutions by means of crystallization at definite temperatures is steadily increasing.

PHYSICAL UNITS

In order to obtain a clear conception in regard to the functioning of mechanical refrigeration systems, it is imperative to understand the physical and thermal properties underlying the production of artificial cold.

Practical Dimensions—Common measures of length are:

$$12 \text{ inches} = 1 \text{ foot}$$
$$3 \text{ feet} = 1 \text{ yard}$$
$$5{,}280 \text{ feet} = 1 \text{ mile}$$

Fig. 1 illustrates the relations between inches, feet, and yards.

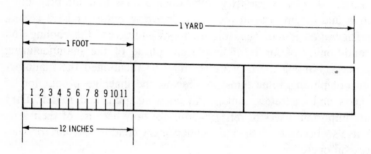

Fig. 1. Illustrating the relations between inches, feet, and yards.

Square Measure—Common measures of area are:

$$144 \text{ square inches} = 1 \text{ square foot}$$
$$9 \text{ square feet} = 1 \text{ square yard}$$

Fig. 2 illustrates the relation between a square foot and a square yard.

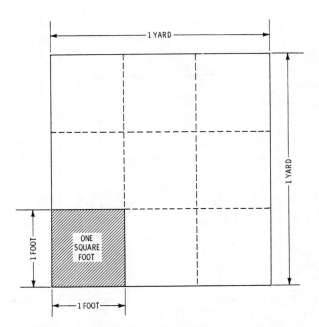

Fig. 2. Illustrating the relations between a square foot and a square yard.

Cubic Measure or Measure of Solids—Common measurements of three dimensional space or volume are:

$$1,728 \text{ cubic inches} = 1 \text{ cubic foot}$$
$$27 \text{ cubic feet} = 1 \text{ cubic yard}$$

Fig. 3 illustrates the relation of one cubic foot compared to one cubic yard.

Mass—The quantity of matter which a body contains is called its *mass*. The space a body occupies is called its *volume*. The relative quantity of matter contained in a given volume is called its

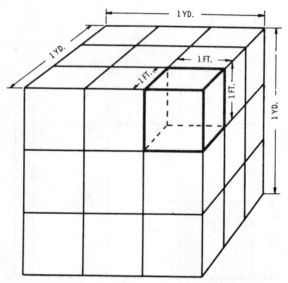

Fig. 3. Showing relative amount of space occupied by a cubic foot as compared to a cubic yard.

density. The relation of volume to mass is expressed by the term density, and is written:

1. density $= \dfrac{\text{mass}}{\text{volume}}$.
2. mass = density × volume
3. volume $= \dfrac{\text{mass}}{\text{density}}$

The relative density of a substance is the ratio of its density to the density of pure water at a temperature of approximately 40°F.

Specific Gravity—This is the ratio between the weight of a given volume of any substance and the weight of the same volume of

14

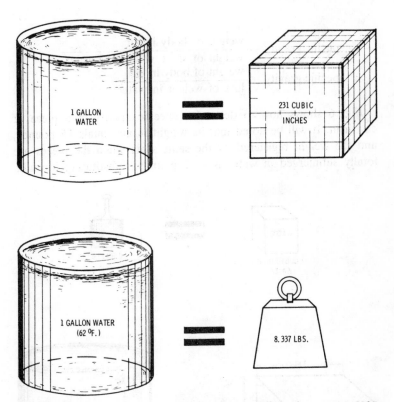

Fig. 4. Illustrating volume and weight of one gallon of water at 62°F.

some other substance taken as a standard. For solids and liquids, this standard is distilled water at a temperature of 39.2°F. Fig. 4 illustrates the volume and weight of one gallon of water at 62°F. In Fig. 5, the weight of one cubic inch of water is compared with one cubic foot. For gases and vapors, some substance must be taken that is in itself a gas, and so the standard for air is *hydrogen*. For solids and liquids, therefore:

1. specific gravity $= \dfrac{\text{weight of body in air}}{\text{weight of same volume of water}}$

2. specific gravity $= \dfrac{\text{weight of body in air}}{\text{loss of weight in water}}$

Fig. 6 shows how to determine specific gravity of a piece of cast iron. It will be noted that its weight in air equals 15 pounds, and the weight registered by the same scale when the pieces are totally submerged in water is 12.9 pounds. Substituting formula,

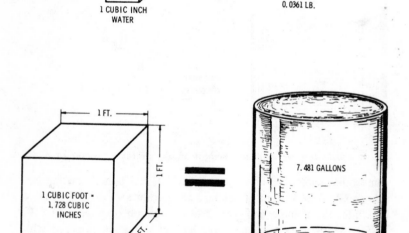

Fig. 5. Showing weight of one cubic inch of water and volume of one cubic foot.

$$\text{specific gravity} = \frac{W}{W\text{-}w} = \frac{15}{15\text{-}12.9} = 7.18$$

ATMOSPHERIC, ABSOLUTE, AND GAUGE PRESSURES

It is of the utmost importance that the refrigeration student understand the meaning of the various kinds of pressure as related to refrigeration.

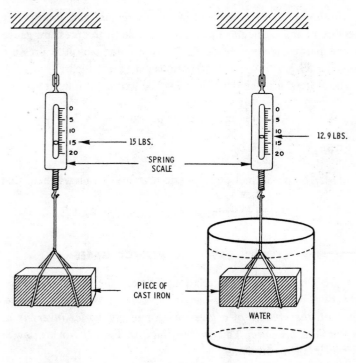

Fig. 6. Illustrating the specific gravity of a piece of cast iron in air and in water.

Atmospheric Pressure

Atmospheric pressure is that pressure which is exerted by the atmosphere in all directions, as indicated by a barometer. Standard atmospheric pressure is considered to be 14.695 pounds per square inch (usually written 14.7) which is equivalent to 29.92 inches of mercury.

Absolute Pressure

Absolute pressure is the sum of gauge pressure and atmospheric pressure at any particular time. For example, if the pressure gauge at one particular time reads 53.7 pounds, the absolute pressure would be 53.7 + 14.7, or 68.4 pounds per square inch.

The aforementioned definitions may be written as follows:

$$\text{Abs. pressure} = \text{gauge pressure} + 14.7$$

where

14.7 is the normal atmospheric pressure it follows then, that

$$\text{Gauge pressure} = \text{abs. pressure} - 14.7$$

BOYLE'S LAW FOR PERFECT GASES

Boyle's law refers to the relations between the pressure and volume of a gas and may be stated as follows: *With temperatures constant, the volume of a given weight of gas varies inversely as its absolute pressure.* This is illustrated in Fig. 7. Boyle's law is written mathematically as

$$P_1V_1 = P_2V_2$$

or,

$$\frac{V_1}{V_2} = \frac{P_2}{P_1}$$

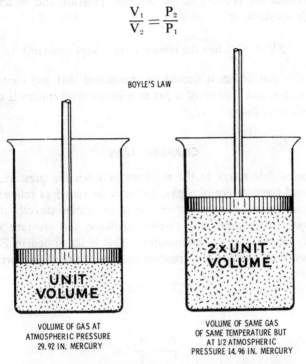

BOYLE'S LAW

VOLUME OF GAS AT
ATMOSPHERIC PRESSURE
29. 92 IN. MERCURY

VOLUME OF SAME GAS
OF SAME TEMPERATURE BUT
AT 1/2 ATMOSPHERIC
PRESSURE 14. 96 IN. MERCURY

Fig. 7. Illustrating Boyle's law for a perfect gas.

where,

P_1 = absolute pressure of a quantity of perfect gas before a
pressure change.

P_2 = absolute pressure after pressure change.

V_1 = volume of gas at pressure P_1.

V_2 = volume of gas at pressure P_2.

Since P_1V_1 for any given case is a definite constant quantity, it follows that the product of the absolute pressure and volume of a gas is constant, or

$$PV = C \text{ (when the temperature is kept constant)}$$

In this connection it should be mentioned that any change in the pressure and volume of a gas at constant temperature is called an *isothermal change*.

CHARLES' LAW

Charles' law refers to the relations between the pressure, volume, and temperature of a gas, and may be stated as follows: *At a constant pressure, the volume of a gas varies directly as the absolute temperature; at a constant volume, the pressure varies directly as the absolute temperature.* This is illustrated in Fig. 8.

When heat is added to a constant volume, the relation is written:

$$P_1T_2 = P_2T_1$$

or,

$$\frac{P_1}{P_2} = \frac{T_1}{T_2}$$

For the same temperature range at a constant pressure:

$$V_1T_2 = V_2T_1$$

or,

$$\frac{V_1}{V_2} = \frac{T_1}{T_2}$$

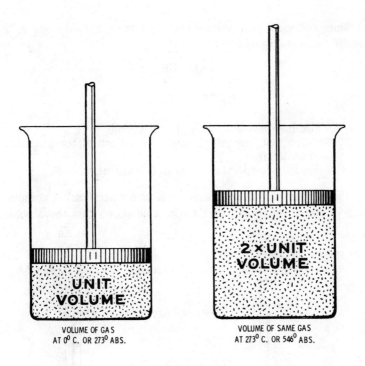

VOLUME OF GAS
AT 0° C. OR 273° ABS.

VOLUME OF SAME GAS
AT 273° C. OR 546° ABS.

PRESSURE UNCHANGED

Fig. 8. Illustrating Charles' law for a perfect gas.

Combined, these laws read:

$$P_1 V_1 T_2 = P_2 V_2 T_1$$

or,

$$\frac{P_1 V_1}{T_1} = \frac{P_2 V_2}{T_2}$$

21

Since volume is proportional to weight, the relation among **P, V,** and **T** for any weight of gas **W,** is:

$$PV=WRT$$

where,

P = absolute pressure of the gas in pounds
R = a constant, depending upon the nature of the gas under consideration
T = absolute temperature in degrees Fahrenheit

Fig. 9 illustrates the absolute units of temperature. A comparison of the absolute and centigrade scale shows that the absolute

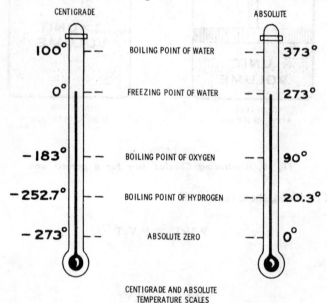

CENTIGRADE AND ABSOLUTE
TEMPERATURE SCALES

Fig. 9. Illustrating absolute units of temperature.

temperature has its zero at 273°C below the freezing point of water. Zero degree centigrade would therefore be 273° absolute. The 10° centigrade would represent 283° absolute temperature.

POWER AND WORK

Power may be defined as the capability of performing mechanical work as measured by the rate at which it is or can be done. Stated in the simplest possible language, *power is the rate of doing work*. If a horse, as shown in Fig. 10, pulls a weight of 220 pounds against gravity at the rate of 2.5 feet per second, and if the friction in the pulling arrangement is neglected, the horse will

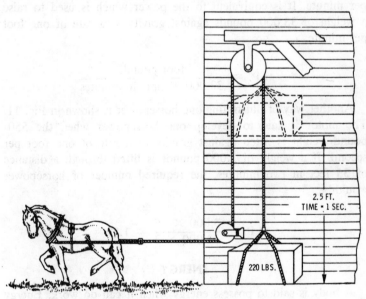

2.5 FT.
TIME = 1 SEC.

220 LBS.

Fig. 10. Illustrating the meaning of one horsepower.

develop one horsepower. The work done in a given time divided by the units of time gives *the average rate of doing work, or the power.*

It may be written:

$$Power = \frac{work}{time}$$

UNITS OF POWER

The most commonly used units of power are the foot pounds per unit time, and horsepower. The horsepower is the rate of doing work at 550 foot pounds per second or 33,000 foot pounds per minute. It is equivalent to the power which is used to raise a weight of 33,000 pounds against gravity at a rate of one foot per minute.

$$H.P. = \frac{foot\ pounds}{33,000 \times time\ in\ minutes}$$

Another way of illustrating one horsepower is shown in Fig. 11. The motor is said to develop one horsepower when the 550-pound weight is lifted against gravity at a rate of one foot per second. If a weight of 3,000 pounds is lifted through a distance of 35 feet in two minutes, the required number of horsepower would be:

$$H.P. = \frac{3.000 \times 35}{33,000 \times 2} = 1.59$$

ENERGY

A body is said to possess energy when it can do work. Energy exists in various forms, such as:

1. Mechanical energy
2. Electrical energy
3. Heat energy (thermal)

Other well known forms are *kinetic* and *potential energy*.

Energy may be transmitted from one form to another by various processes, such as mechanical, thermal, chemical, or electrical, but the energy lost or gained is either kinetic or potential. If the process is mechanical, such as impact, compression, or the application of a mechanical force, work is done. If it is thermal, radiation, or conduction, then heat is added or withdrawn. There are very simple relations that exist between mechanical, electrical, and heat energy. These relationships may be written as follows:

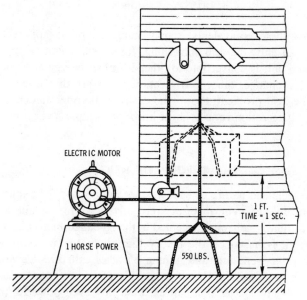

Fig. 11. Another illustration of one horsepower.

1 British thermal unit (Btu) =	778 foot pounds
2546 British thermal units (Btu) =	1 horsepower-hour
39,685 British thermal units (Btu) =	1 kg. calorie
746 watts =	1 horsepower

Other equivalents are:

1 Btu = 0.001036 lb. of water evaporated at 212° F.
0.0000688 lb. of carbon oxidized
0.000393 horsepower-hour
107.6 kg. meters
778 foot pounds
1,055 watt seconds

From these equivalents it may immediately be apparent that heat is an entity, a real something, for it has a unit of measure, and each unit is convertible to other forms of energy at a constant rate of exchange. Since refrigeration is an art that is concerned with the heat problem, those who desire a thorough understanding of the refrigeration process must know the simple facts concerning heat.

THEORY OF HEAT

The technical nature of heat was not understood for a long time, and several different theories were advanced to explain it. The concept that is generally accepted is the so-called *molecular theory* because it is based on the theory that all matter is composed of innumerable, separate, and minute particles called *molecules*. The molecule is so minute that it is considered the smallest independent particle of matter that can exist, so tiny even powerful microscopes cannot reveal it.

Molecular Theory

The molecular theory is based on the supposition that the molecules of a substance are not attached to each other by any bond or cement, but are held together by a force known as cohesion or mutual attraction, a phenomenon somewhat similar to the attraction offered by a magnet for steel particles. The molecules, however, are not physically bound or in contact with each other, like the iron filings, but are actually separated to such an extent in some instances (and usually so at more elevated temperatures) that the space separating two adjoining molecules is larger than either particle. Furthermore, the molecules are not fixed or stationary, but revolve and vibrate within the orbits or limits of their allotted space.

Each substance on this earth is composed of different ingredients or various combinations of molecules and therefore each particular kind and mixture, together with additional peculiarities in physical assembly, have a structure differing from other materials. It is the rapidity of the motion of the molecules composing a body or mass that determines the intensity of its heat. As a specific example to point out the connection between the theory of heat and the molecular theory, a bar of lead may be used for illustration. When cold, the molecules undergo comparatively slow motion. But if the bar is heated, the molecular activity becomes more rapid, until its temperature has been increased to a point where molecular motion becomes so rapid and the individual particles so far separated from each other that, with further assimilation of heat, they become so weakly cohesive they no longer can hold the body in a rigid or solid mass, and it devolves into a liquid.

Further application of heat forces the molecules to greater separation and speeds up their motion to such an extent that the liquid becomes more mobile and volatilization finally results, so that a gas or vapor is produced. The vapor thus formed no longer has a definite volume, such as it had in either the solid or molten (liquid) form, but will expand and completely fill any space that is provided for it. The vapor, of course, contains the same number of molecules that were in the original solid, but with the difference that molecular action is extremely active in the vapor phase, comparatively slow in the instance of the liquid, and slowest in the solid form. The motion of the molecule is somewhat like a bicycle rider; at a slow speed a very small orbit can be adhered to, but with each advance in the rate of travel, larger orbits are required.

To one learning the theory of heat and matter for the first time, it may appear extremely complex. Whether the molecular theory herein described (which is the one accepted by leading scientists), or any other theory is used as a basis of explanation, the facts regarding heat as we know it are in agreement with the molecular theory, and from all tangible proof substantiate the theory in all respects. One of the simplest indications of value in support of the molecular theory is the age-old knowledge concerning expansion and contraction, caused respectively by heat and cold, or, as we look at it from the molecular theory, the rate of molecular activity.

Temperature

Heat and temperature are closely allied, but it must be remembered that heat is energy itself representing the kinetic activity of the molecules composing a substance, while temperature is but a measure of the condition of a mass or body, as it affects our ideas of warmth or cold. Heat is convertible into electrical, chemical, or mechanical energy.

Our ideas of cold and hot are merely ranges of temperature that affect our sense of relative feeling, which we term hot and cold. In a way, heat itself may be likened to water, for of its own accord, it will only flow downhill; that is, it will pass from the hotter (or higher) range of temperature to the colder (or lower) plane.

Two miscible liquids poured together will find their own temperature level, as will a solid and a liquid, or even two solids in intimate contact. For instance, if an ice cube is dropped into a tumbler of tepid water, it will be found that the colder substance will be able to assimilate a certain quantity of heat from the warmer substance. Thus, through this extraction, we find that the water has been cooled or reduced in temperature. Two substances of different temperatures in intimate contact tend to reach an equilibrium or balance by the dispersion of heat by one body and assimilation of heat by the colder. If a thermometer is placed in contact with the substance, the degree or level of its temperature, or the measure of the intensity of its heat, will be indicated.

THERMOMETERS

The instrument in common use for measuring temperature, known as the thermometer, operates on the principle of the expansion and contraction of liquids (and solids) under varying intensities of heat. The ordinary mercury thermometer operates with a fair degree of accuracy over a wide range. It becomes useless, however, where temperatures below $-38°F.$ are to be indicated, because mercury freezes at that point. Some other liquid, such as alcohol (usually colored for easy observation) must be substituted. The upper range for mercurial thermometers is quite high, about $900°F.$, so it is apparent that for ordinary service and general use the mercury thermometer is usually applicable.

The operation of the thermometer depends on the effect of heat on the main body of mercury or alcohol contained in a bulb or reservoir. The liquid will expand or contract (rise or drop) in the capillary tube which is inscribed with the various increments of an arbitrary scale, as shown in Fig. 12. Several thermometer scales are in existence and are used in various countries. The

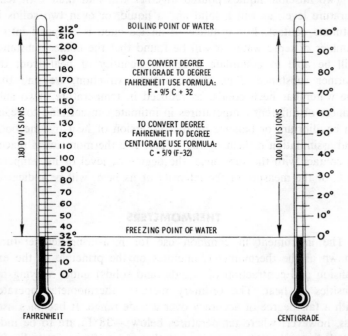

Fig. 12. Illustrating the relation between a Fahrenheit and Centigrade temperature scale.

English or Fahrenheit scale is commonly used in this country. Since the Centigrade scale is so widely used in scientific work in all countries, an illustration of the comparison of thermometers is presented so that any one scale may be converted to another.

The freezing point on the Fahrenheit scale is fixed at 32°. On the Centigrade scale, freezing is placed at zero degrees. On the

Fahrenheit scale, the boiling point of pure water under the normal pressure encountered at sea level is 212°; on the Centigrade scale, 100° is the boiling point.

For instance, if it is desired to convert 50° Centigrade to Fahrenheit, the method would be in accordance with the following formula:

$$F = \frac{9}{5} C + 32$$

Therefore,

$$50 \times 9/5 + 32 = 122° \text{ F.}$$

As previously stated, temperature is a measurement of the intensity of the heat contained in a body, accomplished by means of a thermometer, just as a yardstick is used to measure the length of a body. A thermometer will not, however, indicate the quantity or amount of heat contained in a body.

ABSOLUTE ZERO

In the study of thermometer scales, the question of thermal limits is naturally considered. From the molecular theory we are led to believe that with the removal of heat, molecular action is slowed down accordingly. It must naturally follow that, at some point, all heat will be removed and molecular activity will cease entirely.

The calculation in Fig. 13 indicates that absolute zero is attained at a temperature of 460° below zero on the Fahrenheit scale. Temperatures as low as this have never been reached, although in some instances it has been approached within a few tenths of one degree. Bodies subjected to extremely low temperatures take on characteristics entirely different from those exhibited under normal conditions.

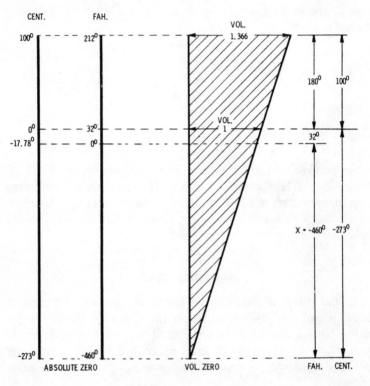

Fig. 13. Diagrammatical illustration of how absolute zero temperature may be determined.

This calculation is based upon the fact that atmospheric air expands 0.366 of its volume on being heated from 32° to 212°F.

It can therefore be assumed inversely, if all possible heat were withdrawn, the volume of air would shrink to zero. With reference to our diagram, the volume of air at 32°F=1. It follows that the volume of air at 212°F=1.366. Constructing our triangles as shown, the following relations are obtained:

$$\frac{32 - \times}{212 - \times} = \frac{1}{1.366}$$

$$\times = \frac{1.366 \times 32 - 212}{0.366} = -460° \text{ F.}$$

UNITS OF HEAT

The quantity of heat contained in a body is not measurable by thermometer which indicates only the temperature or intensity. For example, a gallon of water and a pint of water may have the same temperature, but we are certainly aware that the larger body must have more heat as energy within it, than the smaller.

The unit of heat measure employed in this country is called the British thermal unit, more commonly referred to as the Btu and it is that quantity of heat required to be added to one pound of pure water initially at a temperature of its greatest density (that is 39°F.) to raise its temperature one degree on the Fahrenheit thermometer (in this case to 40°F.). Roughly, a Btu may be said to be the quantity of heat required to raise the temperature of one pound of water one degree on the Fahrenheit scale. This is shown in Fig. 14.

Just as the thermometer is used as a measure of the intensity of the heat of a body, the Btu is used to represent the quantitative energy. For instance, one body at 50°F. may contain twice as many Btu's as another body at the same temperature, because the bodies may be different in size or weight and, of great importance, may have different capacities for absorbing heat.

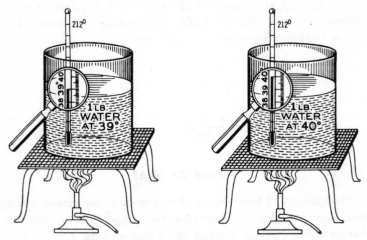

Fig. 14. Showing the unit of heat or Btu.

SPECIFIC HEAT

It could be said that each and every substance on the earth has a different capacity for absorbing heat. Some identical materials, especially natural formations, even give different values for samples secured in different localities. As an illustration of the difference in the heat capacities of materials, let us consider a pound of iron and a pound of water, both at 80°F. If the heat is removed from these bodies and the number of Btu's extracted in cooling each mass to the same temperature is recorded, it will be found that each will give up a different amount. If each body had been at a temperature of 80°F., and was cooled to 60° (a reduction of 20° on the Fahrenheit scale), it would be found that 1 pound of water at 80° cooled to 60° would evolve 20 heat units or 20 Btu.

If the iron (of the same weight) is cooled over the same range, only 2.6 Btu will be extracted (approximately 1/8 of that taken from the same weight of water under identical conditions). We therefore come to the conclusion that all materials absorb heat in different capacities, and by comparing the heat absorbing qualities with a standard, we have a standard of measure, a gauge to compare all substances. This measure is the amount of heat expressed in Btu's required by one pound of a substance to change its temperature one degree Fahrenheit. Since water has a very large heat capacity, it has been taken as a standard, and since one pound of water requires one Btu to raise its temperature one degree, its rating on the specific-heat scale is 1.00. Iron has a lower specific heat, its average rating being 0.130; that of ice, 0.504; of air, 0.238; and of wood, 0.330. The more water an object contains, as in the case of fresh food or air, the higher the specific heat. Materials usually stored in a refrigerator have a high specific heat, averaging about 0.80.

Table 1 lists the average specific heats of a number of common substances. With this table, their relative heat capacities can be compared with water. Observe that metals have limited heat storing powers as compared with water. This is one of the reasons why scalds from hot water burn so deeply, for the water contains so much heat energy that a considerable amount is released and

Table 1. Average Specific Heats

Water	1.000	Pine	0.650
Copper	0.900	Strong brine	0.700
Vinegar	0.920	Oak	0.570
Alcohol	0.659	Ice	0.504
Air	0.238	Glass	0.194
Mercury	0.033	Iron	0.130
Coal	0.241	Sulphur	0.202
Brass	0.094	Zinc	0.095

causes a worse burn than molten metal at a much higher temperature.

In the preceding table, various substances are listed with their average specific values, and by finding this factor, the amount of heat in Btu to be added or taken from a substance of known weight to bring about a change of one degree in its temperature may be calculated.

Specific heat problems may be calculated easily by use of the following formula:

British thermal units $=$ Sp. heat $\times$ W$(t_2\text{-}t_1)$.

Where

$$W = \text{weight of the substance in pounds.}$$
$$\text{Sp. heat} = \text{specific heat of the substance to be heated.}$$
$$t_2\text{-}t_1 = \text{temperature change in deg. F.}$$

Where very accurate scientific work is done, certain allowances are made for the fact that the specific heat of a substance does not remain constant throughout the entire temperature range. Since the difference is not appreciable (except over a long range), the refrigerating engineer usually regards the specific-heat factor as a constant. Other materials, such as liquids and gases, also have specific heats. However, the calculations concerning the heat capacities of gases are further complicated by the pressures as well as the varying temperatures imposed. Despite the tendency to ignore the variance in specific heat and to employ a constant, the values of water are given as follows in Table 2.

The specific heat of various foods and their containers are of interest to the refrigerating engineer in estimating the amount of heat to be extracted in cooling a refrigerator load. The heat that can be felt and detected is termed the *sensible heat*, its name

Table 2. Specific Heats of Water
(Value at 55° F., taken as unity)

Temp. °F.	Spec. Heat	Temp. °F.	Spec. Heat
20	1.0168	140	0.9986
30	1.0098	160	1.0002
40	1.0045	180	1.0019
50	1.0012	200	1.0039
60	0.9990	220	1.007
70	0.9977	240	1.012
80	0.9970	260	1.018
90	0.9967	280	1.023
100	0.9967	300	1.029

denoting it as the heat we can sense or feel and so preventing confusion with other heats. It is the sensible heat which forms the preponderance of the heat load the refrigerating machine is called on to remove in cooling most edibles. Of course ice manufacturing plants and other storage warehouses which freeze edibles are additionally concerned with other heat problems.

Most foods have a high water content and, therefore, a large heat capacity, averaging about 0.80. A few foods are listed in Table 3 so that the specific heats of various edibles can be ascertained and the truth of the statement regarding the water content verified. The specific heats listed are those of fresh foods before freezing.

Table 3. Specific Heats of Foods

Food	Spec. Heat	Food	Spec. Heat
Apples	0.92	Eggs	0.76
Beans	0.91	Fish	0.80
Beef	0.75	Grapes	0.92
Butter	0.60	Milk	0.90
Cabbage	0.93	Peaches	0.92
Cheese	0.64	Pork	0.50
Chicken	0.80	Potatoes	0.80
Celery	0.91	Veal	0.70
Cider	0.90	Watermelon	0.92

An estimate of the heat quantities that must be removed from the food and its containers can be easily accomplished. For instance, if we have 1,000 pounds of cider contained in glass bottles having a weight of 75 pounds, which in turn have been packed in pine boxes totaling 50 pounds in weight, the whole shipment being at a temperature of 80°F., the heat in Btu that would have to be extracted to cool these materials to 50°F. can be calculated as follows:

80° − 50° = 30° difference in each case
1,000 pounds of cider having a specific heat of 0.90, cooled over a 30° range = 1,000 × 0.90 × 30 = 27,000 Btu
75 pounds of glass with a specific heat of 0.194, cooled 30° = 75 × 0.194 × 30 = 30 = 436.5 Btu.
50 pounds of pine wood having a specific heat of 0.650 cooled 30° = 50 × 0.650 × 30 = 975 Btu, or a total of 27,000 + 436.5 + 975 = 28,411.5 Btu.

By observing a thermometer immersed in the cider and taking an average reading, we could calculate at any time during the cooling process just how much of the sensible heat had been removed. In fact, we could calculate any heat load of any material by finding the specific heat value and the cooling range, and if we desired to freeze the product (in this specific case, the cider), an additional factor would have to be considered, namely the *latent heat*.

LATENT HEAT

One of the most mystifying laws to the layman is that of latent heat. The word itself, *latent*, expresses it aptly enough, for it means hidden or not apparent. In order to indicate clearly just what latent heat is, an example will be cited, and an illustration shown in Fig. 15.

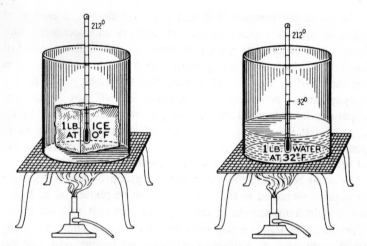

Fig. 15. Apparatus necessary for conversion of one pound of ice at 0°F to water at 32°F.

We are aware that most substances are capable, under proper conditions, of assuming two or more physical states. For instance, lead, when cold, is a solid and when heated and molten, a liquid. Water gives us an outstanding example, for it can assume three states; that is, solid, liquid, and vapor within a relatively short temperature range. Ice, of course, represents the solid state; water, the liquid; and steam, the vaporous or gaseous state.

CHANGE OF STATE

Temperature and heat play important parts in effecting changes from one state to another. For instance, the only quantity that would convert a tumbler of water to either of the other states (that is, a solid or a vapor) would be the addition or extraction of heat.

To prove the function that heat plays in effecting a change of state, let us take a block of ice and perform an experiment with it. In order to simplify the calculations we will utilize a piece of ice that weighs exactly one pound, with a thermometer frozen in the center of it, and we will assume that the block of ice is at a temperature of zero degrees Fahrenheit. We will not go into the apparatus or computations necessary to measure the heat values applied, but we will assume the use of an imaginary Btu meter just as though there existed such a device. Thus, every time a Btu of heat energy is expended it will be registered on our meter.

Prior to beginning the experiment, a graph or squared section of paper is obtained so that the results can be plotted on it. In the lower right-hand section of the paper (a part that will not be required for our log), we will put down the various findings. Setting up the apparatus is a simple matter, for we require only a vessel

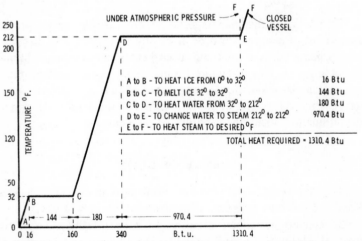

Fig. 16. Diagrammatic representation of amount of heat units required to change one pound of ice at 0°F to steam at 212°F.

and a source of heat, the latter being measurable by our "meter". Place the piece of ice, weighing exactly one pound, in the vessel and indicate the start of the experiment by marking an *A* at the lower left-hand corner of the chart, as shown in Fig. 16, to denote that the ice is at zero degrees Fahrenheit, and that no heat has been added as yet. The specific heat of ice is not as great as that of water; in fact, it is just about half the value, 0.504 to be exact. For this experiment let us assume it is fifty per cent, or 0.5.

Let us now begin to add heat. In accordance with its specific-heat capacity, we will find that every time 0.5 of a Btu is added, the temperature of the ice will increase one degree on the Fahrenheit scale. Continuing to add heat and marking off the progress on the chart, we find that up to 32° Fahrenheit, the number of Btu's required to bring the ice to this degree of sensible heat would be 1 (lb. of ice) × 0.5 (spec. heat) × 32 (degrees rise)= 16 Btu. Thus, from *A* to *B* (a range of 32°) 16 Btu's were required.

At 32° Fahrenheit, an interesting stage is reached. We find that the further addition of heat does not warm up the ice and the thermometer frozen in the test block of ice continues to indicate a sensible heat of 32°. Even providing the ice with a greater quantity of heat causes no observable change in temperature. The only noticeable feature is the melting of ice or conversion of a solid (ice) to a liquid(water). This important transformation is called the *change of state*, due to the fact that a solid is converted to a liquid. If we continued to add heat to the vessel containing the ice and water, we would find that when a total of 144 Btu has been added, the entire block of ice would be converted to water and that the water would have a temperature of 32° F. In other words, to change one pound of ice at a temperature of 32° F. to water at the same temperature, 144 Btu are required to effect this change in state. This we will plot on our chart as line *B* and *C*.

LATENT HEAT OF FUSION

We have had to apply 144 Btu which was taken up by the ice at 32° and caused it to melt and assume its liquid state, without a single indication of any rise or increase in its sensible heat. This masked assimilation of heat is termed *latent heat* and may be said to be the amount of heat units which must be supplied to a solid in order to change it to a liquid without an increase in temperature. It is readily understood that a reversal of the process, that is, for the liquid to assume its solid state (ice), heat must be extracted from the water.

One pound of water at a temperature of 32° F. requires the extraction of 144 Btu to cause it to freeze into a solid block of ice at 32° F. Every solid substance, in varying degrees, has a latent-heat value, and that amount required to convert it or bring about a change of state is termed the *latent heat of fusion*. This heat, assimilated or extracted as the case may be, is not measurable with the thermometer because the heat units are absorbed or expended in inter-molecular work. It separates the molecules from their attractive forces, so that a change of state is effected.

LATENT HEAT OF EVAPORATION

Now let us refer again to the experiment we have under way. We have converted the solid to a liquid, both at 32° F., by adding 144 Btu. Having to deal with water, and knowing that it has a specific-heat factor of 1.00, we may look for a rise of 1 degree in temperature for each Btu added. This will hold until 212° Fahrenheit is indicated on the thermometer, assuming that the experiment is made at atmospheric pressures existing at sea level. Over the 180-degree range of 32 to 212 degrees we will be obliged to add 180 Btu in order to raise the temperature of one pound of water from the former to the latter temperature. This may be plotted as line *C* and *D* on the chart, and the number of heat units recorded on the lower edge.

The further addition of heat would serve to bring out the fact that while the phenomenon of boiling would occur at 212°F., the temperature or sensible heat would not be increased. Just as ice requires a certain quantity of heat units (144 Btu per pound) to melt or convert it from a solid to a liquid without a rise in temperature, we find a similar condition existing. This time a liquid is being converted to a vapor, or steam in this case.

Careful measurements have determined that the conversion of one pound of pure water at 212° F. to steam at 212° F. requires exactly 970.4 Btu when carried out at the normal pressure of the atmosphere encountered at sea level. If we carefully add heat and keep count of the Btu expended, we will find that when all the water has been changed to steam, 970.4 heat units will have been used. Thus, line *D* and *E* may be plotted on the chart, and a note of the number of Btu expended jotted down on the lower right hand corner. The further addition of heat would serve only to heat the steam, such as would be possible if it had been trapped or the experiment performed in a closed vessel so that heat could be applied to it.

STEAM

Steam is the hot, invisible vapor given off by water at its boiling point. The visible white vapor is really a collection of fine watery particles, formed from true steam by condensation.

Steam acts like all true vapors or gases in that it:

1. Has fluidity.
2. Has mobility.

3. Has elasticity.
4. Exerts equal pressure in all directions.

The difference in volume between water and steam at atmospheric pressure is 1,646-to-1, and this wide ratio is manifested by nearly all gases and vapors. The heating of the steam generated in our experiment could be represented by the line *E* and *F*, and would be expended over a considerable range. By referring to the log of our experiment we can trace the heat quantities required to convert ice to water and steam and the action of heat on both liquid and solid. A tabulated form in the lower right-hand portion of the log represents the quantities of heat energy required to effect a change of state, rise in temperature, and other values.

From this experiment it is apparent that heat added to a substance either increases its temperature or changes its state. The heat that brings about the change of state from a solid to a liquid is known as the *latent heat of fusion*, while that required to convert a liquid to a gas is termed the *latent heat of evaporation or vaporization*. One of the interesting facts brought our previously is that a liquid, once brought to the boiling point, does not increase in temperature, but utilizes the heat energy it takes up in converting more liquid to a gas or vapor.

If we were creatures dwelling on another planet and accustomed to a normal atmospheric temperature of 250° or 300°F., we would be able to utilize water to cool substances by immersing them in a bath of water. Since heat and solid are only relative to our senses, materials immersed in a pan of water will lose heat to it, and the heat extracted will be taken up by the water and used to generate steam. Through the extraction or flow of heat from objects so immersed, the water (assumed to be under the same normal sea-level pressures) would remain at 212°F., which would be cooler than the atmospheric temperature of our hypothetical planet. Fortunately for earth dwellers, there are other liquids that boil at temperatures much below that of water.

REFRIGERANTS

Among common liquids that boil at a temperature below that of water is alcohol, with a boiling temperature of 173° F., while ether boils at ordinary summer heat, which is 94° F. Other substances boil at still lower temperatures. They evaporate or vaporize through the absorption of heat at what is in the cool or cold range. Carbon dioxide boils at —110°; ammonia at —28°; sulphur dioxide at 14°; methyl chloride at —10.5°; ethyl chloride at 54°; *Freon 12* at 21.6° and *Freon 22* at 41.4° Fahrenheit, all at atmospheric pressures encountered at sea level. Those materials, solid and liquid, which vaporize or liquefy at comparatively low temperatures, and are suitable for use in refrigeration work, are termed *refrigerant*s. The refrigerants are employed in specially designed apparatus so that the extraction of heat from rooms or perishables can be accomplished as inexpensively as possible.

The latent heat of vaporization of liquid refrigerants varies with the material and with the pressure at which vaporization is allowed to proceed. The latent heat of vaporization in Btu per pound of various refrigerants in common use and volatilizing at zero Fahrenheit is presented as follows:

Ammonia	572.2
Methyl chloride	176.0
Ethyl chloride	173.4
Sulphur dioxide	171.8
Carbon dioxide	117.5
Freon 12	71.0
Freon 22	100.7

From this list, it is observed that ammonia is an excellent refrigerant in that it absorbs a great quantity of heat as compared to other agents. Most large ice manufacturing plants employ ammonia, while for smaller sized units and household apparatus, methyl chloride and sulphur dioxide are used. Formerly, ethyl chloride was widely used, but today practically no machines operate with it, because of its inflammability. Carbon dioxide finds use in transporting ice cream, fish, and similar products, where a great quantity of escaping fumes would endanger human life.

It is very easy to understand that a vessel containing a refrigerant, which is allowed to absorb heat, will cause a cooling or refrigerating effect. Since heat cannot be created or destroyed, it follows that heat removed from one body must show up in some form of energy in another body. Essentially, the removal of heat from one body and its transference and dissipation by another is refrigeration.

USE OF ICE

Where ice is employed, it is the latent heat of fusion that results in the cooling of other materials suffering such loss of heat energy that the heat is taken up by the ice and it reverts to water. The heat-laden liquid (water) is drained away, carrying its heat load out and away from the refrigerator. A graphical illustration of this cycle is shown in Fig. 17.

TON OF REFRIGERATION

Due to the fact that refrigeration was first produced by ice, the rate of removal of heat in a cooling operation was expressed in terms of pounds or tons of ice required per unit time, usually per

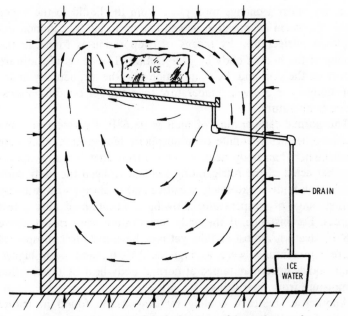

Fig. 17. An example of the ice refrigeration cycle.

day. It has been found previously that one pound of ice absorbs 144 Btu when it melts. One ton of ice consequently absorbs 2,000 × 144 or 288,000 Btu. When one ton of ice melts in 24 hours, the rate is 288,000/24 or 12,000 Btu per hour, or 12,-000/60=200 Btu per minute. This rate has been officially designated as one ton of refrigeration, and is the basis for rating all refrigerating machinery.

EVAPORATION

We have previously discussed the quantities of heat required to bring about a change of state. Considerable heat energy was necessary when a change took place from the liquid to the vapor phase. The term evaporation is well-known to all. A common example of refrigeration by means of evaporation is found in the cooling of the human body by perspiration. The beads of moisture appear on the skin and, by evaporation into the air, actually maintain the body at a lower temperature than the surrounding atmospheric temperature.

The normal temperature of man is 98.6°F. Everyone at some time or other has encountered atmospheric temperatures that were much higher than body heat, never realizing that it was evaporation that acted as the refrigerating element to keep the body cool. The human body is extremely sensitive and is always within a very limited range of temperature, allowing a variation of only a few degrees. For instance, if the body temperature were raised above 108°F., death is almost certain, yet men have lived in atmospheres where temperatures were as high as 140°F., and even higher. Their bodies were maintained at normal body heat by evaporation of moisture from their skins.

Another example of cooling by evaporation found in nature that we have all experienced is the reduction in temperature which usually follows a summer rain. The required heat to bring about the evaporation of the rain water is drawn from the atmosphere and the earth, and thus effects the coolness we note after such precipitation.

PRESSURE

In the previous instances of boiling temperatures, the wording *"at pressures found at sea level"* was used. For instance, water boils at 212° F. when it is heated in a vessel open to the atmosphere and provided the experiment takes place at an altitude at or near sea level or under equivalent pressure. Regardless of how rapidly heat may be added to the open vessel of water, no rise in boiling temperature can be secured, the only result achieved being that steam is formed with greater rapidity, commensurate with the amount of heat. If, however, pressure is allowed to enter as a factor in the conversion of a liquid to a vapor, or vice versa, it will be found that the boiling point is altered. We are all more or less familiar with the story of the man who tried to prepare his eggs on the top of a high mountain where atmospheric pressure, due to altitude, was so low that the water boiled at such a low temperature that it would not cook the eggs. From this simple example, it is apparent that the lower the pressure exerted on the liquid, the lower will be the boiling point.

By way of demonstrating the effect of pressure, let us take a sturdy flask, one capable of withstanding both heat and pressure, and pour in some water. We will assume it to be a glass vessel so that we can view the process and make certain when boiling actually occurs. A stopper provided with three perforations, so that a pressure gauge, thermometer, and a valve can be inserted in the individual openings, is forced tightly into the neck of the flask. The completely assembled apparatus is then placed over a source of heat, such as a gas flame, as depicted in Fig. 18. The exit valve is allowed to remain wide open. Soon the water will boil, and if the experiment is performed at or near sea level, the pressure gauge will register zero pounds of pressure, while the thermometer will indicate a temperature of 212°F. As long as the valve orifice is large enough to offer a free and unobstructed exit to all of the steam formed, no amount of heat will raise the temperature.

Now let us turn the valve so that the opening is slightly restricted. The pressure will build up, and by regulating the amount of gas burned and the exit valve so that a jet of steam is released, we can obtain or impose any pressure we desire on the vessel. Let

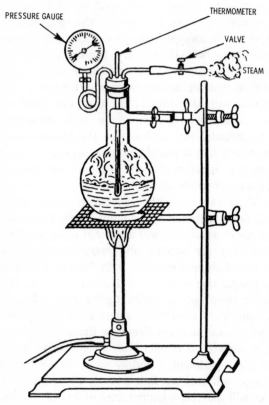

Fig. 18. Apparatus necessary for evolution of pressure-temperature relations of water.

us select a pressure of about 5 pounds as the pressure desired. With proper regulation of the gas and steam valve, this value can easily be obtained and maintained. When secured, let us read the thermometer. By readjusting the steam and the gas valves, let us raise the pressure to 10.3 pounds gauge pressure. At this point we would find the water would start to boil at 240.1° F. Again we would find that no amount of heat added rapidly or otherwise to our flask would raise its temperature above that point, provided the pressure remained constant.

With heat added rapidly, more steam would be formed and we would of course be obliged to open the steam exit valve in order to maintain the pressure at the desired point. If only a little heat were added, we would have to close the valve somewhat to maintain the pressure. By referring to a table giving the properties of saturated steam, various gauge pressures and corresponding temperatures can be determined. For instance, if our boiler were of heavy steel, we could increase the pressure to a point where the gauge would indicate 100.3 pounds, at which point the boiling of the water would occur at 338.1° F. With the increase in pressure, the boiling point advances, and again, in accordance with this pressure-temperature relationship, the boiling point is lowered as the pressure is reduced.

PRESSURE-TEMPERATURE RELATIONS

Most bodies expand when heated, whether of solid, liquid, or gaseous form. If the expansion is restricted, great forces are set up by the body in the effort to expand. Every gas or vapor confined in a closed vessel exerts a certain pressure against the restraining walls of the vessel. The pressure imposed depends on the amount and temperature of the gas. The natural tendency for a confined gas is to expand when the temperature is increased, and if the gas is contained in a vessel with rigid walls, the pressure will increase. This is of such importance that a law has been formulated to express it, stating that the pressure exerted by a gas or vapor in a closed vessel is *directly proportional to the absolute temperature of the gas.*

Low Pressures

Before proceeding with our experiments with lower pressures, it is best that we understand the comparative terms. As previously pointed out, objects at sea level are taken as being subjected to a certain constant pressure. This pressure is due to the weight of the atmosphere, which at sea level is found to exert a pressure of 14.7 pounds per square inch of surface.

The atmosphere is like a high sea, and if we dive into water, similar conditions are encountered, for the deeper we go the greater the pressure becomes, because of the volume above. As we rise, the pressure becomes less. Modern aircraft designers take into consideration the rarefication of the atmosphere with increasing altitude and know that at a certain height the air density will not allow an airplane to rise any higher. This they term the ceiling or density at which further altitude for each particular design is not possible. Since pressue is so instrumental in a great many engineering calculations, a universal standard was necessary. Thus, the pressure existing at sea level was accepted as a standard, being termed zero pounds gauge, or 14.7 pounds absolute.

In the manufacture of gauges, these instruments are usually set to indicate zero pressure at normal atmospheric sea-level density. It must be remembered that this setting at zero is made when the actual and true pressure is in reality 14.7 pounds per square inch, the pressure that the weight of the atmosphere exerts at sea level. Nearly all steam and pressure gauges are set in this fashion and the pressures indicated by these instruments are termed gauge pressures. The usual increments are in one-, five-, and ten-pound readings so that only approximate pressures can be determined. For most commercial applications these roughly calibrated gauges are sufficiently accurate and are quite inexpensive.

For fine work, experimental, and scientific determinations, an-

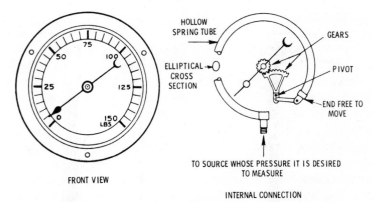

Fig. 19. *The external view and construction details of a typical pressure gauge.*

other pressure scale is employed. This scale is called the absolute pressure and is based on true pressures, for zero on this scale indicates no pressure at all, or in other words, a perfect vacuum. An external view and construction details of a typical pressure gauge is shown in Fig. 19. It consists of a metal tube of elliptical cross section bent into a nearly complete ring and closed at one end. The flatter sides of the tube form the inner and outer sides of the ring. The open end of the tube is connected to the pipe through which the liquid under pressure is admitted. The closed end of the tube is free to move. As the pressure increases, the tube tends to straighten out, moving a pointer through a lever-and-gear arrangement. The scale is graduated directly in pounds per square inch.

On the pressure gauge scale, the normal atmospheric pressure found at sea level (14.7 pounds per square inch) is indicated as zero pounds pressure and below that point the term of pressure is converted to vacuum or inches of mercury. A long glass tube,

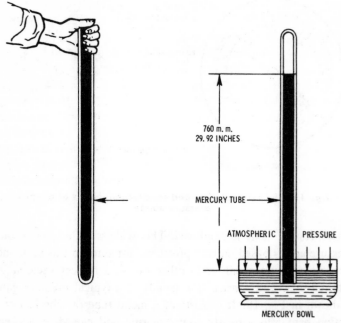

Fig. 20. Balancing the pressure of air with a mercury column.

sealed at its upper extremity, is exhausted of air and filled with mercury as shown in Fig. 20, its lower open end dipping into a reservoir of mercury open to the atmosphere, or to the pressure imposed. Such a device is called a *barometer* and is used to measure the pressure in terms of inches of mercury in place of such a term as pounds under zero gauge pressure. Just as variance in temperature will cause a rise or fall of the mercury level in a thermometer, so will a difference of pressure exerted on the mercury in the reservoir of the barometer bring about a certain reading in terms of inches of mercury. The pressure of the atmosphere, or any other pressure exerting its force on the mercury exposed in the reservoir, drives the liquid up into the evacuated end to a height corresponding with the pressure. In a way, the barometer is much like the thermometer, for it indicates a value by the height of a mercury column, one recording in terms of temperature and the other in terms of an equivalent of pressure.

On the absolute scale, it will be observed that pressures begin from an absolute zero or perfect vacuum, and that a gauge calibrated in this manner will indicate 14.7 pounds at normal sea-level pressures. On the other hand, a gauge calibrated in the fashion employed for the commercial field of refrigeration and air conditioning will indicate this latter pressure as zero pounds, where normal atmospheric conditions prevail.

EFFECT OF LOW PRESSURES

The previous experiments in which we determined the boiling or evaporating points at different pressures indicated that whenever pressure was increased, the boiling point was raised. Making use of the same apparatus, let us investigate the effect of a reduced pressure on the evaporating temperature. To do so, we will again place a quantity of water in the flask, force the stopper containing a pressure gauge, thermometer, and control valve tightly in place so that no leakage can occur to mar the accuracy of our experiment, and place the apparatus over a gas flame. This time, however, instead of using the exit valve for holding the steam within the vessel to cause a pressure to build up, we will connect a vacuum line to it and use it to prevent the steam from being drawn out or evacuated, so that a certain low pressure or inches of vacuum can be maintained within the vessel.

Referring to the pressure scale, Fig. 20, we find that 30 inches of mercury is roughly equivalent to 15 pounds on the gauge-pressure scale, so that a 2-inch vacuum means a pressure of 1 pound less than the sea-level atmospheric pressure. For our first experiment, let us take a pressure of 14 pounds absolute, or 0.7 of a pound less pressure than normally exerted. From a table on the properties of saturated steam, we will find that this corresponds to 1.42 inches of mercury on the gauge-pressure scale.

By regulating the exit valve so that the proper vacuum or low pressure is obtained, we can easily arrive at a point where boiling occurs at the constant pressure we desire. At this point of 14 pounds absolute pressure, we would find that the water boils at 209.55° F. Then, we can open the exit valve a trifle more and regulate it so that a pressure of 12 pounds absolute (5.49 inches of mercury) is maintained. This pressure results in a boiling point of 201.96° F.

The fact is thus brought out that the pressure to which water is subjected has just as much to do with its boiling as does the temperature. This holds true for any liquid, for evaporation can be made to occur at any temperature above its freezing point if the pressure to which it is subjected is made low enough.

HEAT TRANSMISSION

In refrigeration, we are interested in getting the heat contained in a room or refrigerator to a medium that will effect its removal. Ice is a simple method and formerly was widely used. The more modern refrigerator is equipped with a cooling apparatus that supplants ice and provides for more constant and cooler temperatures. Before we can study how heat is taken up and removed mechanically, it is imperative to learn the behavior of heat.

One of the most important laws has already been mentioned; that which refers to the flow of heat from a body of higher temperature to one having a lower sensible heat. Never of its own accord will heat or water flow up hill or in the opposite direction. Therefore, it follows that heat in a refrigerator or room will flow to the cooler object, such as ice or the cooling device.

The transmission of heat may be accomplished in three ways:

1. By conduction.
2. By convection.
3. By radiation.

Conduction

This is the transference of heat by molecular impact from one particle to another in contact. For instance, if the end of a bar of iron is heated in the fire, some of the heat will pass through the bar to the cooler portion. Heat traveling in a body, or from one body to another where the two are in intimate contact, is termed *conduction*. An illustration of this transfer of heat is shown in Fig. 21.

HEAT TRANSFER BY CONDUCTION

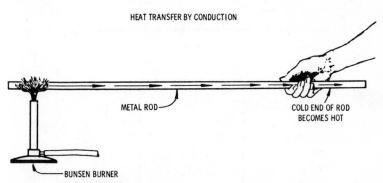

METAL ROD

COLD END OF ROD
BECOMES HOT

BUNSEN BURNER

Fig. 21. Illustrating the transfer of heat by conduction.

Metals are usually splendid heat conductors. Each and every material has a conduction value, some good like the metals, others mediocre, and a few very poor. For instance, heat will quickly pass through a piece of copper but will have considerable difficulty in passing through a piece of cork. The materials that have very low heat conductivities are termed heat insulators. Even the very poorest conductors, or insulation materials, allow a certain

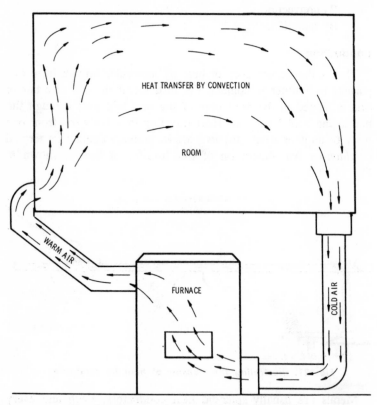

Fig. 22. Showing heat transfer by convection.

amount of heat to pass through. There is no material which offers a perfect barrier or resistance to the passage of heat.

Convection

Convection is the principle used in hot-air heating. Air that is free to circulate, such as in any air body of appreciable size, will be set into motion where a difference of temperature occurs, for it will absorb heat from the warmer wall, become heated, expand and become lighter. The heated portion of the air will rise and cooler air will move into its place, which in turn will become heated. The heated portion of the air eventually moves over to the colder wall, and the heat flows from the air to the colder object. Thus, any body of air capable of motion will transmit heat by convection. Hot-air and hot-water heating systems work on the convection principle. They convey heat by bodily moving the heated substance from one place to another, as shown in Fig. 22.

The most efficient heat insulation known is a vacuum, but except for very small containers, it is structurally impractical to employ it commercially. The next best insulating medium is air subdivided into the smallest possible units so that it is still or stagnant. Air that is contained in spaces of appreciable size, such as between the double walls of refrigerators, will circulate and transmit heat by convection. Cork is an insulation material of a high order and has great resistance to the passage or transmission of heat because of its air content. The air cells in cork are of such minute size that the air trapped in them is so restricted that only a little circulation is possible and is, for all practical purposes, still air, so that little or no convection occurs.

Radiation

Heat energy transmitted through the air in the same way light is sent out by a lighted lamp, a radiant heater, or the sun, is called *radiated energy*. This is illustrated in Fig. 23. Large cold-storage warehouses, auditoriums, theaters, and homes are built with consideration of the heat evolved through radiant energy of the sun. Small household appliances rarely have to consider any radiant-heat factor, for they are used in existing structures without any change in building design and are sheltered from direct heat.

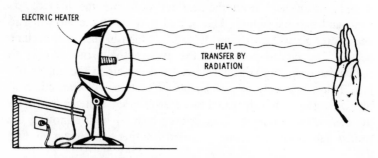

ELECTRIC HEATER

HEAT TRANSFER BY RADIATION

Fig. 23. Illustrating heat transfer by radiation.

CONDENSATION

In a previous experiment we illustrated that a liquid, heated to the boiling point corresponding to the pressure imposed, will assimilate heat and produce a vapor or gas. The heat taken up by the liquid is used to speed up molecular activity until a vapor is evolved. It stands to reason then, that any vapor or gas contains a considerable quantity of heat.

In accordance with the foregoing experiments, we found that heat itself always flows from the warmer to the colder body. To prove this again and illustrate just what condensation is, let us take a vessel, fill it about half full of water, and bring it to the boiling point over a gas flame, as shown in Fig. 24. As soon as steam is generated, let us take a dry, cold plate and hold it at an angle over the jet of steam as it issues from our crude boiler. It will be observed that the steam impinges on the plate and is converted again into water, the droplets forming and dripping off the edge of the plate. This was caused by the hot steam giving up its heat load (latent heat of vaporization) to the cold plate, the heat flowing from the steam to the plate.

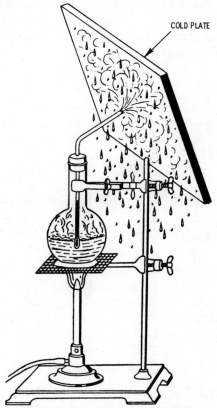

COLD PLATE

Fig. 24. An example of condensation.

To make sure that this is really the case, let us take the vessel we used in a previous experiment and again fill it with water, secure the stopper in place, and apply heat. This time let us set the exhaust valve so that we can maintain a few pounds of steam pressure, perhaps 5 pounds. While steam is generating and we are regulating the valve to get this constant pressure, let us build a condenser. This is easily done; all we need is about 12 feet of copper tubing. Any tubing or material will do, but copper is so easily bent and formed that it is not a difficult task to wind it in a spiral form, such as shown in Fig. 25.

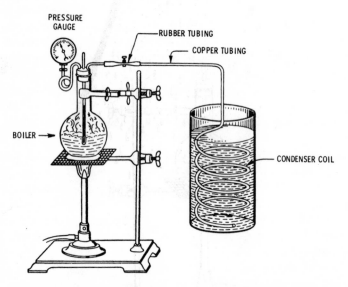

Fig. 25. An example of condensation by steam vapors.

The formed coil is submerged in a pail of cold water with its open end at the bottom. The top end is supplied with a piece of rubber tubing. When the gas and steam valves have been regulated so that there is a constant steam pressure of 5 pounds within the boiler, and a fair amount of steam being exhausted from the exit, quickly connect the rubber tube on the condenser to the steam pipe. It will be observed that the pressure gauge has dropped somewhat, and after the steam has blown out the air contained in our condenser, we will see that no steam is issuing from the open end of the copper coil submerged in the water.

If we weighed the steam-generating apparatus and the condenser equipment before and after the experiment, we would find that the boiler lost weight through evaporation of water, while the condenser gained through condensation exactly what had been lost. Also, if a thermometer has been placed in the condenser water and a reading taken at the start and end of our experiment, it would have been found that the water increased in temperature. In fact, if we ignore various losses, the amount of steam condensed can be estimated from the increase in temperature of the water.

It is apparent that the steam is easily convertible to its liquid form if the heat of vaporization is extracted. Then too, our old rule would apply, not only to steam, but to all vapors and gases; that is, if we increase the pressure we will find that the gas will condense at the lower temperature found in the condenser, for the temperature of the gas will be raised far above the condenser temperature. Thus, heat will flow from the hot gas to the cold condenser; the greater the temperature difference, the faster will be the heat exchange.

In refrigeration and air-conditioning applications, the gases employed as a refrigerating medium have, for any given pressure, a corresponding temperature at which they condense or liquefy. Where both gas and liquid are present in the same vessel, and the closed container is heated to cause boiling, the temperature of both gas and liquid will be the same at the boiling point. If pressure is increased, the boiling point will be raised. Above a certain point the gas will cease to have any latent heat of vaporization, and it will remain as a gas, regardless of the intensity of the pressure imposed.

CHAPTER 2

Refrigerants

Refrigerants are heat-carrying mediums which, during their cycle, absorb heat at a low temperature level and are compressed by a heat pump to a higher temperature where they are able to discharge the absorbed heat. The ideal refrigerant would be one that could discharge to the condenser all the heat that the refrigerant is capable of absorbing in the evaporator or cooler. All refrigerating mediums, however, carry a certain portion of the heat from the condenser back to the evaporator, and this reduces the heat-absorbing capacity of the medium on the low side of the system.

DESIRABLE PROPERTIES

The requirements of a good refrigerant for commercial use are:

1. Low boiling point.
2. Safe and nontoxic.
3. Ease of liquefy action at moderate pressure and temperature.
4. High latent-heat value.

5. Ability to operate on a positive pressure.
6. No effect on moisture.
7. Mix well with oil.
8. Noncorrosive to metal.

Classifications

Refrigerants may be divided into three classes according to their manner of absorption or extraction of heat from the substances to be refrigerated.

Class 1—This class includes those refrigerants that cool materials by the absorption of the latent heat. The temperature and pressure properties of these refrigerants are shown in Table 1.

Table 1. Temperature and Pressure Properties

	Boiling Point °F	Freezing Point °F	Critical Temperature °F	Critical Pressure p.s.i.a.
Freon 14	—198.2	—312	—49.9	542
Freon 13	—114.5	—296	83.8	579
Carbon dioxide	—108.4	—69.9 triple	87.8	1,071
Freon 22	—41.4	—256	204.8	716
Ammonia	—28.0	—107.9	271.2	1,651
Freon 12	—21.6	—252.4	232.7	582
Methyl chloride	—10.76	—143.7	289.6	969.2
Sulphur dioxide	14.0	—98.9	314.8	1,141.5
Freon 114	38.4	—137	294.3	474
Freon 21	48.0	—211.0	353.3	750
Freon 11	74.7	—168.0	388.4	635
Methylene chloride	103.7	—143.0	421	640
Freon 113	117.6	—31.0	417.4	495

Class 2—The refrigerants in this class are those that cool substances by absorbing their sensible heats. They are: Air, calcium-

chloride brine, sodium-chloride (salt) brine, alcohol, and similar nonfreezing solutions.

Class 3—This group consists of solutions that contain absorbed vapors of liquefiable agents or refrigerating media. These solutions function by the nature of their ability to carry the liquefiable vapors that produce a cooling effect by the absorption of latent heat. An example of this group is aqua ammonia, which is a solution composed of distilled water and pure ammonia.

The refrigerants in Class 1 are employed in the standard *compression* type of refrigerating systems. The refrigerants in Class 2 are employed as *immediate cooling agents* between Class 1 and the substance to be refrigerated, and do the same work for Class 3. The latter is employed in the standard *absorption* type of refrigerating systems.

THE *FREON* REFRIGERANTS

The *Freon* family of refrigerants is presently used almost universally in household-type refrigerators. In the past, refrigerants selected for use were chosen principally for their boiling points and pressures, and their stability within the system or unit regardless of other important necessary properties such as nonflammability and nontoxicity. Of course, there are many factors that must be taken into account when selecting a chemical compound for use as a refrigerant other than boiling point, pressure, stability, toxicity, and flammability. They must include molecular weight, density, compression ratio, heat value, temperature of compression, compressor displacement, design or type of compressor, etc., to mention only a few of the major considerations.

Chemical Properties

The *Freon* refrigerants are colorless, almost odorless, and boiling points vary over a wide range of temperature. Those *Freon*

67

refrigerants that are produced are nontoxic, noncorrosive, non-irritating, and nonflammable under all conditions of usage. They are generally prepared by replacing chlorine or hydrogen with fluorine. Chemically they are inert and thermally stable up to temperatures far beyond conditions found in actual operation.

Physical Properties

Pressures required to liquefy the refrigerant vapor affect the design of the system; refrigerating effect and specific volume of the refrigerant vapor determines the compressor displacement; and the heat of vaporization and specific volume of liquid refrigerant affects the quantity of refrigerant to be circulated through the pressure regulating valve or other device. Table 1 covers boiling point at one atmospheric pressure, freezing point, critical temperature, and critical pressures of not only the *Freon* refrigerants, but other commonly used refrigerants as well.

Operating Pressures

Pressures of saturated vapor at various temperatures of typical refrigerants are listed in Table 1. Table 2 lists the pressure of saturated vapor under standard ton conditions. Operating pressures will vary with the temperature of the condensing medium, amount of condenser surface, whether an air- or water-cooled condenser is used, operating back pressure, presence of noncondensible or foul gas in the condenser, circulation of the condensing medium through the condenser, condition of the condenser surface, extent of superheating of the refrigerant gas, and other factors.

Table 2. Operating Pressures
(Standard Ton)

	Pressure p.s.i.g. 86° F.	Pressure p.s.i.g. 5° F.	Compression Ratio
Carbon dioxide	1,024.3	319.7	3.11
Freon 22	159.8	28.33	4.045
Ammonia	154.5	19.57	4.94
Freon 12	93.2	11.81	4.075
Methyl chloride	80.0	6.46	4.48
Sulphur dioxide	51.75	5.87*	5.63
Freon 114	21.99	16.14*	5.42
Freon 21	16.53	19.25*	5.96
Freon 11	3.58	23.95*	6.24
Methylene chloride	9.44*	27.53*	8.57
Freon 113	13.93*	27.92*	8.01

*Inches mercury below one atmosphere.

Freon-12

Freon-12, CCl_2F_2, has a boiling point of $-21.6°$ F., and is extensively used as a refrigerant in both direct and indirect industrial, commercial, and household air-conditioning systems, as well as in household refrigerators, ice-cream cabinets, frozen-food cabinets, food locker plants, water coolers, etc., employing reciprocating type compressors ranging in size from fractional to 800 h.p. *Freon-12* is also used in household refrigerating systems, ice-cream and frozen-food cabinets employing rotary-vane type compressors. *Freon-12* is used in industrial process water and brine cooling to $-110°$ F., employing multistage centrifugal-type compressors in cascade of 100 tons refrigeration capacity and larger.

The health hazards resulting from exposure to *Freon* when used as a refrigerant are remote. *Freon* is in a class of specially nontoxic gases. Vapor in any proportion will not irritate the skin, eyes, nose, or throat, and being odorless and nonirritating, it will eliminate all possibilities of panic hazards should it escape from a refrigerating system. A pound of *Freon-12* liquid expands to 3.8 cu. ft. of vapor at 68° F. room temperature. *Freon-12* is a stable compound capable of undergoing, without decomposition, the physical change to which it is commonly subjected in service, such as freezing, vaporization, and compression. The boiling point is −21.6° F. at the atmospheric pressure of sea level.

The low boiling point permits low temperatures to be reached without the compressor operating on a vacuum. This low but positive pressure prevents moisture-laden air from accidentally entering the system and also permits detection and location of the source of leaks, which is difficult if the refrigeration system operates at a negative back pressure. A halide torch is used for detecting leaks. Under ordinary conditions when no moisture is present, *Freon* does not corrode the metals commonly used in refrigerating systems. In the presence of water, it will discolor brass, steel, and copper, but there is little or no evidence of any serious corrosive action. It is only slightly soluble in water, and the solution formed will not corrode any of the common metals used in refrigeration construction. It is nonflammable and noncombustible under fire conditions or where appreciable quantities come in contact with flame or hot metal surfaces. It requires an open flame at 1,382° F. to decompose the vapor, and then the vapor only decomposes to form hydrogen chloride and hydrogen fluoride, both of which are irritating but are readily dissolved in water. Air mixtures are not capable of burning and contain no elements that will support combustion. Therefore, *Freon* is considered nonflammable. *Freon* is so safe and nontoxic, that the only possible way to cause death with *Freon* is to get concentrations so great as to exclude the oxygen.

Freon-21

Freon-21, $CHCl_2F$, has a boiling point of 48° F. and may be used as a refrigerant in industrial and commercial air-conditioning systems; also in industrial process water and brine cooling to —50° F. employing single or multistage centrifugal-type compressors of 100-ton refrigeration capacity and larger. *Freon-21* has been used in fractional-horsepower household refrigerating systems and drinking water coolers employing rotary-vane type compressors, and has also been used in comfort cooling air-conditioning systems of the absorption type where dimethyl ether or tetraethylene glycol was used as the absorbent.

Freon-22

Freon-22, $CHClF_2$, has a boiling point of —41.4° F., and is used as a refrigerant in industrial and commercial low-temperature refrigerating systems to —150° F., and also in window-type and unit package room coolers and air-conditioning units. *Freon-22* is used in many installations where more efficient operation is desired in providing the necessary lower temperatures for low-temperature locker plants, lower temperatures that result in quicker freezing of foods, greater volume of products handled by the quick-freezing units, home or farm freezers, and countless numbers of low-temperature industrial applications.

Freon-113

Freon-113, $CCl_2F\text{-}CClF_2$, has a boiling point of 117.6° F., and is used as a refrigerant in most all industrial and commercial air-conditioning systems. *Freon-113* is also used in industrial process water and brine cooling to 0° F., employing four or more stage centrifugal-type compressors of 25-ton refrigeration capacity and larger.

Freon-11

Freon-11, CCl₃F, has a boiling point of 74.7° F., and has wide usage as a refrigerant in indirect industrial and commercial air-conditioning systems; also in industrial process water and brine cooling to —40° F., employing single or multistage centrifugal-type compressors of 100 ton refrigeration capacity and larger.

Freon-114

Freon-114, $C_2Cl_2F_4$, has a boiling point of 38.4 F., and is being used as a refrigerant in fractional-horsepower household refrigerating systems and drinking water coolers employing rotary-vane type compressors; also in indirect industrial and commercial air-conditioning systems and in industrial process water and brine cooling to —70° F. employing multistage centrifugal-type compressors in cascade of 100-ton refrigeration capacity and larger.

Freon-13

Freon-13, $CClF_3$, and *Freon-14*, CF_4, are two compounds recently added to the *Freon* family, and have a boiling point of —114.5° F., and —198.2° F., respectively. These will undoubtedly find usage as refrigerants in extremely low-temperature industrial refrigerating systems approximating liquid-air temperatures, and will be employed in cascaded reciprocating-type compressors. The use of these two *Freon* refrigerants will require thorough investigation and research as to the behavior of metals at low temperatures while under stress, lubrication of mechanical compressors, and the possible development of more efficient insulating materials.

Sulfur Dioxide

This was formerly one of the most common refrigerants employed in household refrigerators. It is also known as SO_2, and is a colorless gas or liquid. It is toxic and has a very pungent odor, and is obtained by burning sulfur in air. It is not considered a safe refrigerant, especially in quantities. It combines with water and forms sulfurous and sulfuric acids which are corrosive to metal. Sulfur dioxide has an adverse effect on almost anything with which it comes in contact. It boils at about 14° F. (standard conditions), and has a latent-heat value of 166 Btu per pound.

Surfur dioxide has the disadvantage that it must operate on a vacuum to give temperatures required in most refrigeration work. Should a leak occur, moisture-laden air will be drawn into the system, eventually corroding the metal parts and ruining the compressor. Also, in relation to *Freon* or methyl chloride, approximately 1/3 more vapor must be pumped in order to get the same amount of refrigeration. This means that the condensing unit will either have to be speeded up to give the desired capacity, or the size of the cylinders increased proportionately.

Sulfur dioxide does not mix well with oil. The suction line must be on a steady slant to the machine, otherwise the oil will trap out, making a constriction in the suction line. On many installations it is not possible to avoid traps, and on these jobs sulfur dioxide is not satisfactory. Because of its characteristic pungent odor, comparatively small leaks are readily detected. Even the smallest leaks are readily located by means of an ammonia swab. A small piece of cloth or sponge may be secured to a wire and dipped into strong aqua ammonia or household ammonia and then passed over points where leaks may be present. A dense white smoke forms where the sulfur dioxide and ammonia fumes come in contact. When no ammonia is available, leaks may be located by the usual soap bubble or oil test. The soap solution or oil is put on the tube joints and points where bubbles would be noted.

Note: Liquid sulfur dioxide on any part of the body produces freezing. In any such case a physician should be consulted immediately.

Methyl Chloride

This refrigerant has only a limited use in houeshold refrigeration. It is a good refrigerant, but due to the fact that it will burn under some conditions and is slightly toxic, it does not conform to some of the strict city codes now in force. Roughly speaking, the average relative concentration by weight of different refrigerant vapor in a room of a given size that produces the same effect on a person breathing the air thus contaminated can be approximately specified as follows:

Carbon dioxide	100
Methyl chloride	70
Ammonia	2
Sulfur dioxide	1

In other words, methyl chloride is 35 times safer than ammonia and 70 times safer than sulfur dioxide. To produce any serious effects from breathing methyl chloride, a considerable quantity is required. For instance, in a room 20 × 20 × 10 ft., it would be necessary to liberate about 60 lbs. of methyl chloride to produce any serious effects. Methyl chloride has a low boiling point. Under standard atmospheric pressure it boils to −10.8° F. It is easy to liquefy and has a comparatively high latent value—approximately 176 Btu per pound under standard conditions. It will operate on a positive pressure as low as −10° and mixes well with oil. In its dry state it has no corrosive effect on metal, but in the presence of moisture, copper plating of the compressor parts results, and in severe cases of moisture, a sticky black sludge is formed which is detrimental to the working parts of the system.

Leaks are readily detected by means of special leak-detecting halide torches. Some torches use alcohol as a fuel, normally producing a colorless flame that turns to green when the leak-detector tube picks up very small concentrations of methyl chloride, and to a brilliant blue with stronger concentrations. The space where the torch is being used should be well ventilated to prevent possible harmful effects of breakdown products. Since pressures in all parts of the system are above atmospheric, except in low-temperature applications, a soap bubble or oil test is also effective to locate leaks.

Methyl chloride is not irritating and, consequently, does not serve as its own warning agent in case of leaks as does sulfur dioxide. In some cases, a warning agent is added, such as a small percentage of acrolein (1%). Many consider the addition of 5% of sulfur dioxide a dependable warning agent, but there is some controversy as to the desirability of doing this.

Ammonia

Ammonia is a refrigerant employed in refrigerators operating on the absorption principles. It is also used in large machines for industrial and other purposes. It is a colorless gas with a pungent characteristic odor. Its boiling temperature at normal atmospheric pressure is $-28°$ F., and its freezing temperature is $-107.86°$ F. It is very soluble in water, 1 volume of water absorbing 1.148 volumes of ammonia at $32°$ F.

Ammonia is combustible or explosive when mixed with air in certain proportions (about one volume of ammonia to two volumes of air) and much more so when mixed with oxygen. Because of its high latent-heat value (555 Btu at $18°$ F.) large refrigeration effects are possible with relatively small-sized machinery. It is very toxic, and requires heavy steel fittings. Pressures of 125 to 200 pounds per square inch are not uncommon, and water-cooled units are essential.

There are two common methods for detection of small ammonia leaks. One is the employment of a sulfur candle, which gives off a very thick, white smoke if it comes in contact with escaping ammonia. The other is to test with phenolphthalein paper. The faintest trace of ammonia vapor will cause the moistened paper strip to turn pink, while a larger amount of continued exposure, will turn it into a vivid scarlet color. Phenolphthalein paper can usually be secured from ammonia producers. Both of the aforementioned tests are convenient and accurate.

Carbon Dioxide

Carbon dioxide at ordinary temperatures is a colorless gas with a slightly pungent odor and acid taste. It is harmless to breathe except in extremely large concentrations, when the lack of oxygen would cause suffocation. It is nonexplosive, nonflammable and does not support combustion. The boiling point of carbon dioxide is so extremely low that at 5° F. a pressure of well over 300 pounds per square inch is required to prevent its evaporation. At a condenser temperature of 80° F., a pressure of approximately 1,000 pounds per square inch is required to liquefy the gas. Its critical temperature is 87.8° F. and −69.9° F. is the triple point.

Because of its high operating pressure, the compressor of the carbon dioxide refrigerator unit is very small, even for a comparatively large refrigerating capacity. Because of its low efficiency as compared to other common refrigerants, it is seldom used in household units, but is used in some industrial applications and aboard ships. Leakage of carbon dioxide gas can be tested by making sure that there is pressure on the part to be tested and then use soap solutions at the suspected points. Leakage into condenser water can be tested with the use of "brom thymol blue." The water entering and leaving the condenser should be tested at the same time because of the sensitivity of the test. When carbon dioxide is present, the normal blue color changes to yellow.

Ethyl Chloride

Due to the low pressure at which it evaporates, this refrigerant is not commonly used in household units. In many respects ethyl chloride is quite similar to methyl chloride. It has a boiling point of 55.6° F. at atmospheric pressure and a critical temperature of 360.5° F., with a pressure at this point of 784 pounds absolute. Ethyl chloride is a colorless liquid or gas, with a pungent ethereal odor and sweetish taste. It is neutral toward all metals and, therefore, iron, copper, tin, and lead may be employed in the construction of the unit. Since ethyl chloride softens all rubber compounds or gasket material, it is best to employ only lead gaskets.

From the boiling point, it is apparent that for the lower temperatures required for the preservation of foods, the refrigerant must be evaporated at pressures below atmospheric. This is somewhat of a disadvantage as it is quite difficult to detect leaks in the low or evaporating side, and large leaks would allow air or brine to be filtered or sucked into the system. On the other hand, the low pressure similarly encountered on the high or condensing side, ranging from 6 to 20 pounds gauge, has resulted in the use of rotary compressors. Since the displacement required per unit of refrigeration in the compressor cylinder is excessively large, the rotary method of compression serves to keep down the size of the unit itself, whereas a reciprocating compressor usually presents a rather bulky appearance. Rotary compressors operate with less noise and do not have the pounding found in the reciprocating type, especially in starting up where liquid refrigerants may enter the suction line.

Like methyl chloride, ethyl chloride presents the same difficulties of lubrication and leak detection, with the added disadvantages of operating under low pressures. Frequently, in order to detect leaks, a small quantity of a liquid having a powerful penetrating odor is added to the system. The most common method of leak detection, however, is to put pressure on the system and apply a soapy solution to the suspected points. In locations where there is no danger of explosions, a halide torch can be used. The flame will turn green when held near a leak if ethyl chloride is present.

Isobutane (Freezol)

Isobutane is a colorless gas with a characteristic natural-gas odor. It is stable and does not react with water. It does not decompose to form foreign gases in refrigerating systems and has no corrosive action on metals. Isobutane has a boiling point of 10° F., which permits the production of the desired temperatue at atmospheric pressure with a positive back pressure. Its condensing pressure is approximately 49 pounds gauge at 90° F. When used as a refrigerant, any good grade of refrigerating oil may be employed as a lubricant in the system. The gas has a specific volume of 6.3 cubic feet per pound at 60° F. under normal atmospheric pressure.

PRESSURE-TEMPERATURE CHART

A logarithmic-scaled chart giving the relations between pressure and corresponding temperatures in Fahrenheit degrees of common refrigerants is shown in Fig. 1. The axis of the abscissa shows the temperature and the axis of the ordinate shows the pressure in pounds per square inch gauge and absolute, respectively. To ascertain the pressure of a refrigerant at any particular temperature, follow the desired temperature until the curve of the particular refrigerant is reached. The corresponding pressure is then found on the pressure axis.

PRESSURE -LB./ IN.² GAUGE

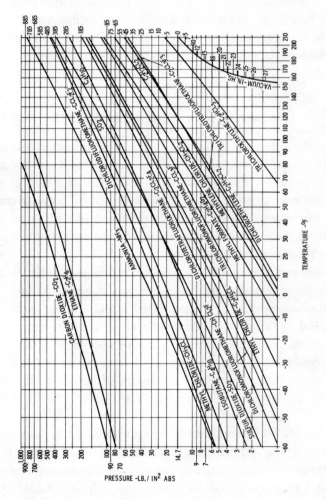

Fig. 1. Showing vapor pressure of refrigerants at various temperatures.

For example, the temperature corresponding to a pressure of 40 pounds gauge for sulfur dioxide is approximately 60° F., and the corresponding temperature at the same pressure for dichlorodifluoremethane (*Freon-12*) is approximately 27° F., etc.

CARE IN HANDLING REFRIGERANTS

In the foregoing discussion it has been observed that one of the requirements of an ideal refrigerant is that it must be non-toxic. In reality, however, all gases (with the exception of pure air) are more or less toxic or asphyxiating. It is therefore important that wherever gases or highly volatile liquids are used, adequate ventilation should be provided, because even nontoxic gases in air produce a suffocating effect.

Vaporized refrigerants, especially ammonia and sulfur dioxide, bring about irritation and congestion of the lungs and bronchial organs, accompanied by violent coughing and vomiting, and when breathed in sufficient quantity, suffocation. It is therefore of the utmost importance that the serviceman subjected to a refrigerant gas should find access to fresh air at frequent intervals to clear his lungs. When engaged in the repair of ammonia and sulfur dioxide machines, approved gas masks and goggles should be used. *Carrene, Freon-12* and carbon dioxide fumes are not irritating and can be inhaled in considerable concentrations for a short period without serious consequences. It should be remembered that liquid refrigerants will refrigerate or remove heat from anything with which they come in contact when released from a container, as in the case of an accident.

HANDLING REFRIGERANT CYLINDERS

It is of the utmost importance to handle cylinders of compressed gas with care (see Fig. 2), and to observe the following precautions:

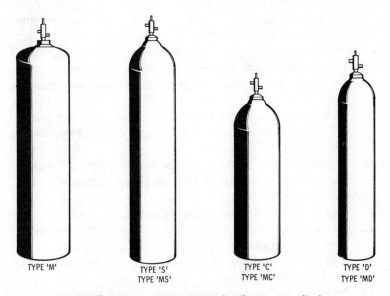

TYPE 'M'   TYPE 'S'   TYPE 'C'   TYPE 'D'
                   TYPE 'MS'   TYPE 'MC'   TYPE 'MD'

Fig. 2. Showing various sizes of refrigerant cylinders.

1. Never drop cylinders nor permit them to strike each other violently.
2. Never use a lifting magnet nor a sling (rope or chain) when handling cylinders. A crane may be used when a safe cradle or platform is provided to hold the cylinders.
3. Where caps are provided for valve protection, such caps should be kept on the cylinders except when the cylinders are in use.

4. Never overfill cylinders. Whenever the refrigerant is discharged from or into a cylinder, immediately thereafter weigh the cylinder and record the weight of refrigerant remaining in the cylinder.

5. Never attempt to mix gases in a cylinder.

6. Never use cylinders for rollers, supports, or for any purpose other than to carry gas.

7. Never tamper with the safety devices in valves or clyinders.

8. Open cylinder valves slowly. Never use wrenches or tools except those provided or approved by the gas manufacturer.

9. Make sure that the threads on regulators or other unions are the same as those on cylinder valve outlets. Never force connections that do not fit.

10. Regulators and pressure gauges provided for use with a particular gas must not be used on cylinders containing different gases.

11. Never attempt to repair or alter cylinders or valves.

12. Never store cylinders near highly flammable substances, such as oil, gasoline, waste, etc.

13. Cylinders should not be exposed to continuous dampness, salt water, or salt spray.

14. Store full and empty cylinders apart to avoid confusion.

15. Protect cylinders from any object that will produce a cut or other abrasion in the surface of the metal.

CAPACITY OF REFRIGERANTS

To determine the allowable shipping capacity of any cylinder, or other authorized container, first find the weight of water it will hold by weighing it full of water and subtracting the tare weight. This water capacity in pounds multiplied by 1.25 will give its allowable shipping capacity for *sulfur dioxide*. The water capacity multiplied by 0.75 will give its allowable shipping capacity for *methyl chloride*. Thus, for example, if a cylinder weighs 120 pounds empty and 243 pounds when completely filled with water, its capacity is 243—120 or 123 pounds of water. It will hold 1.25 × 123 or 154 pounds of *sulfur dioxide,* and 0.75 × 123 or 92 pounds of methyl chloride.

A Simple Refrigeration System

The principle of using the latent heat of vaporization of a liquid, such as sulfur dioxide, for producing refrigeration can be

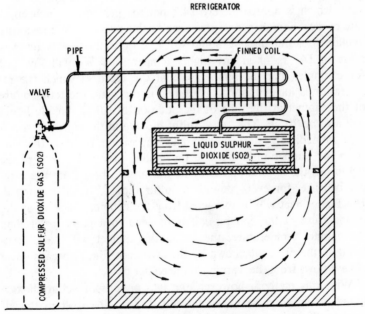

Fig. 3. Illustrating a simple refrigeration cycle.

illustrated very easily by thinking of a refrigerator of very simple design, similar to the one shown in Fig. 3. The refrigerator is made up of a box that is completely insulated on all six sides to prevent the entrance of heat by conduction, convection, and radiation. We then place in the top of the cabinet a series of finned coils, with one end connected to the cylinder charged with sulfur dioxide. Through this end we will charge, for example, two pounds of sulfur dioxide into the coil after which the compressed cylinder will again be sealed and disconnected from the line, with the charging end of the pipe open to the atmosphere.

Since the liquid sulfur dioxide is exposed to the air, the only pressure to which the liquid is subjected is to atmospheric pressure, which is approximately 14.7 pounds per square inch absolute or zero pounds gauge pressure. At this pressure, as previously explained, sulfur dioxide liquid will boil or vaporize at a temperature of 14° F, or at any higher temperature. We will say, just for example, that the temperature of the room in which the refrigerator is located is 70° F. If this is the case, the temperature of the cabinet at the time of the addition of sulfur dioxide liquid will also be 70° F. The liquid sulfur dioxide in the coils will therefore immediately start boiling and vaporizing because the surrounding temperature is above the boiling point (14° F.) of the liquid. As the liquid boils away, it will absorb heat from the cabinet because, for every pound of sulfur dioxide liquid vaporized, 168 Btu of heat will be extracted from the cabinet. As soon as the temperature of the cooling coil is reduced to a point lower than the cabinet temperature, the air in the cabinet will start circulating in the direction shown by the arrows in Fig. 3, because heat always flows from the warmer to the colder object.

With this method, however, the two pounds of sulfur dioxide liquid would soon be vaporized and the gas given off to the air outside the cabinet, and refrigeration would then stop until a new charge was placed in the cooling coil. Sulfur dioxide is expensive and difficult to handle and some means must therefore be used to reclaim the vapor in order to use the original charge continuously. The inconvenience of recharging the coil must also be prevented, and the refrigerator must be built so that it will automatically maintain proper food-preservation temperatures at all times with absolutely no inconvenience to the customer. This is accomplished by the compressor pulling the warm sulfur dioxide gas from the cooling unit and pumping it into the condenser where it is changed to a liquid ready to return to the cooling unit.

CHAPTER 3

Compression System of Refrigeration

The process of refrigeration is most commonly accomplished by the evaporation of a liquid refrigerant, thereby extracting heat from the medium to be cooled. The refrigeration cycle is then composed chiefly of four further steps, whose purpose is to remove this heat from the evaporating refrigerant by again putting it in the liquid state in order that it may be used repeatedly in a continuous process.

The type of compressors generally used in home refrigerators may be grouped according to their construction as *reciprocating* and *rotary*. The principal components of a compression system refrigeration are:

1. Compressor
2. Condenser
3. Drier-strainer
4. Capillary tube
5. Evaporator (freezer unit)
6. Accumulator

In modern systems, the capillary tube method is employed to control the flow of refrigerant to the evaporator, whereas older systems are generally provided with an expansion valve for refrigerant control or metering purposes.

THE REFRIGERATION CYCLE

A thorough understanding of the cycle of operation, that is, what takes place inside a refrigerator, is necessary before a correct diagnosis of any service problems can be made. Thus, only by a thorough study of the fundamentals will one be able to master the field of refrigeration.

A cycle by definition, is *an interval or period of time occupied by one round or course of events in the same order or series.* The word *cycle,* as applied here, means a series of operations in which heat is first absorbed by the refrigerant, changing it from liquid to a gas, then the gas is compressed and forced into the condenser where the heat is absorbed by the circulating air, thus bringing the refrigerant back to its original or liquid state. With reference to Fig. 1, the cycle of operation consists of the following steps:

1. The compressor pumps refrigerant through the entire system. It draws cool refrigerant gas in through the suction line from the evaporator freezer coils. At the same time, it compresses the gas and pumps it into the discharge line. The compressed gas sharply rises in temperature and enters the condenser.

2. The condenser performs a function similar to that of the radiator in an automobile, that is, the condenser is the cooling coil for the hot refrigerant gas. In the condenser, the heat is expelled into the room air outside the cabinet. During this process, the refrigerant gas gives up the heat

Compression System of Refrigeration

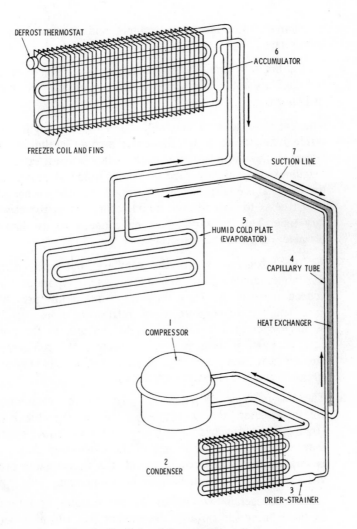

DEFROST THERMOSTAT

6
ACCUMULATOR

FREEZER COIL AND FINS

7
SUCTION LINE

5
HUMID COLD PLATE
(EVAPORATOR)

4
CAPILLARY TUBE

HEAT EXCHANGER

1
COMPRESSOR

2
CONDENSER

3
DRIER-STRAINER

Fig. 1. Typical refrigerant flow diagram.

it removed from inside the cabinet and changes into a liquid state.

3. As the hot refrigerant liquid leaves the condenser to enter the capillary tube, a drier-strainer removes any moisture or impurities.

4. The capillary tube is carefully calibrated in length and inside diameter to meter the exact amount of liquid refrigerant flow required for each unit. A predetermined length of the capillary tube is usually soldered along the exterior of the suction line, forming a heat exchanger which helps to cool the hot liquid refrigerant in the capillary tube. The capillary tube then connects to the larger diameter tubing of the evaporator.

5. As the refrigerant leaves the capillary tube and enters the larger tubing of the humid plate and evaporator, the sudden increase in tubing diameter forms a low pressure area, and the temperature of the refrigerant drops rapidly as it changes to a mixture of liquid and gas. In the process of passing through the evaporator, the refrigerant absorbs heat from the storage area and is gradually changed from a liquid and gas mixture to a gas.

6. The low-pressure refrigerant gas leaving the evaporator coil now enters the accumulator. The accumulator is a large cylinder designed to trap any refrigerant liquid which may not have changed to gas in the evaporator. Since it is impossible to compress a liquid, the accumulator prevents any liquid from returning to the compressor.

7. As the refrigerant gas leaves the accumulator, it returns to the compressor through the suction line which is part of the heat exchanger, thus completing the cycle.

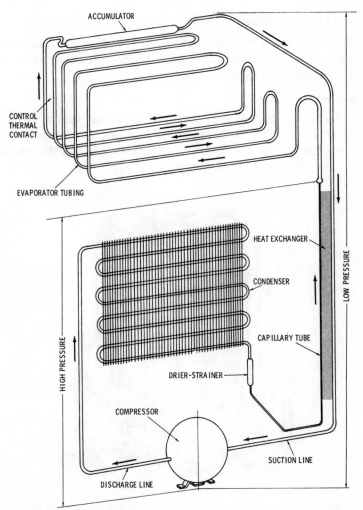

Fig. 2. Illustration showing the low-pressure and the high-pressure side of a refrigeration system.

Compression System of Refrigeration

High-pressure Side

The high-pressure side of the system is that containing the high-pressure refrigerant, and consists of the condenser and capillary tube including the compressor.

Low-pressure Side

This is that part of the system where the refrigerant is in a gaseous state at low temperature and pressure. It consists of the evaporator and suction line. The low-pressure and high-pressure side of a refrigeration system are shown in Fig. 2.

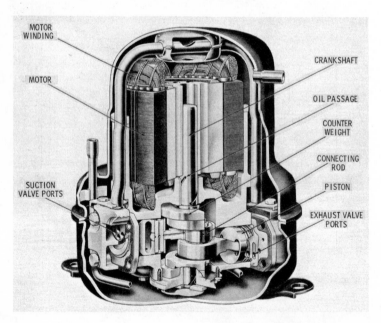

Courtesy Tecumseh Products Co.

Fig. 3. Cutaway view of a typical twin-cylinder sealed compressor used in household refrigerators.

COMPRESSORS

These are usually of the hermetic or sealed bype, although numerous refrigerators of the older models are of the so-called open type. The open-type compressor is one in which the motor is connected to the compressor by means of a belt, whereas in the hermetic type, the motor and compressor are connected directly to the same shaft and sealed into the same compartment to furnish an airtight and dust-proof assembly. A hermetic-or sealed-type compressor is shown in Fig. 3. The hermetically sealed unit provides a compact assembly and will, as such, require less space, with the additional advantage of the elimination of a shaft seal and stuffing boxes. Also, the elimination of the belt and pulley will result in the lessening of noise and maintenance.

CONDENSERS

Since the refrigerant leaves the compressor in the form of high-pressure vapor, some method must be found to bring the vapor back into liquid form. It is the function of the condensing unit to condense the vapor back to a liquid so that it can be reused in the refrigeration cycle. Condensers are of two main types—air-cooled by means of a forced fan draft, and air-cooled by natural air circulation. The most common condenser construction is shown in Fig. 4, and consists of copper tubing or coils upon which fixed fins have been inserted to assist in removing the rapid accumulation of heat. This cooling process is further provided by means of a fan (driven either by the compressor motor or by an independent motor) which forces air through the condenser.

Other condensers are made up of corrugated plates welded together, the corrugations forming tubes in which the gas is condensed. In this form of condenser, the air passes over the outside surface of the plates and removes the heat by condensation from the refrigerant gas.

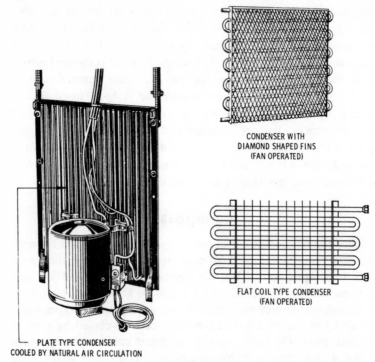

CONDENSER WITH
DIAMOND SHAPED FINS
(FAN OPERATED)

FLAT COIL TYPE CONDENSER
(FAN OPERATED)

PLATE TYPE CONDENSER
COOLED BY NATURAL AIR CIRCULATION

Fig. 4. Various types of condensers showing construction principles.

DRIER-STRAINER

As previously noted, the function of the drier-strainer is to remove moisture and impurities from the refrigeration system. A typical drier-strainer, Fig. 5, consists essentially of a tubular metal container, or housing, arranged for connection into the

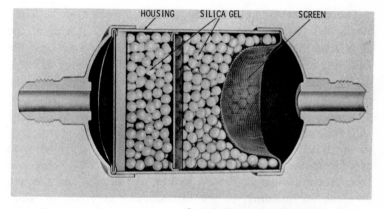

Fig. 5. Illustrating a typical drier-strainer.

refrigerant circuit. The drying and purifing agent is usually pure silica-gel which, in addition to a cup-shaped inlet screen, provides the filtering and drying action.

CAPILLARY TUBES

The capillary tube is essentially an expansion device used as apart of the refrigerant circuit. It consists normally of a miniature tube, the length of which depends upon the size of the condensing unit and the kind of refrigerant used. The bore or inner diameter is very small and the length varies greatly from a few inches up to several feet. Because the capillary tube offers a restricted passage, the resistance to the refrigerant flow is sufficient to build up a high enough head pressure to produce condensation of the gas. The operating balance is obtained by properly proportioning the size and length of the tube to the particular unit on which it is to be used.

The refrigerant employed has a direct influence on both the length and the diameter of the capillary tube. The size of the inner tube diameter must, in any event, be such as to keep the tube full of liquid under normal operating conditions. Because of the minute size of the tube bore, it is important that the refrigerant circuit be kept free from dirt, grease, and any kind of foreign matter, since these obstructions may close up the tube and thus make the unit inoperative. To prevent obstructions to the free flow of refrigerants, a strainer-drier is provided, as noted in the refrigerant circuit diagram (Fig. 6). If the refrigerant tube becomes plugged, the evaporator will defrost and the unit may run continuously, or the thermal-relay cuts out, in which case both the suction and discharge pressures will be abnormally high.

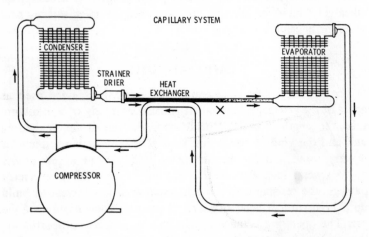

Courtesy Refrigeration Research Co., Inc.

Fig. 6. Illustrating capillary installation in typical refrigerating circuit.

EVAPORATORS

The function of the evaporator is to absorb heat from the refrigerator cabinet, the heat being introduced by food placed in the refrigerator, by insulation loss, and by door openings. Evaporators used in present day designs are of the direct-expansion type because of its simple construction, low cost, and compactness, and also because it provides a more uniform temperature and rapid cooling. The evaporator consists simply of metal tubing which is formed around the freezer compartment to produce a cooling area for freezing of ice cubes, and to provide the desired cooling effect for the food storage compartments. Fig. 7 illustrates various types of frozen food compartments.

In operation, when the refrigerant leaves the capillary tube and enters the larger tubing of the freezer shelves, the sudden increase in tubing diameter forms a low-pressure area, and the temperature of the refrigerant drops rapidly as it changes to a mixture of liquid and gas. This cold mixture passes through the top shelf (or top freezer plate in some models), then to the bottom shelf, descending through each additional shelf until it reaches the accumulator. In the process of passing through the shelf tubing, the refrigerant will absorb heat from the food storage area and will gradually change from a liquid and gas mixture to a gas.

ACCUMULATORS

The accumulator is a large cylindrical vessel designed to trap any refrigerant liquid which may not have changed to gas in the evaporator. It is in this manner that any liquid refrigerant remaining in the low side of the system is prevented from entering the suction line to the compressor.

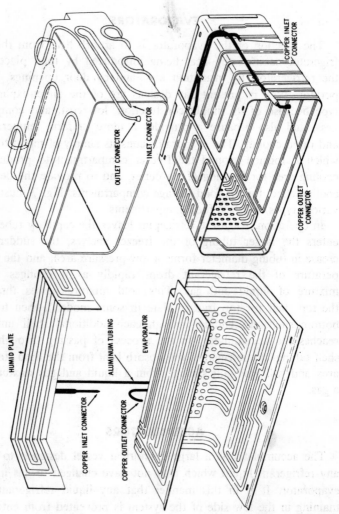

Fig. 7. Typical evaporator arrangement in household refrigerators.

CONTROL METHODS

The most common method of temperature control presently employed in household refrigeration units, is the thermostatic control. The apparatus consists principally of a thermostatic bulb (Fig. 8), which is fastened to the evaporator (chilling unit) and connected to the bellows by means of a capillary tube.

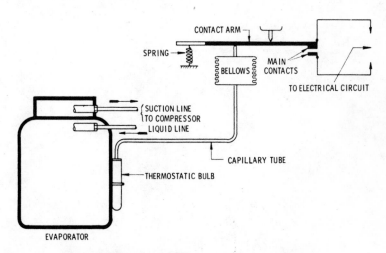

Fig. 8. Diagram showing the temperature control.

The bulb and tube are charged with a highly volatile fluid. As the temperature of the bulb increases, gas pressure in the bulb-bellows assembly increases, and the bellows pushes the operating shaft upward against the two spring pressures. The shaft operates the toggle or snap mechanism. Consequently, the upward travel of the shaft finally pushes the toggle mechanism off center, and the switch snaps closed, starting the motor. As the motor runs, the control bulb is cooled, gradually reducing the pressure in the bulb-bellows system. This reduction of bellows pressure allows the spring to push the shaft slowly downward until it has finally traveled far enough to push the toggle mechanism off center in the opposite direction, snapping the switch open and stopping the motor. The control bulb then slowly warms up until the motor again starts and the cycle repeats itself.

CHAPTER 4

Absorption System of Refrigeration

The absorption system of refrigeration differs from that of the conventional compression type mainly in that it uses heat energy instead of mechanical energy to change the condition required in the refrigeration cycle. The heat energy required may be obtained from a gas flame, an electric heater, or a kerosene flame. The principal advantages in the absorption system of refrigeration lies in the fact that, since no moving parts are involved, the repairs and maintenance cost will be at a minimum. The comparison between the functioning of an *absorption system* and a *compression system* of refrigeration is principally as follows: *The absorption system uses heat (usually a gas flame) to circulate the refrigerant, while the compression system employs a compressor to circulate the refrigerant.* There are four components of the absorption system which compare with the four components of the compression system, as follows:

1. The boiler or generator compares with the stroke of the compressor.

2. The condenser and evaporator serves the same purpose in an absorption system as that in the compression system of refrigeration.
3. The absorber compares to the low side, or the suction of the pump.

PRINCIPLES OF OPERATION

After the proper heat has been applied to the generator, the ammonia will vaporize from the water. The vapor bubbles, in trying to escape, will carry slugs of water up the percolator tube. The vapor and water are allowed to separate so that the vapor is free to continue upward into the condenser. Here, with proper air circulation, the ammonia vapor will be condensed to a liquid. It then flows through a liquid trap into the evaporator. When the evaporator shelf is level, the proper slope is established in all coils to induce a gravity flow downward.

At the time the unit is charged, a small amount of hydrogen is introduced. At this point of the cycle of the unit, hydrogen flows upward into the evaporator and tends to mix with the ammonia vapor and encourages more evaporation. It is this evaporation process which produces refrigeration. Since the mixture of hydrogen and ammonia vapor is considerably heavier than hydrogen alone, the normal tendency for this mixture is to flow downward. It is encouraged to do this, and in so doing it is forced to pass upward through the absorber.

Water, which has been separated from the ammonia by heat, is flowing downward through the absorber. The water temperature has been reduced so that it will again absorb the ammonia quite readily, and the water and ammonia solution flows back to the generator for recirculation. Since the hydrogen has been washed free of ammonia (and lightened), it flows upward again through the evapoator. When the absorption system is working normally, all of these actions are continuous. A thermostatically controlled gas valve, with the feeler attached to the evaporator coil, will vary the heat input and consequently the amount of refrigeration that the load of the refrigerator requires.

ABSORPTION REFRIGERATION CYCLE

The freezing system of the gas refrigerator is made up of a number of steel vessels and pipes welded together to form a hermetically sealed system. All the spaces of the system are in open and unrestricted communication so that all parts are at the same total pressure. The charge includes an aqua-ammonia solution of a strength of about 30% concentration (ammonia by weight) and hydrogen.

The elements of the system include a *generator* (sometimes called boiler or still), a *condenser*, an *evaporator,* and an *absorber*. There are three distinct fluid circuits in the system an *ammonia circuit* including the *generator, condenser, evaporator,* and *absorber*; a *hydrogen circuit* including the evaporator and absorber; and a *solution circuit* including the generator and absorber. A diagram of this circuit is shown in Fig. 1.

Heat is applied by a gas burner or other source of heat to expel the ammonia from solution. The ammonia vapor thus generated flows to the condenser. In the path of flow of ammonia from the generator to the condenser are interposed an *analyzer* and a *rectifier*. Some water vapor will be carried along with the ammonia vapor from the generator. The analyzer and rectifier serve to remove this water vapor from the ammonia vapor. In the analyzer, the ammonia passes through a strong solution which is on its way from the absorber to the generator. This reduces the temperature of the generated vapor somewhat to condense water

103

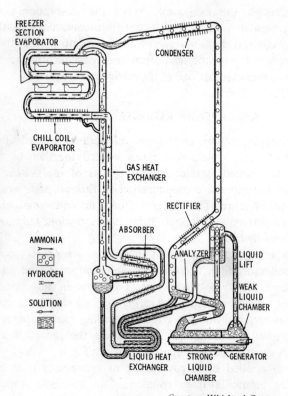

Courtesy Whirlpool Corp.

Fig. 1. Operating cycle of a gas-absorption refrigerating system.

vapor, and the resulting heating of the strong solution expels some ammonia vapor without additional heat input. The ammonia vapor then passes through the rectifier where the residual small amount of water vapor is condensed by atmospheric cooling and drains to the generator by way of the analyzer.

The ammonia vapor, which is still warm, passes on to the section of the condenser where it is liquefied by air cooling. The condenser is provided with fins for this purpose. The ammonia thus liquefied flows into the evaporator. A liquid trap is interposed between the condenser section and the evaporator to prevent hydrogen from entering the condenser. Hydrogen gas enters the lower evaporator section and flows upward, in counter-flow to the downward flowing liquid ammonia. The effect of placing a hydrogen atmosphere above the liquid ammonia in the evaporator is to reduce the partial pressure of the ammonia vapor in accordance with Dalton's law of partial pressures.

Under Dalton's law, the total pressure of a gas mixture is equal to the sum of the partial pressures of the individual gases. Consequently, in the evaporator, the partial ammonia vapor pressure is less than the total pressure by the value of partial pressure of the hydrogen. The lesser ammonia vapor pressure results in evaporation of the ammonia, with consequent absorption and cooling of the surroundings which are in a well-insulated enclosure. The cool, heavy, gas mixture of hydrogen and ammonia vapor formed in the evaporator leaves the top of the evaporator and passes downward through the gas heat exchanger to the absorber.

Since the weight of a gas is proportional to its molecular weight, and the molecular weight of ammonia is 17 and the molecular weight of hydrogen is 2, the specific weight of the strong gas is greater than that of the weak gas. This difference in specific weights is sufficient to initiate and maintain circulation between the evaporator and the absorber. The gas heat exchanger transfers heat from one gas to the other. This saves some cooling in the evaporator by precooling the entering gas. A liquid drain at the bottom of the evaporator is connected to the down-flow space of the gas heat exchanger. In the absorber, a flow of weak solution (water weak in ammonia) comes in direct contact with the strong gas. Ammonia is absorbed by water, and the hydrogen (which is practically insoluble) passes upward from the top of the absorber through another chamber of the gas heat exchanger into the evaporator. The liquid and gas flow in opposite directions.

From the absorber, the strong aqua-ammonia solution flows through the liquid heat exchanger to the analyzer, and then to the strong liquid chamber of the generator. The liquid heat exchanger precools the liquid entering the absorber and preheats the liquid entering the generator. Further precooling of the weak solution is obtained in the finned air-cooled loop between the liquid heat exchanger and the absorber. Actual unit construction includes additional refinements which increase efficiency, but the cycle described previously is typical of the cycle in any absorption refrigerator. Refrigeration is accomplished by a continuation of the cycle described herein.

THE FLUE SYSTEM

The flue system is composed of a combustion chamber where the gas-air mixture is burned. The flue extension is to provide a draft for an adequate flow of secondary air and a dilution flue to cool the products of combustion and carry them to the top of the refrigerator.

The combustion chamber is properly known as the generator flue because it is attached to the generator. A flue baffle, is normally located at the back or top end of the generator. The purpose of the flue baffle is to distribute the heat. The flue baffle should always be located in its correct position, otherwise the efficiency of the unit will be affected.

The flue extension is made of nonmetallic materials and is attached to the generator flue. On horizontal generator flue systems, a clean-out cover is located at the rear of the unit. The flue baffle may be removed through the opening when the clean-out cover is removed. When the unit is in operation, the clean-out cover must be in place for proper draft.

The dilution flue is a nonmetallic pipe which extends from the top of the generator flue extension to the top of the cabinet. Air for dilution is induced at the bottom of the loose fitting dilution flue, and mixes with products of combustion as it travels to the top of the cabinet.

GAS CONTROL DEVICES

An absorption system refrigerator requires various gas control devices for its operation, which are shown in Fig. 2.

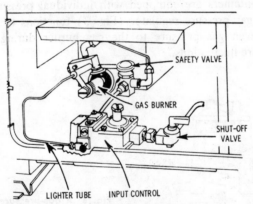

Fig. 2. Gas components in typical absorption refrigeration system.

1. Shut-off valve.
2. Pressure regulator (for piped gas only).
3. Input control valves.
4. Gas burner.
5. Thermostat.

107

The gas components may easily be removed as an assembly for service when required, provided that the gas shut-off valve is closed and that the electric supply is disconnected.

Gas Shut-off Valve

The gas shut-off valve, as the name implies, is a simple *on* and *off* valve to enable the serviceman to cut off the gas supply when necessary for repairs and service.

Pressure Regulators

These are normally provided on all piped gas refrigerating units except those using straight liquid petroleum (LP) gas, since LP gas containers are equipped with individual pressure regulators. The gas pressure regulator (Fig. 3) functions to provide a constant even gas pressure to the gas burner during all main line pressure fluctuations.

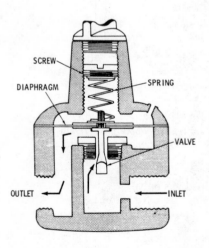

Fig. 3. A gas-pressure regulator.

The action of the gas pressure regulator is very simple. A valve is suspended on a flexible diaphragm in a way that will cause the valve to come in contact with the valve seat when the diaphragm opens, allowing the gas to pass. The pressure of the gas will move the diaphragm up or down, controlling the amount of gas.

Pressure applied from above the diaphragm, either by spring pressure or by weights (depending upon the type of regulator), will tend to open the valve. Therefore, the outlet pressure of the regulator can be adjusted by turning a screw to change the spring tension or, on dead weight regulators, by adding or removing weight.

Input Controls

The input control consists essentially of two automatically operated gas valves which are electrically controlled by means of the refrigerator thermostat. The most common type of controls are of General Controls or White Rodgers manufacture, as shown in Fig. 4. As will be noted in the illustrations, these controls function in a similar manner, although they differ in their operation. The input control consists of:

1. A felt filter to remove gum and foreign materials from the gas.
2. A diaphragm-type pressure regulator to adjust maximum flame gas pressure when the control is used on piped gases.
3. Two identical electrically operated gas valves which alternate opening and closing as the refrigerator thermostat cycles. One valve supplies gas for a maximum burner flame, while the other releases gas for an intermediate flame.

109

4. A bypass to supply gas for a burner pilot flame when both valves are closed due to no electrical power.
5. A plate containing two orifices to reduce the gas flow for the intermediate and pilot flames.
6. A push-button valve gas release for burner lighting.

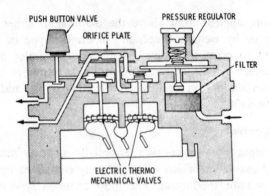

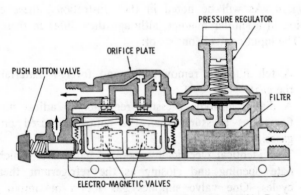

Courtesy General Controls and White Rodgers

Fig. 4. Diagram showing the components of a gas input control assembly.

When the refrigerator is to be operated on LP gas, the pressure regulator cap screw is replaced with one having a long narrow pin. The pin locks the pressure regulator in an open position. The gas is regulated at the supply tank.

Gas Burners

The gas burner assembly (Fig. 5) consists essentially of a *turbulator, orifice spud,* and *thermal safety valve.* The function

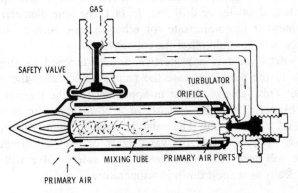

Fig. 5. Diagram illustrating the typical gas burner operation.

of the turbulator, as its name implies, is to create turbulence in the gas stream as it enters the mixing tube. This turbulence will have two effects. The one which is apparent and readily understood is that it aids in mixing primary air and gas. The second effect is that the air-gas ratio is automatically adjusted so that with proper air-shutter adjustment, the flame will be all blue on maximum flame and will have stability on pilot flame. All piped gas-burner turbulators have two grooves in the conical end, and the head of the turbulator must always fit tightly into the rear

111

side of the orifice. All LP gas-burner turbulators have a single groove in the conical end and are spring-loaded for adjustment to the gas pressure.

The burner orifice required on gas refrigerators is so small that a slight change in its dimensions changes its capacity. For this reason, each orifice spud is individually flow tested and rated to capacity. All orifice spuds having the same rated capacity have a comparative flow accuracy of plus or minus 3% for orifice spuds used with piped gas. The number marked on the orifice spud is not the hole diameter or drill size. In fact, the hole diameter may vary somewhat to compensate for other factors, such as surface resistance, which would affect the capacity.

The safety valve is a protective device designed to stop the gas flow to the burner in case the flame should leave the generator flue. This valve is similar in appearance to the thermo valve on the burner. The valve consists of a bi-metallic disc to which is attached a valve stem. The valve is open at room temperature. However, by overheating the valve body or the heat conductor, the disc will snap the valve closed. The safety valve will reset automatically as it cools down in temperature.

Thermostats

The thermostat is an automatic gas valve in the burner supply line which controls the flow of gas to the burner to supply either a maximum or minimum flame, depending upon control dial setting and thermostat bulb temperature. The thermostat shown in Fig. 6 identifies the different parts of the thermostat and their relative position to each other. The working parts of the thermostat are enclosed in an outer case. In the lower part of the case is a gas passage, imposed in which is a gas valve. Under the valve is a spring which pushes the valve toward a closed position.

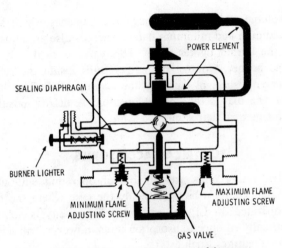

Fig. 6. Illustrating the absorption refrigerator thermostat valve.

Above the gas passage is a power element consisting of a bulb connected to a flexible diaphragm by a capillary tube. In this system is a small quantity of gaseous hydrocarbon. Motion of the power element is transmitted to the gas valve by the valve pin. When the bulb is warm, the gas expands and exerts a pressure in the power element, which pushes the valve open. When the bulb is cold, the gas contracts, the pressure inside the power element is reduced, and the valve spring pushes the valve closed. From the foregoing description, it is evident that there is a throttling action and that the valve may be in any position between wide open and fully closed, depending upon the thermostat dial setting and the thermostat bulb temperature.

To prevent the gas supply to the burner from being completely closed off when the valve is closed, a bypass or minimum flame passage is provided. Adjustment screws on the thermostat control the volume of gas flow through the passages which supply gas for maximum and minimum flame. There is also an adjustment screw on the burner lighter valve. This valve is used only when lighting the burner. Control of temperatures inside the refrigerator is accomplished by turning the control dial. The highest number on the dial is the coldest position. A defrost position is provided for manual defrosting.

ELECTRICAL ACCESSORIES

Gas refrigerating units are capable of operating without any electrical connections, which is usually the case where the refrigerator is operated on LP gas and where electricity is not available. Electrically equipped absorption units, however, will add certain desirable features, such as:

1. Cabinet lights.
2. Automatic defrosters.
3. Air circulator fans.
4. Air circulator thermostat, etc.

Cabinet Lights

These are wired in the conventional manner, the interior light bulb being energized by the light switch when the cabinet door is opened.

Defrost Timer

These are manufactured to operate the electrical defrost heater at certain time intervals, usually once every 12 or 24 hours. Fig. 7 illustrates a typical selfstarting electrical defrost timer operating upon the well-known electric clock principle. The dial on the timer should be set to the correct time of day when the refrig-

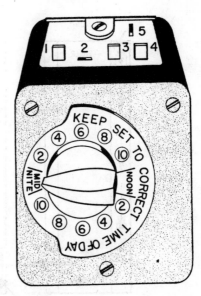

Fig. 7. A typical defrost timer.

erator is installed, and should be reset to the correct time any time the electric service is interrupted.

The 24-hour defrost timer contains an electric switch which makes contact for a period of about 20 minutes, beginning at the 2 A.M. position on the timer. This means that if the dial is set to the correct time, defrosting will occur automatically at 2 A.M. each day. The defrost water will drain from the chill coil onto the lower surface of the chill cover and then into a drain elbow which directs the water to an evaporation pan.

Air Circulator Fan

The air circulator fan, as the name implies, is generally designed to become operative when the ambient temperature becomes unduly high. The additional air movement provided by the

115

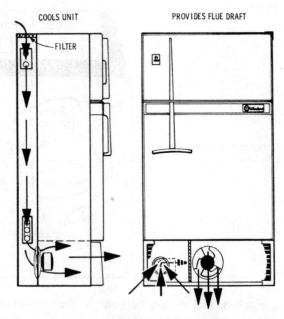

COOLS UNIT   PROVIDES FLUE DRAFT

FILTER

Courtesy Whirlpool Corp.

**Fig. 8. Illustrating the air circulation fan arrange-
ment in a typical refrigerator.**

air circulator will provide more cool air for cooling the condenser.
At the same time, the movement of cooler air at the rear of the
cabinet will reduce the amount of heat transfer to the inside of
the cabinet, as shown in Fig. 8. The thermostat which controls
the air circulator fan is preset to "cut in" at approximately 100° F.
and to "cut out" at approximately 80° F. This means that the
fan will not operate until the temperature of the thermostat reaches
100°, and once it has started to operate, the fan will remain in
operation until the thermostat temperature has dropped to 80° F.
The electrical components are shown in Fig. 9.

116

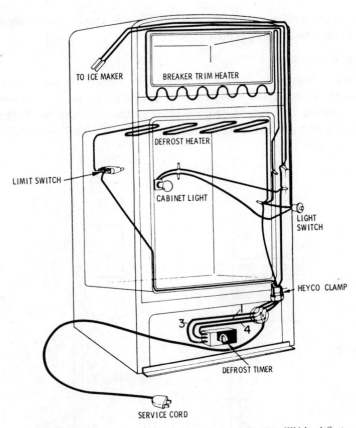

TO ICE MAKER

BREAKER TRIM HEATER

DEFROST HEATER

LIMIT SWITCH

CABINET LIGHT

LIGHT SWITCH

HEYCO CLAMP

3

4

DEFROST TIMER

SERVICE CORD

Courtesy Whirlpool Corp.

Fig. 9. Arrangement of electrical components used in an automatic defrost refrigerator.

INSTALLATION AND SERVICE

Before starting the refrigerator installation, turn off all other gas appliances, such as gas ranges, gas furnaces, gas water heaters, gas spaceheaters, etc. Next, shut off the gas supply at the main inlet or outlet at the gas meter.

Air Circulation

All refrigerators must have proper air circulation for proper operation. When the refrigerator is in operation, air enters from the bottom and travels upward through the rear section of the cabinet and out at the top, as shown in Fig. 10. This air circula-

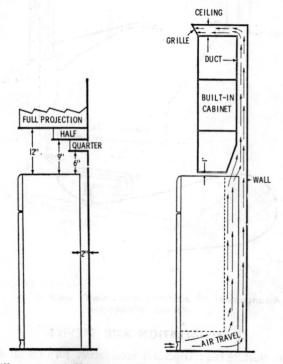

Fig. 10. Illustrating the proper clearance arrangement for the proper air circulation.

118

tion takes place naturally unless prevented by insufficient clearance or blocked air passages. Proper air circulation will usually result when the refrigerator is installed indoors directly in front of a wall allowing a minimum distance of two inches of clearance from the back of the refrigerator to the wall, and at least a twelve-inch clearance above the top of the refrigerator.

When the recommended top clearances cannot be obtained, an air duct should be installed. The air duct should have about the same width as the refrigerator and be approximately seven inches deep. This duct may return the air to the room at ceiling height or may exhaust it through a suitable vent in the roof.

Leveling

The equal distribution of the liquid within the freezing compartment requires the unit to be installed and maintained in a level position, both front, back, and side to side. The leveling of the refrigerator can conveniently be accomplished by shimming with small wooden strips or other available material.

Gas Line Connection

When connecting the gas line, use tubing and fittings as prescribed by local codes. Install the gas line so that the refrigerator can be disconnected at the inlet valve without damage to the controls. On liquid petroleum(LP) gas installations, a gas pressure regulator in the gas line is not needed since the regulator at the gas supply tanks should maintain constant gas pressure at the burner. Fig. 11 shows typical gas connection methods.

The installation shown will not permit the refrigerator to be disconnected between the gas cock and the thermostat. Therefore, to disconnect the refrigerator, it is necessary to shut off the gas supply from the meter. By using a tubing connection between the gas cock and gas filter, or between the gas filter and thermostat,

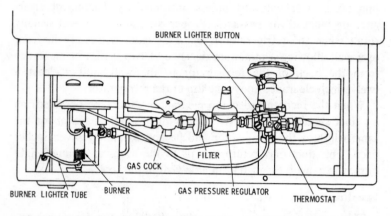

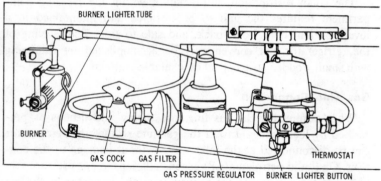

Fig. 11. Gas connections for vertical and horizontal installations.

the controls can be installed in a way which will permit the refrigerator to be easily disconnected for service.

Piping Material—Standard weight wrought-iron pipe coupling with the American Standard wrought-steel and wrought-iron pipe shall be used in installation of appliances supplied with utility gases. Threaded copper or brass pipe in iron-pipe sizes may be used with gases not corrosive to such material. Gas pipe shall not be bent. Fittings shall be used when making turns in gas pipe.

The connection of steel or wrought-iron pipe by welding is permissible. Threaded pipe fittings (except stockcocks or valves) shall be of malleable iron or steel when used with steel or wrought-iron pipe and shall be copper or brass when used with copper or brass pipe. When approved by the authority having jurisdiction, special fittings may be used to connect either steel pipe or wrought-iron pipe.

Piping Material for LP Gases—Gas piping for use with undiluted LP gases shall be of steel or wrought-iron pipe complying with the American Standard for wrought-steel and wrought-iron pipe, and brass or copper pipe, or seamless copper, brass, steel, or aluminum tubing. All pipe or tubing shall be suitable for working pressure of not less than 125 pounds per square inch. Copper tubing may be of the standard K or L grade, or equivalent, having a minimum wall thickness of 0.032 inch. Aluminum tubing shall not be used in exterior locations or where it is in contact with masonry or plaster walls, or insulation.

Defective Material—Gas pipe or tubing and fittings shall be clear and free from burrs and defects in structure or threading, and shall be thoroughly brushed, chipped, and scale blown. Defects in pipe, tubing, or fittings shall not be repaired. When defective pipe, tubing, or fittings are located in a system, the defective material shall be replaced.

Gas pipe, tubing, fittings, and valves removed from any existing installation shall not be used again until they have been thoroughly cleaned, inspected, and ascertained to be equivalent to new material. Joint compounds shall be applied sparingly and only to the male threads of pipe joints. Such compounds shall be resistant to the action of LP gases.

121

BURNER ORIFICE CLEANING

The burner orifice must be cleaned when the refrigerator is installed and each time a new orifice is installed. This is necessary because the orifice is so small that a particle of dirt can materially change its operating characteristics. Dirt in the orifice can also cause an unstable flame and burner outage. Clean the orifice after

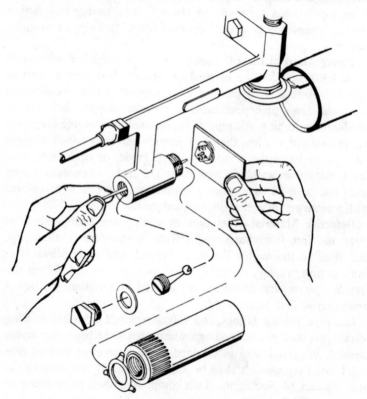

Fig. 12. Showing typical method for orifice cleaning.

it has been installed on the burner body. The air-shutter barrel, mixing tube, seal screw, and turbulator must be removed.

Use a round toothpick, as shown in Fig. 12, sharpened on an emery board, to clean the orifice. Insert in the orifice and rotate with light pressure. Blow away any dust but do not rub the orifice with the fingers. If the burner is installed on a refrigerator, use a mirror for observation.

BURNER AIR ADJUSTMENT

The entire flame must be free of all yellow after the adjustments have been completed. Do not make this adjustment if there is an abnormal flue draft. On models having a filter above the condenser, check to be sure the filter is clean and in place. Tighten the air-shutter barrel securely on the burner body. This position should result in a yellow flame. Rotate the air-shutter barrel in the opposite direction, increasing the primary air until the yellow just disappears from the entire flame. From this point, continue to turn the air-shutter barrel in the same direction until the flame becomes noisy, unstable, or until the stop is reached. The desired setting for proper combustion is approximately midway between these two points.

CLEANING THERMOSTAT VALVE

To clean the thermostat valve, turn off the gas supply to the refrigerator. If the cleanout cap is inaccessible, disconnect the flare nuts at the inlet and outlet of the thermostat. Remove the screws attaching the thermostat to the cabinet, and turn the thermostat until the cleanout cap is accessible. Be careful not to pinch or break the capillary. Remove the cleanout cap and gasket, spacer, valve spring, and valve. Clean the valve seat in the thermostat,

123

using the eraser end of a pencil covered with a clean cloth. Blow into the valve seat to make certain all dirt has been removed. Clean the flat face of the valve with a clean cloth.

GAS PRESSURE ADJUSTMENT

The maximum flame gas pressure must be determined and adjusted for each refrigerator when installed or reinstalled in a different location. The pressure was determined at the time the burner orifice spud was selected. The maximum flame provides the

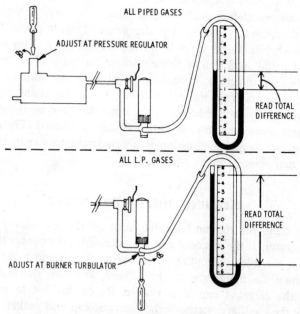

Fig. 13. Showing manometer method of gas pressure measurement for piped and L.P. gas.

correct heat input for the greatest capacity of the refrigerator unit. The unit cooling capacity will be decreased if the heat input is more or less than the specified rating.

Adjustment to the intermediate and pilot flame gas pressure is not necessary, and provision for such has not been made. The orifice plate on the input control meters the gas flow for the lower flame settings. To adjust the maximum flame gas pressure, proceed as follows:

1. Make sure the appliance cord is connected to a power source and the thermostat is turned to a numbered position. (Maximum flame valve must be open in the input control.)
2. Remove the seal screw from the side of the burner and connect a water-filled manometer, as shown in Fig. 13.
3. Light the burner and allow the generator flue to warm.
4. *On piped gas*: Remove the seal screw and turn the adjusting screw in the pressure regulator on the input control counterclockwise to decrease the pressure; or clockwise to increase the pressure.

FLAME STABILLITY

After completing the control adjustments, always check the flame for stability. Disconnect the appliance cord from the power source, thus reducing the flame to a pilot. If the pilot flame appears jumpy or wobbly, rap the bottom cross rail of the cabinet several times lightly, using a wrench. If the flame is unstable, the rapping will cause the flame to go out. If the flame is stable, the rapping will not affect it. An unstable flame is usually caused by incorrect primary air adjustment, loose turbulator, and/or dirt in the orifice. When the test for flame stability has been completed, reconnect the appliance cord.

125

REMOVING AND REPLACING REFRIGERATOR UNIT

To remove and replace the refrigerator unit, proceed as follows:

1. Remove all trays, baffles, and other parts from the freezing compartment to permit its removal through the freezing compartment opening at the rear of the cabinet. If the unit has a separate food compartment cooling coil, remove the grille and thermostat bulb.

2. On models with a permanently insulated section between the freezer compartment and food compartment, remove the trim around the freezer compartment, remove the rubber plug from the drain hole, and remove the screws on the sides of the freezer.

3. Move the refrigerator away from the wall and remove the rear panel, dilution flue, and top louver.

4. On models having push-button defrost, disconnect the electric cord from the wall receptacle. Carefully pry out the complete push-button assembly from the trim. Remove the side and top-door opening trim. Remove the defrost thermostat feeler from the clamp on the freezer by loosening the screws from the inside of the freezer. Remove the thermostat support screws from the liner. Pull the assembly downward out of the cabinet. Now remove all the wires from the thermostat terminals. The defrost heaters, when used, may be removed from the freezer coils after the unit is out of the cabinet by prying off the retaining clamps. Install the heater on the replacement unit while the unit is out of the cabinet by reversing the above proceedings.

5. Remove the unit retaining bolts and, on models with a gas heat exchanger (or tubes) embedded in the cabinet insu-

lation, remove the screws from the cover plate. Carefully lift the unit out of the cabinet.

6. Remove and install on the replacement unit the stryofoam insulation and freezer drain pan, if present. When replacing the unit, it is necessary to disconnect the front chill-coil supports in order to remove the plastic drain chute from beneath the freezer section. After the drain chute has been removed from the inoperative unit, reconnect and securely tighten the supports on both units.

7. Install the replacement unit by reversing the removal procedure. Make sure that the gasket and/or sealing compound around the freezing compartment opening is properly placed in position to assure a satisfactory seal. On models with embedded gas heat exchangers, place sealing compound around the edge of the cover plate and attach the plate securely to the cabinet. The tubes protruding through this plate should also be carefully sealed.

8. On models equipped for automatic defrosting, the drain tube should be properly sealed around the tube and cover plate on the cabinet side.

REFRIGERATOR MAINTENANCE

The following pointers should be observed for proper adjustments and maintenance of gas refrigerators.

Lighting the Burner

Lighting the burner is a rather simple operation provided the manufacturer's instructions accompanying the unit are followed. The lighting procedure is generally as follows:

1. Be sure the gas valve is turned on.
2. Push the lighter button.

3. Light the gas at the end of the burner tube.
4. Continue to push the lighter button until the burner valve clicks open and the burner flame ignites. (Should the burner flame go out, wait five minutes before relighting.)

Do not leave the burner lighted unless all final adjustments have been made. The burner flame should burn a blue color and must enter the flue opening.

Cold Control

The position of the thermostat dial should depend upon the refrigeration load. When the food load is heavy, turn the dial toward a colder position, and when the food load is light turn the dial to a less cold position. A colder setting will be required in summer than in winter. Experience and observing the effect of the various thermostat settings will usually provide the operator with the required knowledge after a short period of time.

Stopping Refrigeration

When necessary to discontinue refrigeration for any length of time, turn off the gas supply. Remove the ice cube trays and empty and dry them. Dry the interior of the refrigerator. Leave the door partly open to ventilate the cabinet interior and keep it fresh.

Refrigerator Too Cold

Low refrigerator temperature may be caused by any or a combination of the following:

1. If the minimum flame is set too large, the thermostat will not be able to control the temperature in the food storage compartment due to the fact that some refrigeration will be

taking place even when the thermostat valve is completely closed.

2. Dirt on the valve seat will keep the valve open slightly. Gas passing through the valve will cause the minimum flame to be too large, giving the same effect as just described.

3. The refrigerator is designed for operation at normal room temperatures. Location in unheated rooms will cause foods to freeze.

4. The highest number on the control dial is the coldest setting. If the food storage compartment temperature is too cold, turn the dial to a warmer setting.

Refrigerator Not Cold Enough

If any of the basic adjustments are incorrect, the efficiency of the unit may be impaired. Therefore, the things to check on a complaint of a refrigerator not cold enough include the basic adjustments for proper air circulation, level, and right burner flame. In addition, the following items may cause a complaint of poor refrigeration:

1. Check the door gasket seal and repair if necessary.

2. If a "built-in" refrigerator is improperly vented, there may not be enough air circulation over the condenser to cool the unit efficiently. Check for proper air circulation.

3. Check for leaky cabinet seals when the service history shows that the unit has been changed, or if there is evidence pointing to wet insulation.

4. On models which depend on circulation of air around the evaporator for cabinet cooling, the efficiency of the unit will decrease as ice builds up on the evaporator. Some models located in extremely humid climates may need defrosting several times a week for peak efficiency.

5. Dirty condenser fins will prevent the air from circulating through the fins for proper cooling, and as a result, the efficiency of the unit will decrease in proportion to the amount of dust and lint on the fins.
6. The flue must be clean and have proper draft. A visual inspection of the flue will show whether the flame is entering the flue.
7. The highest number on the control dial is the coldest position. If the complaint is that the refrigerator is not cold enough, the control dial may not be set to a cold enough position.
8. If the maximum flame pressure setting is in excess of the recommended pressures, the unit may be overloaded and will not perform as efficiently as it should.
9. Dirt in the orifice spud may partially close the opening and limit the amount of gas which can be burned.

No Refrigeration

A complaint of no refrigeration can be caused by the following:
1. Check cause for burner flame outage.
2. If the evaporator is warm and the control dial is set on the coldest position, it should not be difficult to adjust the maximum flame screw to obtain the correct pressure at the burner. If this is impossible, change the thermostat.

Unit failure will seldom be experienced. Before condemning a unit, be sure that the following requirements have been fulfilled:

1. Clean the condenser and be sure that there is enough clearance above the refrigerator for proper air circulation.
2. Level the unit front to back and side to side, checking from the bottom shelf of the freezer section.
3. Adjust burner.

Burner Flame Goes Out

The burner will react to adverse conditions more noticeably when it is operating on minimum flame. Any difficulty with flame outage can usually be discovered by looking at the minimum flame and by checking minimum flame pressures. Burner outage is usually caused by the following:

1. If the burner is spaced too close to the generator, the minimum flame will be pulled away from the heat conductor, causing the heat conductor to cool off and close the automatic shut-off valve. The burner space illustrations are shown in Fig. 14.
2. Check to be sure that the correct orifice is in the burner and use a manometer to set the recommended pressure.

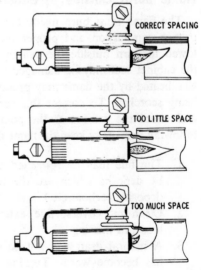

Fig. 14. Illustrating the correct and incorrect burner-to-generator spacing arrangement for proper flame.

CORRECT SPACING

TOO LITTLE SPACE

TOO MUCH SPACE

131

3. Dirt in the orifice spud may partially close the opening. A visual inspection of the orifice and cleaning are necessary to correct this condition.

4. Always check for flame stability after working on a burner, or when there is a complaint of burner outage. To test flame stability, turn the control dial within its operating range until the flame is maximum size. Then gradually turn the dial in the opposite direction until the flame begins to reduce in size. Observe the flame as it reduces from maximum flame to minimum flame. If the flame is jumpy or distorted as it passes from maximum to minimum size, it is probably unstable. A further check for stability can be made by snapping the fingers or tapping two wrenches together. An unstable flame will react to the sound waves.

Flame Burns Outside of Generator Flue

The flame must burn inside the generator flue at all times for proper combustion and proper refrigeration. If the flame is allowed to burn outside the generator flue for even five minutes, the cabinet seal may be damaged and the insulated section which was heated by the flame may produce odors due to the insulation being scorched. To correct this complaint, replace the insulation and reseal the cabinet at the points affected by the flame. The following items may keep the flame from entering the flue:

1. The flue may be restricted by objects dropped into it, or by deposits which are the result of combustion. (Sulphur deposits, carbon, etc.)

2. Clean-out covers, flue extensions, flue elbows corroded, loose, or missing.

3. A natural draft will not be established in the flue until it has become warm. Turning the thermostat to the coldest

position and setting the air adjustment for a hard flame will help the flame to enter the flue. Blowing through a short length of tube into the generator flue opening will also cause the flame to enter, unless the flue is stopped up. Final air adjustment should be made after the flame enters the flue.

4. A burner spaced too far away from the generator flue will cause the flame to back out when it is controlling at minimum flame.

5. If the minimum flame is too small, the generator flue may cool off, stopping the natural draft. This can also occur if the refrigerator is located in an extremely cold room even with the correct minimum flame.

6. The refrigerator should not be vented to another room, to the attic, or to the outside. Down drafts caused by improper venting may force the flame out of the flue.

Manual Defrosting

Most complaints of "incomplete defrosting" or "defrosting takes too long" are usually caused by too large a minimum flame. To correct this condition, check to be sure that the burner has the correct orifice spud and that the minimum flame pressure is correct. Dirt on the thermostat valve seat may cause the minimum flame pressure to be incorrect. If it is impossible to obtain the correct minimum flame pressure by turning the minimum flame adjustment screw, clean the thermostat valve and valve seat.

Automatic Defrosting

A list of the most common causes of defrost problems on 24-hour automatic, or on push-button defrost models is combined in this section because of the related nature of the two types of automatic defrost.

1. Connect an ohmmeter or test core to the heater and check for continuity or for a short. If the heater is found to be defective, replace it.
2. The defrost heater must have good contact with the section of the evaporator which is to be defrosted. Check to be sure that the heater clamps are holding the heater in contact with the section of the evaporator which is to be defrosted.
3. Failure of the electrical power supply to the heater could cause complaints of no defrosting. This could be caused by an electrical short, the service cord not plugged in, or by a blown fuse.
4. Place a long screwdriver against the timer case and press an ear to the handle. If the power cord is plugged in and the clock is running, the gear train sound should be audible. To test the timer electrically, disconnect the power cord and remove the timer. Check for continuity between terminals 1 and 4. This is the clock circuit and it should have continuity at all times. If no continuity exists, replace the timer. Check for continuity between terminals 3 and 4. Continuity should exist when the dial is turned to the 2 A.M. position. If no continuity is found, replace the timer.
5. The push-button defrost control is a "fail-safe" mechanism and will not start a defrost cycle if the power element has lost its charge. If the refrigerator is located at an altitude greater than 5,000 ft. above sea level, the defrost mechanism must be recalibrated to accomplish a complete defrosting cycle.

Odors Inside the Refrigerator

Odors inside the refrigerator may be the result of storing odorous unwrapped foods, or by infrequent cleaning. Odors will also develop if a refrigerator has been in use and is stored for any length of time with the door closed. If, by any chance, the flame has burned outside of the generator flue, it is possible that a phenolic odor due to burned insulation may develop in the cabinet. To remove this odor, the section of the insulation which has been burned must be replaced.

To remove any of these odors, first remove the source, then wash with a solution of baking soda and water (approximately one tablespoon to a quart of water). In extreme cases, use activated charcoal to remove the odor.

Odors Outside The Refrigerator

Odors outside the refrigerator are usually the result of poor combustion caused by the flame burning outside the flue, touching the generator flue, or wrong primary air adjustment. Gas leaks can also cause odors outside the refrigerator. Use a soap-bubble solution to find gas leaks.

Frost Forms Rapidly

Rapid formation of frost can be caused by a bad door seal, uncovered foods or liquids, high humidity, excessive usage, or a bad cabinet seal. Keep in mind that the moisture which forms the frost must enter the cabinet in one of the ways mentioned previously. To reduce the amount of frost, the user can be cautioned against excessive door openings on hot humid days. All foods and liquids should be covered before placing in the refrigerator.

135

Loose Gas Connection

All gas connections should be leak tested with a soap-bubble solution before putting the refrigerator into operation. Gas leaks, no matter how small, should be corrected. Be sure that all seal washers and seal screws are tightened on burners, thermostats, etc.

Inoperative Light Switches

A visible check of the light switch may be made when the power cord is plugged in by manually pushing the button in and out to see if the switch is sticking, and to see if the light is going off and on.

TROUBLE CHARTS

The chart listed on the following pages gives the more common troubles encountered in the repairs of absorption-type household refrigerators. The trouble and possible cause are given with the method used for remedying the defect.

ABSORPTION REFRIGERATION TROUBLE CHART

No Refrigeration

Possible Cause	Possible Remedy
Burner	Check to see that the flame provides proper heat input.
Electrical power (when available)	Check for 115 volt a.c. at front terminal board.

Partial Refrigeration

Possible Cause	Possible Remedy
Unlevel unit	Check unit for levelness. Adjust levelers at bottom corners if necessary.
Air filter	Check air filter above condenser. If dirty, wash in detergent and instruct

	user. If missing, replace and check for dirty condenser.
Air circulation	Check to see that cabinet fans are operative.
Thermostat	Check to see that thermostat is on numbered position calling for refrigeration.
Usage	Instruct user regarding excessive door openings, excessive ice usage, improper loading and storage, and commercial usage.
Improper Defrosting	Check to see that evaporator air chambers are defrosted (air flow not restricted). Check to see that defrost heater circuit is not energized.
Flue baffle	Check for omission.
Vapor seal	Check door gasket for good seal. If interior liner sweats or frosts, check and reseal all cabinet openings for good vapor seal.
Cabinet lights	Check to see that lights do not burn when door is closed.
Gas pressure	Check to see that maximum flame gas pressure is correct. Be sure maximum flame valve is open on input control.
Burner orifice	Disassemble burner and clean orifice. (Dirty orifice will restrict gas flow and reduce heat input.)
Inefficent unit	Performance test unit before replacing.
Burner thermal valve	Check to see that valve opens during burner lighting.
Hi-Temp safety valve	Check to see that valve has not failed in "closed" position.

Burner Outage (Customer complaint may be "no refrigeration.")

Possible Cause	Possible Remedy
Burner valve heat conductor	Check to see that heat conductor impinges on intermediate flame. (If necessary, turn thermostat dial to "Off" position to obtain intermediate flame.)
Burner orifice	Disconnect appliance cord from power supply. Check pilot flame for stability.
Air circulation	Check to see that absorber fan is operative. Check to see that air filter above condenser is not dirty or restricted. (Note: A restricted filter will increase generator draft, pulling flame from burner. This will give flame characteristic of being noisy.)
Input control	Check to see that both valves are operative and that there are no internal leaks. Check to see that orifice plate is for type of gas used and orifices are not restricted or oversize.

Improper Defrosting (Improper defrosting will probably not be noticed by user. The complaint would likely be "not enough or no refrigeration").

Possible Cause	Possible Remedy
Defrost timer	Check to see that motor runs and defrost heater circuit is energized at 2 A.M. position.
Defrost heater	Check for resistance and proper thermal contact with unit defrost liquid trap. (Note: heater will glow if contact is inadequate.)
Defrost switch	Check for thermal contact with freezer evaporator. Replace switch

if inoperative. If stuck "closed" heater will be energized too long during defrosting and will cycle on the safety switch. If stuck "open", freezer fan will not operate at any time.

Safety switch

Check for thermal contact with heater heat conductor. Check for continuity.

Operates Too Cold

Possible Cause
Thermostat

Possible Remedy
Check numbered position. Set on lower number if possible. Instruct user. Check that capillary tube is inserted full length of well evaporator. Check calibration.

Exterior Condensation

Possible Cause
Location

Insulation

Possible Remedy
Instruct user regarding very damp location (basement, for example). Check adjacent insulation area for void. Fill void with fiberglass or equivalent.

Interior Condensation

Possible Cause
Heaters

Usage

Vapor seal

Possible Remedy
Check adjacent antisweat heaters for resistance. Replace if inoperative.
Instruct user regarding uncovered foods and liquids.
Check and adjust door gasket for good seal. Check and reseal any cabinet openings (unit, evaporator, cabinet, fans, etc.).

Odor

Possible Cause
New appliance

Possible Remedy
Inside storage compartment will have "new" odor for a few min-

139

utes when door is first opened. Instruct user this is normal. When burner is lighted and heated for first time, odor will occur; this is normal. Advise user.

Inoperative Freezer Fan.
Possible Cause
Defrost switch

Possible Remedy
Check to see that thermal switch in series with fan motor has cooled to "closing" temperature. Advise user it is normal for fan to be temporarily inoperative because of switch following installation, defrosting, and restarting when warm. Check for thermal contact and continuity when cold.

Fan motors

Check to see that motor is operative.

Noisy Burner
Possible Cause
Dirty air filter

Possible Remedy
Wash filter. Do not adjust burner primary air until filter has been checked.

Burner primary air

Rotate burner air-shutter barrel to reduce primary air. Flame must not be yellow when adjustment is completed.

Excessive generator draft

Check for obstruction in area of condenser air intake.

CHAPTER 5

Compressors

The function of any compressor in a mechanical refrigeration system is to establish a pressure difference in the system, and thus create a refrigerant flow from one part of the system to the other. It is this difference in pressure between the high and low sides that forces liquid refrigerant through the control valve and into the cooling unit. The vapor pressure in the cooling unit must be above the pressure at the suction side of the condensing unit to force the low-side vapor to leave the cooling unit and flow to the condensing unit.

Compressors employed in household refrigeration units may be divided into several classes:

With respect to their construction and operation as:

1. Single cylinder.
2. Twin cylinder.

With respect to the method of compression as:

3. Reciprocating.
4. Rotary.

With respect to drive employed as:

5. Direct drive.
6. Belt drive.

With respect to location of prime mover as:
7. Independent (belt drive).
8. Semi-hermetic (direct drive, motor and compressor in separate housings).
9. Hermetic (direct drive, motor and compressor in same housing).

Modern household refrigeration compressors are usually of the reciprocating sealed type whereas older refrigerators are normally of the open type, with the compressor belt driven by the motor each being mounted separately. The reciprocating compressor consists of one or two cylinders mounted either horizontally or vertically. The cylinder motion is effected by the crankshaft arm, which is fastened to one end of a connecting rod. The other end of the connecting rod is fastened to the piston by means of a piston pin. It is in this manner that the connecting rod and crank arm transfer the rotation of the crankshaft to the reciprocating or back-and-forth motion of the piston.

HOW THE COMPRESSOR WORKS

The passage of the refrigerant from and to the compressor is controlled by means of a discharge and suction valve located on a specially designed valve plate which forms the lower part of the cylinder head. The flapping action of the valve permits the flow of refrigerant out through the discharge valve port only, and only through the suction valve port. Thus, when the piston moves away from the valve plate (suction stroke), a pressure reduction takes place. Because the pressure in the cylinder is now below that in the suction line, a flow of refrigerant occurs that pushes open the suction valve and permits a certain quantity of refrigerant to enter the compressor.

As the motion of the piston reverses and moves toward the valve plate (compression stroke), it increases the pressure which forces the suction valve to close. A further compression, as the piston moves close to the valve plate, opens the discharge valve and forces the refrigerant into the discharge line, thus causing what is known as the high-side pressure of the refrigerant.

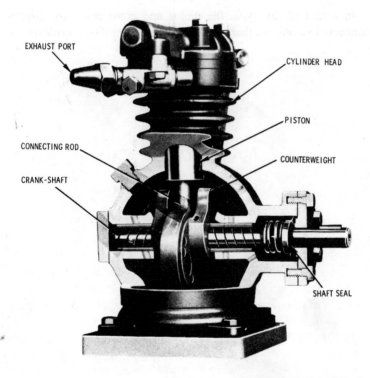

EXHAUST PORT

CYLINDER HEAD

PISTON

CONNECTING ROD

COUNTERWEIGHT

CRANK-SHAFT

SHAFT SEAL

Courtesy Multiplex Mfg. Co.

Fig. 1. Cutaway view of a single cylinder belt-driven reciprocating refrigeration compressor.

It is in this manner that the suction stroke fills the cylinder with vaporous refrigerant, whereas the compression stroke compresses it and forces it out of the cylinder; the valves are actuated only by the difference in pressure. A belt-driven single-cylinder compressor is shown in Fig. 1.

HERMETIC UNITS

In a unit of this type, the motor and compressor are directly connected to one another; the motor and compressor work on the

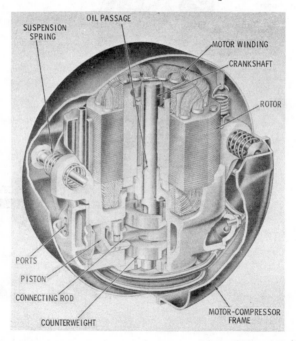

Courtesy Tecumseh Products Co.

Fig. 2. Cutaway view of a single cylinder reciprocating hermetically sealed refrigeration compressor.

same shaft and are enclosed in a common casing. Some of the advantages of a hermetically sealed unit are that no shaft seal or belt are required, and the more compact assembly takes less space. In a unit of this type (shown in Fig. 2), the revolutions per minute (rpm) obviously are the same for both compressor and motor. This factor has a very important bearing on the size and design of the unit; it determines the type of refrigerant, the type of controls to be used, etc.

The servicing of hermetic units does not differ in any important respect from that of the belt units in which the compressor and motor are separately mounted. Because the unit is completely sealed in and tested at the factory, trouble is seldom found with the compressor-motor assembly, and the source of the trouble is in almost every case found in other parts of the system. The motor, located above the compressor, operates in a vertical position, whereas the compressor operates horizontally. This construction method permits operation of the compressor in oil, simplifying the lubricating problem. The suction intake is placed so that the suction vapor must travel through the holes in the motor rotor in order to get to the top of the shell and then to the intake tube.

Any oil or liquid refrigerant is separated from the vapor by centrifugal force due to rotation of the motor rotor, as vapor passes up through the holes in the rotor. Consequently, oil and liquid separation is assured, oil is eliminated, and with it, the danger of valve breakage. Oil is picked up in a small slot on the end of the crankshaft which acts as a centrifugal pump, and the oil is forced into the lower main bearing. From this point it follows the spiral groove in the bearing up to the crankcase, where it lubricates the thrust plate, connecting rod, and piston. Oil is then pumped through a tube by vapor action, up to a small reservoir beside the upper main bearing and is then fed into and spiraled up through the bearing from where it drops back to the sump. Fig. 3 shows other typical reciprocating compressors used in the refrigeration and air conditioning industry.

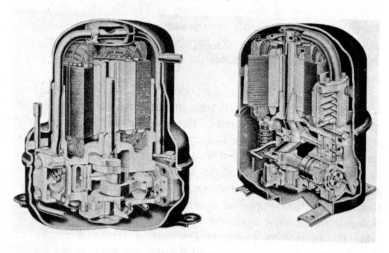

Courtesy Tecumseh Products Co.

Fig. 3. Cutaway views of a typical sealed reciprocating compressor used in the refrigeration and air conditioning industry.

ROTARY-TYPE COMPRESSORS

In the rotary compressor, compression of gas is obtained by means of a sleeve or roller moving in a closed cylinder. In one type, the roller slides or rolls on an eccentric on the drive shaft inside a stationary concentric ring known as the pump chamber. In another type, the roller revolves concentrically with the shaft inside an off-center ring.

The pump chamber of a typical rotary compressor is shown in Fig. 4. Here, compression is obtained by means of an eccentrically driven roller moving in a gyrating manner in a closed cyl-

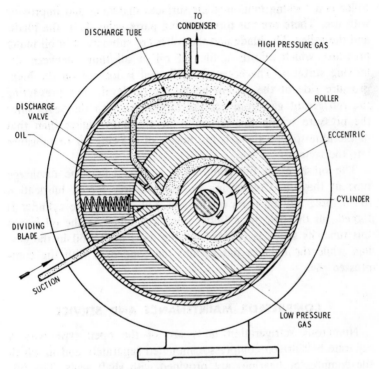

Fig. 4. Illustrating the working components in a typical rotary compressor.

inder. The inlet and discharge passages are separated by a blade which, under oil pressure, always maintains contact with the roller surface. The unit is designed with adequate clearance between the roller and cylinder, and a film of oil under pressure serves as a seal between the surfaces. The roller does not revolve at shaft speed, but simply rolls slowly around the eccentric portion of the shaft. The contact between the blade and the

147

roller is a rocking motion, their surfaces matching and improving with use. There are but three moving parts—the shaft, the blade, and the roller. The blade and the roller are submerged in oil under pressure, which affords a film of oil at all times between the moving surfaces. The eccentric-shaft seal is located on the high-pressure side of the system below the oil level, thus preventing the refrigerant gas from coming in contact with the seal. Since the pressure within the system is at all times higher than that of the atmosphere, there is no danger of drawing air or moisture into the system.

The oil level in the compressor is just below the discharge tube at the top. Condensing pressure insures forced lubrication to all three moving parts of the unit. Oil entering the cylinder is forced out through the cylinder discharge tube. As the oil leaves this tube, its speed is reduced leaving most of the oil in the casing, while the balance passes into the condenser with the compressed gas.

COMPRESSOR MAINTENANCE AND SERVICE

Numerous refrigeration units are of the open type with a separate belt-driven compressor mounted separately and in which the compressor bearings are provided with shaft seals. The following information will assist in servicing this type of unit:

Shaft Seal

The function of the seal in an open-type refrigerating compressor system is to prevent the gas from escaping the compressor at the point where the shaft leaves the compressor housing. This, in the early stages of the refrigeration industry, was a difficult problem to solve. The shaft, of necessity, must revolve, and yet the refrigerant must not be allowed to escape when there is a pressure within the crankcase. Neither must air be allowed to enter when the pressure in the crankcase is below zero pounds pressure. The solution to the problem of crankshaft leaks was found in the development of a bellows-type seal, which is now an important part of most compressors.

The seal is an assembly of parts consisting of a seal ring fastened to a bellows which, in turn, is fastened to a seal flange, as shown in Fig. 5. A spring surrounds the bellows, with one end resting

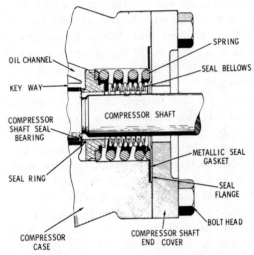

Fig. 5. Showing a typical shaft seal assembly.

against the seal ring and the other against the seal flange. The face of the seal ring is lapped flat and smooth. When assembled in the compressor, the seal ring presses against a shoulder on the shaft that has also been lapped, forming a gas- and oil-tight joint at this point. The bellows provides the degree of flexibility necessary to keep the seal ring in perfect contact with the shaft. The seal flange is clamped against a gasket around an opening in the side of the compressor. The compressor shown in Fig. 2 is of the hermetic type and needs no shaft seal.

To determine if a compressor is leaking at the seal, proceed as follows:

Close both shut-off valves by turning the stem to the right as far as possible. To insure adequate refrigerant pressure in the compressor crankcase and on the seal bearing face, attach a refrigerant drum containing the correct refrigerant to the suction shut-off valve outlet port. When making this connection, there should be a gauge in the line from the drum to the compressor to accurately determine the pressure of the refrigerant in the compressor.

Test pressures for this purpose should be approximately 70 to 80 pounds. If the compressor is located in a cool location, it may be necessary to raise the pressure in the drum by adding heat. In this process, care must be taken not to exceed 100 pounds, as pressure greater than this may damage the bellows assembly of the seal. With this pressure on the crankcase of the compressor, test for leaks with a halide torch, moving the finder tube close to the seal nut, the crankshaft, the seal-plate gasket, and the point at which the seal comes in contact with the seal plate. If this process does not disclose a leak, turn the flywheel over slowly by hand, holding the finder tube close to the aforementioned parts.

After the leak has been detected, locate the exact place where it is leaking, if possible. If the leak is around the seal-plate gasket, replace the gasket. If the leak should be at the seal seat or nut, replace with a new seal plate, gasket, and seal assembly.

To replace the seal, observe the following instructions:

1. Remove the compressor from the condensing unit.
2. Remove the flywheel, using a puller. Leave the flywheel nut on the crankshaft so that the wheel puller will not distort the threads.
3. Remove the seal guard, seal nut, and seal assembly.
4. Remove the seal plate and gasket.
5. When assembling the seal, put a small quantity of clean compressor oil on the seal face plate and the seal.
6. To reassemble, reverse these operations, making sure the seal plate is bolted in place and the seal guard is at the top.

Pistons and Rings

Pistons employed in the majority of compressors are made of the best grade of cast iron or aluminum. They are carefully machined, polished, and fitted to the cylinders with close tolerances. There are several different designs of pistons. Some early models were not equipped with piston rings, but were lapped to the cylinder in a very close fit.

At present, however, two or more piston rings are employed, as shown in Fig. 6. Their function is to insure proper lubrication and sealing of the piston and the cylinder walls. Pistons, when assembled, should fit the cylinder walls so that, when inserted, they do not drop of their own weight but must be urged through with the fingers. This fit is usually obtained by allowing 0.0003 in. clearance per inch of cylinder diameter. Thus, a 1-1/2″ cylinder would have a 0.00045 in. clearance between the piston and the cylinder wall.

If the cylinder walls are scored, they must be honed after reboring to assure a high degree of wall finish. This will maintain cylinder proportions over long periods of time. After the

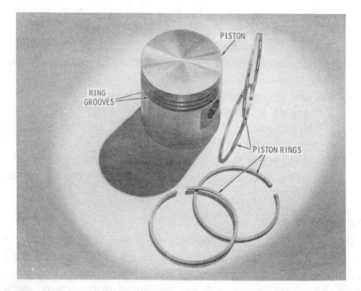

Fig. 6. Showing construction principles of a typical piston and rings.

rings have been fitted, the compressor should be operated over-
night to permit the rings to wear in. The compressor should then
be drained and flushed with petroleum spirits or dry-cleaning
fluid and dehydrated before being returned to service.

Connecting Rods and Wrist Pins

The connecting rod forms the link between the piston and
the crankshaft, as shown in Fig. 7. One end is connected to the
piston by means of a hardened, ground, and highly polished
steel wrist pin. The connecting rod is very similar to the type employed in an automobile engine.

Several different methods are used to secure the piston wrist
pin and connecting rod. In some designs, the wrist pin is tightly

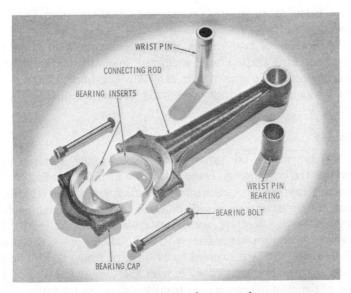

Fig. 7. Connecting rod construction.

clamped to the connecting rod with the moving bearing surface in the piston, while others have a bushing in the connecting rod which allows the pin to turn freely in both the piston and connecting rod. Other types have the wrist pin held solidly in the piston. Connecting rods are usually made of high-grade cast iron or drop-forged steel.

Crankshafts

The crankshafts are commonly made of steel forgings machined to the proper tolerances for the main and connecting-rod bearings. The double crank is employed in all two-cylinder compressors, while the single crank is used on the single-cylinder type. Crankshafts are equipped with counterweights and are carefully balanced to insure smooth and vibrationless compressor operation.

Some types of compressors are equipped with what is known as an eccentric shaft. This is a different application of the crankshaft principle. It employs an assembly consisting of the main shaft with an eccentric and an outer eccentric strap, as shown in Fig. 8.

Valves

The function of the valves is to direct the flow of refrigerants through the compressor. These valves are named according to the function they perform, as *suction* and *discharge* valves. The location of the valves varies with different designs, although suction and discharge valves are usually assembled to a plate located on top of the compressor assembly. These valves are usually made of thin steel and are referred to as discs or feeds, depending on their shape and construction. It is of the utmost importance for the efficiency of the compressor that the valves seat properly.

In one model employing reed valves, the suction or inlet valve is 0.008 in. thick, whereas the discharge or outlet valve is 0.006 in. thick. Most valve plates are fitted with a spring arrangement retaining the valve reed. Typical compressor valve assemblies are shown in Fig. 9.

It may often be found that the suction-valve reed is held off its seat by corrosion and dirt lodged under it, leaving the cylinder open on the low side. In this case there will be no refrigeration, the condenser will not get warm, and the power consumption of the motor will be low. To determine if the suction valve is causing these conditions, connect the compound and pressure gauges, then start the unit. If the suction valve is at fault, the pressure gauge will not show an increase in pressure, and the compound gauge will not show any decrease in pressure and will

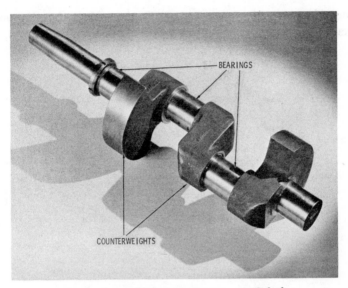

Fig. 8. Two cylinder compressor crankshaft.

fluctuate. Flushing the suction valve may wash the obstruction away and permit the valve to function normally.

If the discharge-valve reed is held off its seat by something lodged under it, such as corrosion or dirt, the cylinder will remain open on the high side, and there will be no refrigeration. To determine if the discharge valve leaks, connect the compound and pressure gauges and operate the unit until the low-side pressure is reduced to normal. Shut off the unit and immediately place an ear close to the compressor. If the valve leaks, a hissing noise of the gas escaping will be heard. The low-side pressure will rise rapidly, and the high-side pressure will fall rapidly, equalizing the pressures. The rapidity of this action determines how badly the valve leaks. Flushing the discharge valve may

155

wash the obstruction away and permit the valve to function normally.

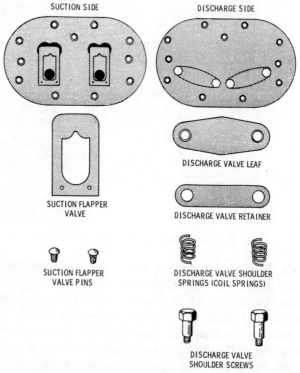

SUCTION SIDE   DISCHARGE SIDE

SUCTION FLAPPER
VALVE

DISCHARGE VALVE LEAF

DISCHARGE VALVE RETAINER

SUCTION FLAPPER
VALVE PINS

DISCHARGE VALVE SHOULDER
SPRINGS (COIL SPRINGS)

DISCHARGE VALVE
SHOULDER SCREWS

Fig. 9. Details of a typical compressor valve assembly and parts. The suction side forms the bottom and the discharge side the top of the removable valve plate.

In some designs, the suction valve is located in the piston head. The refrigerant enters the compressor crankcase from the suction line, and is drawn from there through the suction line and into the cylinder. When the piston has completed its suction stroke and begins its compression stroke, the piston valve closes, trapping the refrigerant vapor above the piston. As the compression stroke is continued, the vapor is forced out through the discharge valve, and the cycle continues.

In a design of this type, the discharge valve is usually located on a separate plate, held between the top of the cylinder and the cylinder head. The valve plate has a hole for refrigerant passage, located directly above the piston, and a valve seat to which the valve is attached. The discharge valve is the dividing point between the low-pressure refrigerant gas in the compressor base and the high-pressure refrigerant gas which has been compressed by the piston and forced through the discharge valve into the cylinder head.

Compressor Efficiency Test

An efficiency test is a check on the relative amount of useful work that the compressor will accomplish. Strictly speaking, the efficiency of any machine is taken as the ratio of the power output to the power input in the same unit. This is usually written:

$$\text{efficiency} = \frac{\text{output}}{\text{input}}$$

The factors that determine the efficiency of a compressor are:

1. The degree to which the piston valve remains closed on the up stroke.
2. The degree to which the discharge valve remains tight when the piston is on the down stroke.

To test the compressor efficiency, proceed in the following manner:

1. Stop the compressor and install a compound gauge on the suction-line valve and a pressure gauge on the discharge-line valve.

2. Close the suction valve and operate the compressor until about 25-in. of vacuum is obtained on the compound gauge, then stop the unit and note the gauge readings. If the compressor will not pull a 25-in. vacuum or better, it is probable that air is leaking by the discharge valve and the piston valve.

3. If the head pressure drops and the vacuum-gauge reading remains practically constant, it is probable that there is an external leak at one of the points on the head of the compressor, or at the gauge and shut-off valve connection.

4. To repair either a leaky suction valve or discharge valve, remove the head of the compressor and remove the discharge valve plate carefully. In disassembling the discharge valve, caution should be used so as not to disturb the actual conditions prevailing during the test. It is possible for some dirt, scale, or other foreign matter to get under the valve disc and on the seat, causing poor performance. If there is no evidence of dirt or foreign matter, check the seat on both the discharge valve and piston assembly for low spots or scratches. If these are found, replace the discs or the valve plate completely.

Generally the trouble can be found at either the suction valve or the discharge valve. Badly scored seats on either side of the discharge or suction valve require replacing with new assemblies. Removal of deep scores changes the valve lift, further endangering the efficiency. After the repairs are made, thoroughly clean the parts with gasoline or other solvent and reassemble them, using new gaskets. Repeat the efficiency test to insure that the trouble has been eliminated.

Stuck or Tight Compressor

The reason for a compressor becoming *stuck* is usually a result of moisture in the system or lack of lubrication. When this occurs, the compressor should be thoroughly cleaned. The compressor should be completely disassembled and the parts thoroughly cleaned and refitted. New oil and refrigerant should be put into the cleaned system.

A tight compressor will result when a cylinder head, a seal cover, or similar part has been removed and not replaced carefully, or when the screws have been tightened unevenly. This will develop a misalignment causing a bind in the moving parts, which may cause the compressor to become *stuck*.

Compressor Knocks

A knock in the compressor may be caused by a loose connecting rod, eccentric strap and rod, eccentric disc, piston pin, crankshaft, or too much oil in the system. A compressor knock can be determined by placing the point of a screwdriver against the crankcase and the gear against the handle. It will not be possible to determine what causes the knock until the compressor is disassembled.

Sometimes it may be possible to determine a looseness of the aforementioned parts without completely disassembling the compressor. First remove the cylinder head and valve plate to expose the head of the piston. Now rotate the compressor by hand and press down on the top of the piston with the finger. Any looseness can be felt at each stroke of the piston. The loose part should be replaced.

It is always well to check the compressor oil level before analyzing and determining compressor repairs. Oil knocks are usually caused by adding too much oil in the servicing of the unit. It should never be necessary to add oil to a system unless there has been a leakage of oil. A low charge is sometimes diagnosed as a lack of oil. Always make sure that a low oil level is actually due to lack of oil rather than to a low charge before adding oil.

Lubrication

In conventional reciprocating compressors the lubrication is accomplished by the so-called *splash system*. Special *dippers* or *slingers* fastened to the crankshaft distribute the crankcase oil to the pistons, pin bearings, cylinder walls, crankshaft bearings, and seal. Perhaps the most important point for the serviceman to remember in connection with compressor service, is to check the amount of oil in an open-type compressor. This is accomplished as follows:

After the unit has been operated for several minutes, attach a compound gauge to the suction service valve and close the valve. The unit should be pumped down to balance the pressure (zero on the gauge) then stopped. Allow a few minutes before removing the oil filler plug and carefully measure the oil level. This level should be checked with the manufacturer's instructions concerning the oil level required for the unit in question. Only oil specifically recommended by the manufacturer for the particular unit and refrigerant should be used when adding oil.

COMPRESSOR REMOVAL

To remove a compressor from the unit, proceed as follows: Attach a compound gauge to the suction-line valve. Close the suction-line shut-off valve and run the compressor until 20 to 25 inches of vacuum are obtained, then close the discharge shut-off valve. Before removing any fittings, crack the suction-line valve to bring the gauge reading back to zero. Before removing service valves, loosen the pressure gauge and relieve the pressure in the head of the compressor. Remove the cap screws holding the suction and discharge valves to the compressor. If the compressor is to be taken away from the premises for repairs, place service valves over both the discharge and suction-line openings. This prevents air and moisture from entering and oil from leaking out. Loosen the nuts that hold the compressor to the base and bend the tubing away from the compressor just enough to permit the assembly to be lifted out. Care should be taken not to loosen the mounting pads and washers on which the compressor rests.

COMPRESSOR REPLACEMENT

The installation of a compressor is roughly a reversal of the process of removing it. First place the mounting pads and washers in position. Place the compressor carefully on the base in the same position it occupied before removal. Bolt the compressor in place. Replace the suction and discharge valves, using new gaskets. After the compressor and valves are bolted in place, the compressor must be evacuated to remove the air.

BELT ALIGNMENT

The importance of proper belt alignment in open units must be kept constantly in mind when service necessitates changing of a compressor, motor, or motor pulley. To determine the correct belt alignment and tension, proceed as follows:

The correct belt tension for a V-type belt is to have the tension so adjusted that it is possible to depress or raise the belt 1/2 in. from its original position with the fingers without undue pressure. With the compressor and motor in their respective positions and in line as nearly correct as possible, loosen the setscrew on the motor pulley so that the pulley turns freely on the motor shaft. It may be necessary on older motors to dress down the motor shaft with emery cloth. A little oil should be added to insure that the motor pulley turns freely. At this point, attach the belt with the proper tension, turn the fly wheel forward several times, then backwards several times. The point at which the belt is in correct alignment will be that position where there is no in or out travel of the motor pulley on the motor shaft, whether the flywheel is turned forward or backward.

The movement of the motor pulley outward when the flywheel is turned forward, or inward when the flywheel is turned backward (or vice versa), indicates that the motor pulley is out of plane with the flywheel; the motor must be readjusted so that this condition does not exist. Close observance of the aforementioned procedure will result in a greatly increased length of time the belt will remain in a serviceable condition.

RUNNING TIME CHECK

The percentage of running or operating time of the unit, assuming the unit functions normally, depends upon the amount of work being done. The amount of work needed depends upon the size of the refrigerator cabinet to be cooled, the temperature of the air that surrounds it, and the amount of heat that must be extracted from it. The amount of heat that leaks into the refrigerator depends upon the temperature of the room, the frequency and length of time of the door openings, and in the amount and temperature of the food placed in the refrigerator. Climatic conditions also affect the operations of a refrigerator. Thus, a refrigerator will operate more efficiently in a dry climate than in a climate of high humidity.

Keeping the aforementioned factors in mind, the length of the "on" and "off" period on the average well-adjusted refrigerator should be somewhat as follows:

At 75° F. room temperature, the "on" period should be around 2 to 4 minutes, and the "off" period around 10 to 15 minutes. In many cases where a complaint is received that the refrigerator is operating too much, a check may very easily be made by connecting a self-starting electric clock to the motor terminals. It is evident that since the clock will operate only when the motor operates, the total running time of the compressor will be registered.

COMPRESSION RATIO

The compression ratio in a refrigerant system is defined as the absolute head pressure divided by the absolute suction pressure, or

$$\text{Compression ratio} = \frac{\text{Ab head pressure}}{\text{Ab suction pressure}}$$

It should be noted that the ordinary compound gauge does not register atmospheric pressure but reads zero when not connected

163

to a pressurized system. To obtain the absolute head pressure or absolute suction pressure at zero gauge or above, fifteen pounds must be added to the gauge reading.

Example—At zero gauge or above, we have

Absolute head pressure = gauge reading + 15

Absolute suction pressure = gauge reading + 15

Example—When the low side is reading in the vacuum range, we have

Absolute head pressure = gauge reading + 15 pounds

$$\text{Absolute suction pressure} = \frac{30 - \text{gauge reading in inches}}{2}$$

The calculation of compression ratio can be illustrated by the following examples:

Head pressure = 160 pounds

Suction pressure = 10 pounds

Compression ratio =

$$\frac{\text{Ab. HP}}{\text{Ab. SP}} = \frac{160 + 15}{10 + 15} = \frac{175}{25} = 7:1$$

Example

Head pressure = 160 pounds

Suction pressure $= 10$ inches of vacuum

Absolute head pressure $= 160 + 15 = 175$ pounds

Absolute suction pressure $= \dfrac{30 - 10}{2} = \dfrac{20}{2} = 10$

Compression ratio $= \dfrac{\text{Ab. HP}}{\text{Ab. SP}} = \dfrac{175}{10} = 17.5:1$

ENERGY CONSUMPTION

The electrical energy (usually referred to as the power consumption) used by a refrigerator depends on all the factors that influence the "on" and "off" period in addition to the size of the motor employed. Motors used generally range in size from 1/2 to about 1/3 horsepower, depending upon the size of the unit, type of refrigerant employed, and various other factors.

Experience has shown that in the northern half of the country, a good average range for the summer months is 25 to 30 kilowatt-hours per month and 20 kilowatt-hours for other months. In the southern half of the country, these figures (especially for the summer months) will be somewhat higher.

REFRIGERATION SYSTEM LUBRICANTS

The necessity of providing lubrication to prevent frictional contact on metal surfaces is universally recognized. The correct lubrication of refrigeration machinery demands special consideration; the employment of incorrect oil or the excessive use of even the most suitable oil will create objectionable operating conditions. An excessively heavy oil will not be distributed properly to the working parts and will therefore fail to do the required job. An excessively light oil will not cling and will not satisfactorily seal the pistons and rings from the by-pass of the gas back into the suction port and crankcase. Because of this fact, the selection of the proper oil should be made with care. It must be viscous enough to give proper lubrication. In a rotary compressor, the oil acts as a lateral seal, and efficiency depends on its proper functioning. Due to superheating at the discharge valves, the oil must be able to withstand high temperatures.

Reputable refiners who have assisted in lubrication research are now able to supply proper oils and, from experience, can advise a potential user which oil will best serve his purpose. The soundest advice on lubrication, therefore, is to use the oil that experience has shown to be the best. This information can generally be secured from the manufacturer of the machine or a refiner actively engaged in supplying oils for refrigeration work.

Lubrication of Motor and Fan Bearings

Lubrication of the motor and fan bearings usually can be accomplished by feeding the oil through a piece of wicking or felt from a reservoir directly to the bearings in continuous small quantities. It is necessary, therefore, to use an oil that is light enough in body to pass through the wick but heavy enough to form a proper film on the bearing surface at operating temperatures. It must also have a low "pour point" so that it will flow freely to the bearings when starting cold. The best oil will resist deterioration due to oxidation and polymerization, which cause stickiness and decreased lubrication. The use of properly refined oil will eliminate most of these difficulties. When one considers the small amount required, and the costly damage that may result from using an inferior oil, it can be seen that the best oil is the cheapest over a long period of time.

Compressor Lubrication

There are so many types of refrigerating compressors that it is impossible to specifically determine which lubricant fits all requirements. Even when compressors and machines are quite similar in design, they are apt to require individual consideration for proper lubrication.

Speed, clearance, temperature conditions, etc., have an important bearing and the system of operation and the refrigerant used are the determining factors. Most oils are chosen for a given job as a result of actual tests. Therefore, servicemen in the field will always profit by using the oil specified by the manufacturer of the unit being serviced or an oil known to answer the same specifications. Buy oils from reputable refiners only, preferably those who have had real experience in refrigeration problems.

Types of Lubrication

Compressors are usually lubricated by splash, although a semi-forced feed is occasionally used; in certain types a separate oil pump is required. There are two systems of oil circulation—one in which the oil circulates through the low side, and the other in which it does not.

As the temperature of the gas discharged from the compressor rises, the vapor pressure of the oil carried with it will also rise, and the amount of oil that can be separated will be larger. In addition, the quantity of oil carried over can be increased by the mechanical action in the crankcase of the compressor, and foaming can be induced by the release of dissolved refrigerant during the suction stroke of the piston. This latter difficulty may be quite pronounced in a machine charged with methyl chloride. If the gas and oil from the compressor are discharged into a chamber, baffles or centrifugal force can be employed to separate the oil from the gas and return it to the intake of the machine. This system is very satisfactory when employing refrigerants that dissolve oil or in a dry system where the velocity of the gas carries the oil back to the compressor. In commercial installations, the oil usually circulates through the low-pressure side. In a dry system, the high velocity of the gas keeps the oil moving. In a flooded system, the evaporation of the refrigerant leaves the oil behind, and special arrangements are used for its return.

If sufficient care has not been exercised in removing all impurities from the oil, emulsification in the liquid refrigerant can result. The effect would be the same as excessive solubility, since it can change the liquid level of the refrigerant in the evaporator. It can also result in decreased free flow of the refrigerant and prevent proper boiling in the evaporator. This causes a temperature that disagrees considerably with the corresponding pressure.

Glycerol

In addition to mineral oils, some attention has been paid to glycerol. Glycerol was used at a time when it was thought that a lubricant, in order to be suitable for use, must either be insoluble or only slightly soluble in methyl chloride. Since it was difficult to secure glycerol with a sufficiently low moisture content, its use was limited. The establishment of the completely soluble mineral oils as suitable lubricants for methyl chloride machines eliminated glycerol, except for a few special cases.

Specification of Oils

As a result of the experience of manufacturers and service engineers over a period of years, certain characteristics have become quite generally accepted as specifications for oils suitable as lubricants in refrigerating compressors charged with sulfur dioxide or methyl chloride. By means of these specifications, it is possible to guarantee that an oil (from experience) is known as satisfactory.

TABLE I

Specifications for Oil

Characteristic	Sulfur Dioxide	Methyl Chloride
Viscosity Saybolt Universal seconds at 100° F. at 5° F.	 70-200 1600-10,000	 150-320 5,000-30,000
Pour Point, °F.	—20 and below	—10 and below
Moisture, % by weight	0.01 passes 25-30 KV test	0.01 passes 25-30 KV test
Acidity, ASTM	0.01 mg. KOH/g.	0.01 mg. KOH/g.
Wax separation, from oil-refrigerant mixtures	 Not important	Important in low temperature units
Flash Point, °F.	320-400	320-400
Sligh oxidation number	10 or less	10 or less
Saponifiable matter	None	None
Sulphur %	Not important	0.15% or less
Specific gravity	.860-.870	.870-.890
Color	White or pale	White or pale
Carbon Residue % (Conradson)	.005-.01	.005-.01
Solubility, room temp- erature		
Oil in liquid refrigerant	Max. approx. 5% by Weight	Soluble all proportions
Liquid refrigerant in oil	Max. approx. 14% by weight	Soluble all proportions
Gaseous refrigerant in oil	Depends on pressure and temperature	Depends on pressure and temperature

Specifications for these oils are given in Table 1, and wherever possible, numerical values are assigned. In most cases, a range of values is given. Selection of these values is to some extent arbitrary, since it is not possible to limit definitely the range of values, or even in some cases to relate an exact value for a characteristic to the performance of the oil. Not all the characteristics given need to be specified when buying an oil, since some are vastly more important than others. There must be some connection between specifications and performance, otherwise specifications will be meaningless and of little value. In the final analysis, performance alone determines the value of an oil. Specifications are merely a convenient means of rating the value based on performance.

CHAPTER 6

Refrigeration Control Devices

In order to be of service, it is necessary that the refrigeration unit function without attention; that is, it must be made fully automatic in its operation. This automatic operation is obtained by the use of certain control devices whose function it is to connect and disconnect the compressor at periodic intervals as required to keep the stored food at the low temperatures required.

Refrigerators are usually equipped with the conventional capillary tube for refrigerant control and a temperature control switch for motor-compressor control. The motor and compressor in such systems are located in a common enclosure and are therefore termed a *sealed system*. Among the several advantages of the sealed system is its compactness, with an accompanying saving of space in the unit, in addition to the simplicity of the necessary control components.

Because of the numerous instances where older household refrigerators are still in use, it is important that the serviceman have a thorough knowledge in the operation of a few common types of these older systems. This will enable him to understand others, since they all work on the same basic principles. In general, these controls may be divided into two classes, namely:

1. Those employing a mechanical means for their operation.
2. Those employing an electrical arrangement for their operation.

Often, however, the two may be combined and the system made to function as a result of the combination. An automatic expansion valve (Fig. 1), is an example of a control which is purely mechanical, while a thermostatic type of control is a device for motor-compressor control and is an example of a control in the electrical class.

While the function of a refrigerating system is the removal of heat and the consequent governing or maintaining of desired temperatures, many types of controls are employed other than merely temperature controls to complete the system. A great many controls have an indirect bearing on the temperature, although their primary purpose is to definitely operate some part of the system. The compression method of refrigeration has two main types of controls. They are:

1. Refrigerant controls (liquid, vapor).
2. Motor controls.

Refrigerant controls are usually exercised by employment of the following:

1. Automatic expansion valve.
2. Thermostatic expansion valves.
3. Capillary or choke tube.

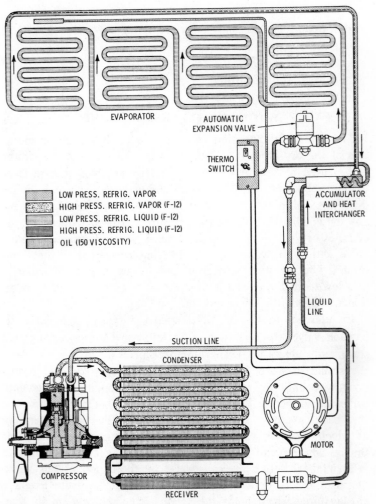

LOW PRESS. REFRIG. VAPOR
HIGH PRESS. REFRIG. VAPOR (F-12)
LOW PRESS. REFRIG. LIQUID (F-12)
HIGH PRESS. REFRIG. LIQUID (F-12)
OIL (150 VISCOSITY)

EVAPORATOR

AUTOMATIC
EXPANSION VALVE

THERMO
SWITCH

ACCUMULATOR
AND HEAT
INTERCHANGER

LIQUID
LINE

SUCTION LINE

CONDENSER

MOTOR

COMPRESSOR

FILTER

RECEIVER

Fig. 1. Illustrating the refrigerant circuit and component arrangement when using an automatic expansion valve as a means of controlling the refrigerant.

173

Motor controls are usually exercised by the use of:

1. Pressure control.
2. Thermostatic control.

AUTOMATIC EXPANSION VALVE

The automatic expansion valve is used on household evaporators of the dry type. It is located at the inlet to the evaporator and is used to control the flow of refrigerant from the receiver to the evaporator. The purpose of the expansion valve is to reduce the high-pressure liquid to a low-pressure liquid as it enters the cooling coil. When the pressure has been reduced by the compressor suction to a predetermined value depending on the valve setting, the valve opens, admitting refrigerant to the evaporator. The admitted refrigerant evaporates almost immediately at a low temperature and is pumped away before admitting additional refrigerant to the evaporator.

In reference to Fig. 2, which shows a typical automatic expansion valve, the operation is as follows: The condensing unit starts and reduces the evaporator back pressure to a point where the spring pressure forces the valve bellows, yoke, and needle downward until the valve is opened. This condition exists until sufficient refrigerant is allowed to pass through the valve to raise the back pressure enough to overcome the spring tension, at which time the valve tends to close. Thus, during the time the condensing unit is in operation, a nearly constant pressure is maintained within the evaporator by the action of this valve. During the idle period, the rising evaporator pressure exerts a closing force which holds the valve needle securely on its seat, thereby reducing the flow of refrigerant.

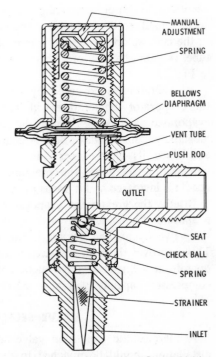

Fig. 2. Typical automatic expansion valve.

MANUAL ADJUSTMENT

SPRING

BELLOWS DIAPHRAGM

VENT TUBE

PUSH ROD

OUTLET

SEAT

CHECK BALL

SPRING

STRAINER

INLET

Courtesy of American Standard Control Division

THERMOSTATIC EXPANSION VALVES

The thermostatic expansion valve differs from the automatic expansion valve in that its action is governed by the temperature, whereas the automatic expansion valve is governed entirely by pressure. In construction, it is similar to the automatic expansion valve except that it has, in addition, a thermostatic element. This thermostatic element is charged with a volatile substance (usually a refrigerant that is the same as that used in the refrigeration system in which the valve is connected). It functions according to the pressure-temperature relationship and is connected (clamped) to the evaporator suction line of the evaporator and to the bellows operating diaphragm of the valve by a small sealed tube. A cutaway view of a thermostatic expansion valve is shown in Fig. 3.

Its operation is governed by the temperature, thus a rise in the evaporator temperature will increase the temperature of the evaporated gas passing through the suction line to which the thermostatic expansion valve bulb is clamped. The bulb absorbs heat, and since its charge reacts in accordance with the pressure-temperature relations, the pressure tending to open the valve needle is increased and it opens proportionally.

Briefly, the greater the evaporator gas temperature rise in the evaporator, the wider the valve opens, and vice versa. The wider the valve opens, the greater is the percentage of coil flooding. This improves the heat transfer. It also causes the compressor to operate at a higher average suction pressure. Hence, an increase compressor capacity will also increase overall system capacity.

VALVE SELECTION

A thermostatic expansion valve selected or specified for any installation should be matched to the individual application. To do this is far more complex today than in years past. Valve selection involves several important factors that must be given careful consideration. They include:

1. Refrigerant used in system.
2. Refrigeration load.
3. Suction temperature.
4. Liquid inlet temperature.
5. Type of evaporator.
6. Operating conditions.

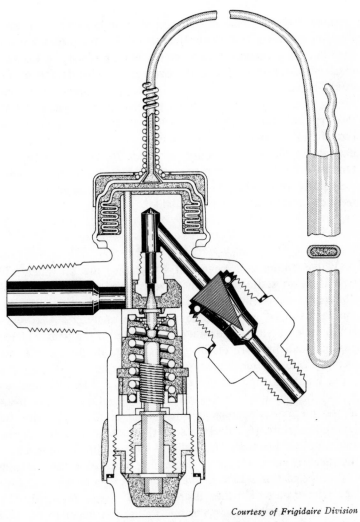

Courtesy of Frigidaire Division

Fig. 3. A typical thermostatic expansion valve.

Many different refrigerants are used today. A valve to be selected for any given application should be designed specifically for the refrigerant in the particular system. Capacity of the valve must be matched to that of the evaporator. Manufacturers' literature indicates valve capacities covering a broad application range. The type of evaporator installed in the system dictates the type of expansion valve selected. If the evaporator has considerable pressure drop, or is equipped with a distributor, an external equalizer valve must be used. Equally important, the type of evaporator and the type of installation should be considered in order to properly apply the various types of power element charged valves that are available.

OPERATION

A diagrammatic arrangement illustrating the operation of a typical thermostatic expansion valve is given in Fig. 4. Here the illustration shows that part of the refrigeration system in which the temperature and pressure are being analyzed. Also shown is the cycle of action indicating the changes in the values of temperature and pressure at the various points of the cycle as well as the direction of movement of the valve needle.

By following the oval cycle of action in a clockwise direction, it will be observed that when the temperature (T_1) decreases at the thermostatic power element bulb at the evaporator outlet, the pressure (P_1) decreases in the bulb and in the thermostatic power bellows. The bellows then contract, thus closing the needle valve (N) and decreasing the refrigerant pressure (P_2) at the suction side of the valve and the inlet of the evaporator. The temperature (T_2) then decreases, due to the throttled action of (N), causing the temperature (T_1) at the outlet to the compressor to increase.

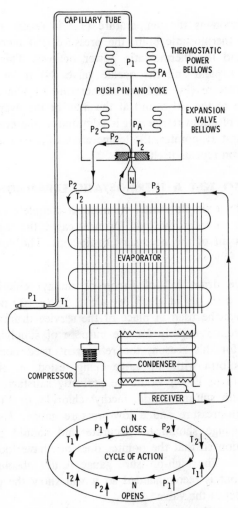

Fig. 4. Diagram illustrating the working principles of a thermostatic expansion valve.

179

Just as soon as the temperature (T_1) increases at the outlet and at the thermostatic bulb, the pressure (P_1) increases in the the bulb and the thermostatic power bellows. This causes the bellows to expand and the needle valve (N) to open. The refrigerant pressure (P_2) and the temperature (T_2) increase at the suction side of the valve and at the inlet of the evaporator as a new supply of liquid refrigerant is admitted to the evaporator. As the refrigerant evaporates, the temperature (T_1) decreases and the cycle of action repeats itself.

HOW TO TEST A THERMOSTATIC EXPANSION VALVE

It is quite a simple matter to make a complete and accurate test of these valves in the field. In most cases, the regular service **kit contains all** of the necessary equipment. The equipment required is as follows:

1. Service drum full of Freon or methyl chloride (in the shop, a supply of clean dry air at 75 to 100 pounds pressure can be used in place of the service drum). The service drum is merely for the purpose of supplying pressure and, for this reason, the refrigerant used does not have to conform with the valve being tested; in other words, a drum of Freon would be perfectly satisfactory for testing with sulfur dioxide, methyl chloride, or Freon valves.
2. A high-pressure and a low-pressure gauge. The low-pressure gauge should be accurate and should be in good condition so that the pointer does not have too much lost motion. The high-pressure gauge is not absolutely necessary, but is recommended so it will show the pressure on the inlet of the valve.
3. Fittings and connections are required to complete the hook up, as shown in Fig. 5.

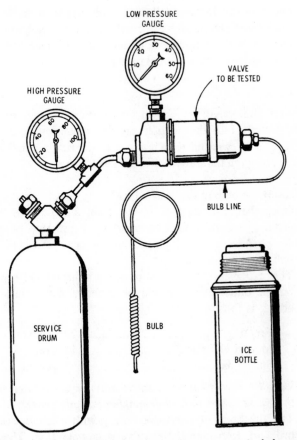

Fig. 5. *Illustrating the necessary equipment to test a typical thermostatic expansion valve.*

4. Some finely crushed ice is necessary, and one of the most convenient ways of carrying this around is to keep it in a thermos bottle. Otherwise, a milk bottle or other con-

tainer is satisfactory. Whatever the container is, it should be completely filled with crushed ice. Do not attempt to make this test with the container full of water and a little crushed ice floating around on top.

Procedure

Connect the valve, as shown, with the low-pressure gauge screwed loosely into the adapter on the expansion valve outlet. The gauge is screwed up loosely so as to provide a small amount of leakage through the threads. Proceed as follows:

1. Insert the bulb in the crushed ice.
2. Open the valve on the service drum and be sure that the drum is warm enough to build up a pressure of at least 70 pounds on the high-pressure gauge connected in the line to the valve inlet.
3. The expansion valve can now be adjusted. The pressure on the outlet gauge should be different for various refrigerants as follows:

   Freon ....22 pounds
   Methyl chloride ....15 pounds
   Sulfur dioxide .... 3 pounds

   Note: Be sure to have a small amount of leakage through the gauge connection while making this adjustment.
4. Tap the body of the valve lightly with a small wrench in order to determine if the valve is in operation. The needle of the gauge should not jump more than one pound.
5. Now screw the gauge up tight so as to stop the leakage through the threads and determine if the expansion valve closes off tightly. With a good valve, the pressure will increase a few pounds and then either stop or build up

very slowly. With a leaking valve, the pressure will build up rapidly until it equals the inlet pressure.

6. Again loosen the gauge so as to permit leakage through the threads, and then remove the feeler bulb from the crushed ice and warm it up with the hand or by putting it in water at about room temperature. The pressure should increase rapidly, showing that the power element has not lost its charge. If the pressure does not increase when this is done, it is a sign that the power element is dead.

   Note: *With the new gas charged expansion valves, the amount of charge in the power element is limited and the pressure will not build up above the specified pressure. This pressure is always marked on the power element and must be considered when testing gas charged valves.*

7. With high pressure showing on both gauges, as outlined in the preceding paragraph, the valve can be tested to determine if the body bellows leaks. This should be done by loosening up the packing nut and using a halide leak detector or soap suds to detect the escape of gas. When making this test, it is important that the gauge and other fittings are screwed up tight so as to eliminate leakage at other points.

Precautions

Be sure that the service drum has liquid in it and is warm enough to build up sufficient pressure. The high-pressure gauge used as shown in Fig. 5 will save a lot of trouble because it will show when there is not enough pressure on the inlet side of the valve. During the winter time especially, the service drum may become cold and develop insufficient pressure to make a satisfactory test. Be sure that the thermos bottle or other container is full of finely crushed ice and does not have merely a little ice floating on top of the water.

CAPILLARY TUBE SYSTEMS

The capillary tube or restrictor system is presently in universal use on household refrigerators because of the simplicity in operation, since it contains no valves or adjustments. Because of its nature, this type of system requires more accurate design to meet the particular requirements. The restrictor, in a sense, is a fixed control having no movable element responsive to load variations. Its element of variable control lies only in the natural variation of the factors affecting the rate of flow of the refrigerant. The most important of these are the pressure difference, the volume, and the density of the refrigerant. The refrigerant circuit and component arrangement are shown in Fig. 6.

The positive force to push the refrigerant through the restrictor is the pressure differential between the inlet and outlet—the inlet being the condenser pressure and the outlet the evaporator pressure. Acting against this positive force is the resistance offered by the friction within the restrictor. The temperature of the condensing medium has a greater effect on the pressure difference than the load change. The friction loss or pressure drop in the restrictor depends on the velocity, density, volume, and viscosity of the refrigerant, and on the diameter and length of the restriction.

The velocity depends on the volume and density of the refrigerant delivered by the compressor. The volume and density depends on the temperature and pressure of the refrigerant and whether it is in a liquid or vapor state. The viscosity of the pure refrigerant changes very little. However, the presence of oil will affect the viscosity by increasing the pressure drop. The diameter and length of the restrictor are fixed quantities in any unit.

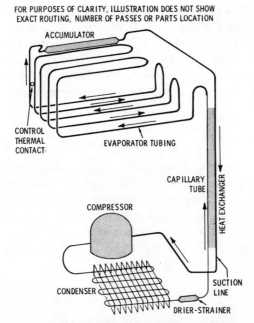

FOR PURPOSES OF CLARITY, ILLUSTRATION DOES NOT SHOW
EXACT ROUTING, NUMBER OF PASSES OR PARTS LOCATION

Fig. 6. Illustrating refrigerant circuit and component arrangement in a typical capillary and sealed household refrigeration system.

The restrictor or capillary tube system accomplishes the reduction in pressure from the condenser to the evaporator without the use of a needle valve or pressure reducing valve, but by using the pressure drop or friction loss through a long small opening. With this system there is no valve to separate the high-pressure zone of the condensing unit from the low-pressure zone of the unit and evaporator. Therefore, the pressures through the system tend to equalize during the off cycle, being retarded only by the time required for the gas to pass through the small passage of the

185

restrictor. The expansion system is sometimes referred to as being the dry system while the low-side float system is the flooded system. This is sometimes true, but not necessarily so, for the expansion valve may be used on a flooded system where the evaporator is so designed as to take the low-pressure vapor out of the top with the evaporator practically filled with liquid refrigerant.

ELECTRICAL SYSTEM

The electrical wiring may differ considerably from unit to unit, depending on the protective feature of the motor-compressor as well as the defrosting circuit or circuits. All systems are made up of a cabinet wiring harness which includes the line cord, compressor leads, light switch, control leads, and warmer wire leads (where used). In its simplest form, the wiring components (Fig. 7) consist of the following:

1. Motor-compressor.
2. Light switch.
3. Temperature control.

Some refrigerator units use natural draft for condenser cooling, whereas others use forced draft provided by a cooling fan usually located underneath the cabinet.

The functional requirements of the motor and compressor devices are:

1. Starting of the unit.
2. Stopping of the unit.
3. To protect the unit against overload caused either by high refrigerant pressure or excessive current drawn by the motor.

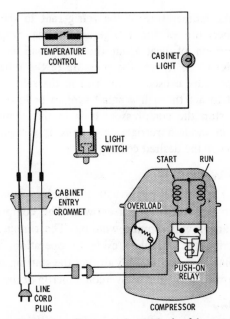

Fig. 7. Wiring diagram of a typical refrigerator.

The motor control mechanism in modern household refrigerators is actuated by a conventional thermostatic control switch.
The length of the operating period of the compressor determines
the quantity of the refrigerant pumped and the amount of cooling
produced. In order to function properly, the compressor must be
started when the temperature of the evaporator has risen to a predetermined point and stopped when the temperature has dropped
to another predetermined point, both of which must be at such
levels as to maintain the desired storage space temperature. This
temperature in most household refrigerators is approximately 45°
F. The start-stop controls for the motor-compressor are operated

187

directly by the temperature of the refrigerant in the evaporator. As the temperature of the refrigerant in the evaporator rises due to absorption of heat from the food load in the unit or from the water to be frozen, the pressure of the refrigerant rises. The rise in pressure caused by the rise in the refrigerant temperature is used to act through a small syphon bellows on a switch to start and stop the compressor. It is in this manner that the temperature in modern refrigerating units is automatically controlled to provide the desired cooling.

Compressor Wiring

Compressor motor sizes vary with the cabinet capacity and are from 1/12 to about a 1/3 horsepower. The compressor motor employs a starting and running winding. The running winding is energized during the complete cycle of operation, whereas the starting winding is energized only during the starting period, when additional torque is required to overcome inertia of the unit.

Starting Relay

At the moment of starting, when the temperature control closes the electrical circuit, a surge of electric current passes through the running winding of the motor and through the relay coil. This energizes the starting relay coil and pulls up the starting relay armature, closing the starting winding contacts. The current through the starting winding introduces a second out-of-phase, magnetic field in the stator and starts the motor. As the motor speed increases, the running winding current is reduced. At a predetermined condition, the running winding current, which is also the current through the starting relay coil, drops to a value below that necessary to hold up the starting relay armature. The armature drops and opens the starting winding contacts and takes the starting winding out of the circuit. The motor then continues to run on the running winding as an induction motor. A schematic diagram of a motor with an overload protector and starting relay is shown in Fig. 8.

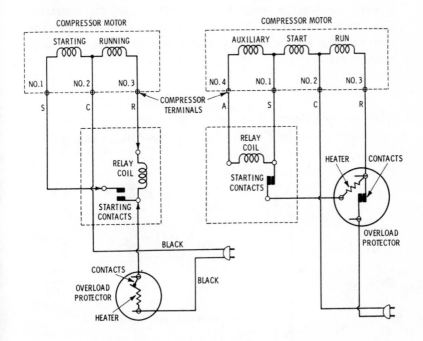

Fig. 8. A schematic wiring of a motor circuit with overload protectors and starting relay.

Overload Protector

In series with the motor windings is a bimetallic overload protector. Should the current in the motor windings increase to a dangerous value, the heat developed by passage of current through the bimetallic overload protector will cause it to deflect and open

189

the controls. This breaks the circuit to the motor windings and stops the motor before any damage can occur.

After an overload or a temperature rise has caused the bimetallic overload protector to break the circuit, the bimetallic strip cools and returns the contact to the closed position. The time required for the overload switch to reset varies with room temperature.

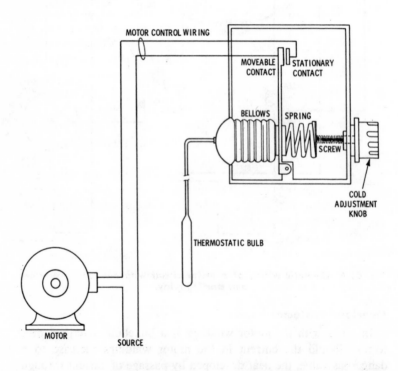

Fig. 9. Simplified illustration showing the working principles in a bulb bellows system of temperature control.

Temperature Control

The temperature control or thermostatic switch as the device is sometimes called, is the connecting link between the evaporator and the electrical system. Briefly, this control mechanism (Fig. 9) consists essentially of a thermostatic bulb (which is clamped to the evaporator), together with a capillary tube and bellows. These three interconnected elements are assembled in one unit and charged with a few drops of refrigerant, such as sulfur dioxide, or a similar highly volatile fluid.

As the temperature of the bulb increases, gas pressure in the bulb-bellows assembly increases, and the bellows pushes the operating shaft upward against the two spring pressures. The shaft operates the toggle or snap mechanism. Consequently, the upward travel of the shaft finally pushes the toggle mechanism off center and the switch snaps closed, starting the compressor.

As the compressor runs, the control bulb is cooled, gradually reducing the pressure in the bulb-bellows system. This reduction of bellows pressure allows the spring to push the shaft slowly downward until it has finally traveled downward far enough to push the toggle mechanism off center in the opposite direction, snapping the switch open and stopping the compressor. The control bulb then slowly warms up until the motor again starts and the cycle repeats itself. The thermostatic control is set to close the compressor circuit at a certain evaporator temperature and open the circuit at another predetermined temperature, and in this manner any desired cabinet temperature may be maintained.

CHAPTER 7

Cabinet Defrosting Systems

Since the accumulation of frost on the evaporator has a direct relationship to the ambient temperature and humidity, the successful performance of any refrigerator depends upon maintaining cabinet and freezer temperatures within a range that will promote the most favorable conditions for keeping perishables and frozen foods. It should be noted that each time the refrigerator door is opened, some of the heavy cold air within the cabinet escapes and mixes with the warm room air. This process creates a low-pressure area within the cabinet, which draws in warm room air.

The rapid increase in cabinet air temperature results in an accumulation of excess moisture on the evaporator and cold surfaces within the refrigerator. An additional result of frequent door openings is that the temperature control will almost immediately energize the unit, which will run until the cabinet air temperature has been lowered to a degree corresponding to the setting of the temperature control switch. Naturally, with a greater number of door openings, the unit will operate with greater frequency and for longer periods of time, with a corresponding higher power consumption and an increase in frost accumulation on the evaporator. One method of minimizing refrigerator door openings is to remove all the required food and dishes at one time, instead of opening the refrigerator door for each dish required during preparation of a meal. When all the necessary food is removed at one time and placed on an adjacent work counter surface, door openings may be decreased as many as seven to ten times that usually required.

MANUAL DEFROSTING

Periodic defrosting is essential to the efficient and economical operation of any refrigeration system. The defrosting operation should be performed when the frost accumulation on the cooling unit becomes approximately 1/4″ thick, and regardless of the thickness of the frost, the unit should be defrosted and the moisture removed once every two weeks, or more often if conditions require. If large quantities of moist food are stored, or if the weather is exceptionally humid, it may be necessary to defrost more often.

NEED FOR DEFROSTING

The need for defrosting is readily apparent if the following factors are considered:

Cabinet air temperatures are controlled by means of a temperature control, the control bulb of which is attached directly to the cooling unit and frequently insulated from the circulating air by a rubber insulator. The bulb is therefore directly affected by the temperature of the cooling unit, but is affected only slightly by the temperature of the air in the cabinet. Since the cooling unit is the coldest spot inside the cabinet, moisture in the form of frost deposits on the outside surface of the cooling unit is increased considerably.

Position of Control or Switch

On refrigerators equipped with a defrosting switch, all that is necessary to defrost the unit is to turn the control to the *defrost* position (it is not necessary to turn it off or allow the door to remain open). Allow the switch to remain in this position until all the frost has melted. To defrost refrigerators not equipped with a defrosting switch, all that is necessary is to set the *on* and *off* switch to the "off" position.

Hot Water Defrosting

In order to hasten the defrosting period, particularly in warm weather when it is desired to preserve the ice cubes and allow only a small rise in cabinet air temperatures, pans or containers of hot water can be placed in the cooling unit after turning the control switch to the "off" position. The unit will then defrost in about 20 to 30 minutes.

Defrosting Tray

It is obvious that before a defrosting operation, the defrosting tray should be empty and correctly located to receive the water from the melting ice of the cooling unit. After the defrosting is completed, the defrosting tray should be emptied, the interior of the refrigerator cleaned, and fresh water placed in the ice-cube trays.

AUTOMATIC DEFROSTING

Automatic defrosting is accomplished by providing an electric heater (or heaters) consisting of a conventional ohmic resistor encased in tubing which, by various control methods, supplies the heat necessary to prevent excessive moisture accumulation on the

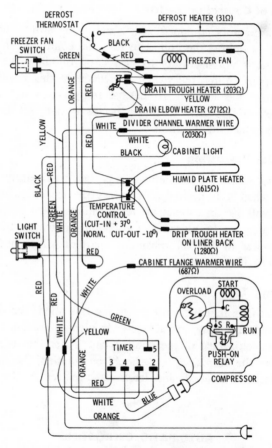

Fig. 1. Wiring diagram of an electrical circuit used in a typical automatic defrost refrigerator.

evaporator. The defrost heater operates in a cyclical manner. The heater may be energized on cut-out periods of the unit only, or it may be operated by a control timer mechanism starting a defrost cycle once every 12 or 24 hours, as shown in Fig. 1.

The freezer and fresh-food compartments usually have a common drainage system. During a defrost cycle in the freezer com-

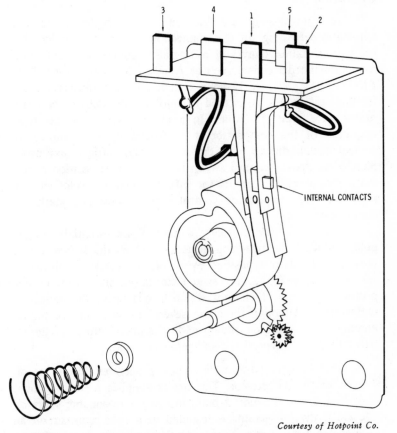

INTERNAL CONTACTS

Courtesy of Hotpoint Co.

Fig. 2. A defrost timer showing contact and terminal arrangement.

partment, the water runs down special drain tubes to a collector or pan under the cabinet where the water is evaporated into the room air.

Operation

There is no mystery or magic connected with the principle of automatic defrosting. In this connection it should be noted that the various manufacturers of refrigerators employ different terms for automatic defrosting, such as *NO-FROST, FROST-PROOF, FROSTFREE,* etc. A 12-hour system means a refrigerator defrosting system (Fig. 2) is used to automatically defrost the evaporator once every 12 hours. In a defrost system of this type, operation of the compressor is controlled by the temperature control switch during both the defrost and refrigeration cycle. Should the defrost control switch be in a defrost position during a thermostat cycle (compressor off), the defrost cycle will not start until the temperature control switch closes and starts the compressor.

The defrost controls usually employed are essentially single-pole, double-throw switching devices in which the switch arm is moved to the defrost position by an electric clock, as illustrated schematically in Fig. 3. The switch arm is returned to the normal position by a power element which is responsive to changes in temperature. Although there are several methods to accomplish automatic defrosting depending upon the manufacturer of the refrigerating unit, a typical system operates as follows:

A small (usually 10-watt) liner heater operates during the off cycle of the compressor. This heater supplies a small amount of heat to the thermostat bulb, insuring a reasonably short *off* cycle if the refrigerator is installed in a cold room or on an unheated back porch. When the thermostat in the fresh-food

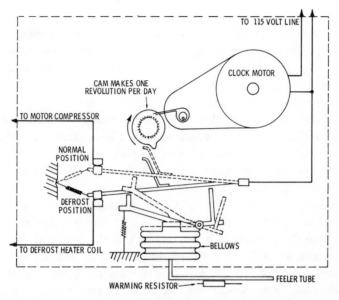

TO 115 VOLT LINE

CLOCK MOTOR

CAM MAKES ONE
REVOLUTION PER DAY

TO MOTOR COMPRESSOR

NORMAL
POSITION

DEFROST
POSITION

TO DEFROST HEATER COIL

BELLOWS

WARMING RESISTOR

FEELER TUBE

Fig. 3. Pictorial view of an electric clock motor and contact arrangement in a typical automatic defrost refrigerator.

compartment has energized the compressor, the refrigerant circulates through the cooling coil in the food compartment and passes through a restrictor into the cold coil in the freezer compartment. The refrigerant expands and evaporates, absorbing heat from the fresh-food and freezer compartments.

A fan in the freezer compartment circulates the air from the bottom, up through the coil, and out through the fan. This air-flow pattern is unchanging and always goes from the bottom, up under the coil cover plate, through the coil, and out through the orifice in the coil cover plate. Moisture is removed from the air as it passes through the coil and is deposited on

199

the colder surface of the coil. Since all of the moisture is deposited on the coil, there will be no frost on any other part of the freezer compartment or on any food packages stored in this area. Because frost cannot accumulate on the coil indefinitely, some provision must be made for its removal. This is done by means of an automatic defrost cycle.

The automatic defrost cycle for the freezer compartment is controlled by a timer which has a 12-hour electrically-driven movement. A revolving cam in the timer operates the defrosting contacts. The timer operation is governed by the compressor since the timer motor operates only when the compressor is running. The only time that the timer motor operates independently of the compressor is during a defrost cycle (when the compressor is not running). If it is assumed that the compressor will run 50% of the time, there will be at least one automatic defrost a day in the freezer compartment. If the compressor should run 100% of the time (under extreme ambient conditions), there would be a maximum of two defrost cycles during a 24-hour period.

The Defrost Sequence

The defrost sequence is as follows:

1. The timer turns off the compressor and the freezer compartment fan. At the same time, it energizes the heater on the coil and the heater on the drain trough. At this point, the compressor and fans are not operating, but the heaters are activated.
2. The heater melts the frost on the coil, and the resulting water drains down into the trough through a tube in the bottom of the freezer compartment.

3. When the temperature at the bimetal thermodisc reaches approximately 65°, the coil heater is turned off. The coil should be completely defrosted by this time. Approximately 10 minutes will elapse from the start of the defrost cycle to the time when the coil heater is cut off. If, for any reason, the bimetal disc should fail to function when the interior evaporator temperature reaches 65°, the timer will cut off the coil heater after approximately 18 minutes from the start of the defrost cycle. The food will not be affected by the defrost cycle because the fan is off and warm air is not being circulated. The food packages are protected by the insulating cold air in the evaporator and the insulation afforded by the plate covering the cold coil.

4. The drain heater stays on for approximately 8 minutes after the coil heater has been shut off by the thermodisc, and is cut off by the action of the timer. This 8-minute delay in cutting off the drain-trough heater is to insure that all the water is drained from the trough before the refrigeration cycle begins again.

5. Since the defrost cycle interrupted an *on* cycle, the compressor is activated immediately to bring the coil down to the proper temperature as quickly as possible. There is, however, an additional 5-minute delay before the fan operation is resumed. This is to prevent the circulation of warm moist air.

Defrost Timer Operation

Figs. 4, 5, and 6 show the action of a typical defrost timer during normal operation, as well as the variation in the electrical circuit during the defrost cycle. Fig. 4 indicates the circuit conditions during normal operation. One side of the power line goes

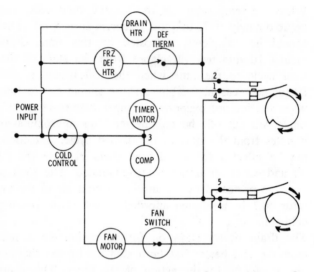

Fig. 4. Electric circuit during normal operation.

to the timer motor and to contact terminal #1. The other side of the power line runs through the cold control in the fresh-food compartment and to the other side of the timer motor. This same side of the power line also goes to one side of the compressor, and then to one side of the fan motor. Contact terminal #1 makes contact with terminal #4, which goes to the other side of the compressor. Terminal #4 also makes contact with terminal #5 which goes to one side of the fan switch. When the fan-switch plunger is depressed, and terminals #4 and #5 are making contact, the fan motor is energized.

The condition shown in Fig. 5 is the one that exists at the beginning of the defrost cycle. Terminals #1 and #4 have separated, which interrupts the power to the compressor. Terminals

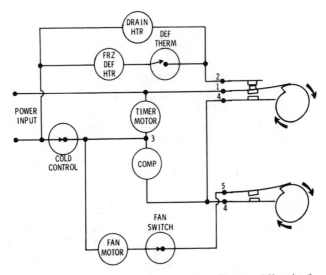

Courtesy of Hotpoint Co.

Fig. 5. Electric circuit at start of defrost cycle.

#4 and #5 are also separated, which interrupts the power to the fan switch, de-energizing the fan motor. Timer terminals #1 and #2 make contact, sending power to one side of the drain heater and to the cold coil thermostat. The other side of the drain heater and one side of the coil heater connect to one side of the power line. This connection energizes the drain-trough heater. The coil heater is energized when the thermodisc closes.

Fig. 6 shows the electrical situation after approximately 18 minutes of the defrost cycle have expired. Terminals #1 and #2 break contact and de-energize both the coil heater and the drain heater. Remember that in normal operation, the cold coil thermostat will de-energize the coil heater after approximately 10 minutes of the defrost cycle. Terminals #1 and #4 make con-

203

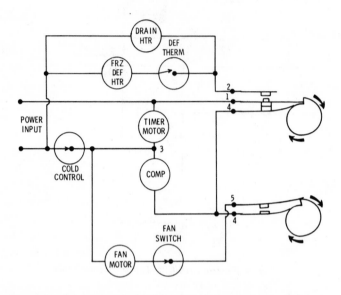

Fig. 6. Electric circuit near end of defrost cycle.

tact and energize the compressor, while terminals #4 and #5 are still open to allow the 5-minute delay before the evaporator fan starts again. After the 5-minute delay, terminals #4 and #5 make contact and the evaporator fan is energized once again. The action of the timer in breaking the circuit of the cold coil heater is purely a mechanical one. If the cold coil thermostat is operating properly, it will remove the coil heater from the circuit after approximately 10 minutes of the defrost cycle, or when the temperature at the point of the cold coil thermostat reaches either 55 or 65 degrees.

204

DEFROST THERMOSTAT TESTING

The freezer compartment defrost thermostat contacts are usually set to a temperature change of about 15 degrees. Since a test might be made just after a freezer defrost cycle, it could appear that the defrost thermostat was inoperative because the contacts were still open. In order to make a more positive check the following steps are recommended.

1. Disconnect the power cord.
2. Remove the breaker strip from the fresh-food compartment.
3. Connect the probes of a test lamp to the ends of the defrost thermostat leads. Refer to the wiring diagram on the cabinet for the correct color code. (Needle-type probes are best for this test, since they can be inserted into the connectors.)
4. Plug the test lamp into the wall receptacle. If the test lamp has a bright glow, the contacts are closed, but in case the lamp has a dull glow, the contacts are open and additional testing is necessary.
5. It is important that the refrigerator line cord be disconnected, otherwise an erroneous reading will be made, or the defrost and drain-trough heater could be energized. Points A and *B* in Fig. 7 show the circuit being tested and the points at which the test lamp is connected. If the initial test has shown the freezer thermostat contacts open, the serviceman should use a can of refrigerant for the next part of the test. Leave test lamp connected to points *A* and *B*.
6. Remove the food from the freezer compartment and take off the freezer cover plate. Spray the defrost thermostat

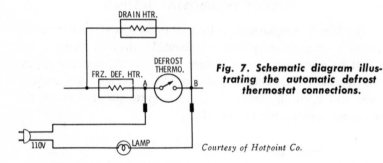

Fig. 7. Schematic diagram illustrating the automatic defrost thermostat connections.

Courtesy of Hotpoint Co.

with a can of refrigerant for about 15 seconds. This should reduce the temperature to the vicinity of 15°, thus closing the contacts. When the contacts close, a click will be heard and the test lamp will glow brightly. *If the contacts do not close after approximately three sprayings of refrigerant, and the lamp retains its dull glow, then the serviceman has made a positive check and should then replace the thermostat.* The serviceman having tested the thermostat in the freezer and finding it operating normally, should test the freezer heater.

CHAPTER 8

Household Freezers

Household freezers are manufactured in various sizes to suit family requirements. The purpose of household freezers is to facilitate maximum food storage over a period of time. They are usually termed as horizontal or vertical units, depending on individual requirements and installation space available. Household freezers are usually manufactured in capacities of from 13 to 20 cubic feet, and are normally equipped with hermetically sealed condensing units.

CYCLE OF OPERATION

The operation of the refrigeration system can best be described with reference to the refrigerant flow diagram shown in Fig. 1. The temperature of the freezer is regulated by a conventional temperature control, which starts the motor-compressor when the evaporator requires refrigeration, and stops the motor-compressor when the evaporator has been sufficiently cooled. When the temperature control contacts close, the motor-compressor starts operating and reduces the pressure in the evaporator. The refriger-

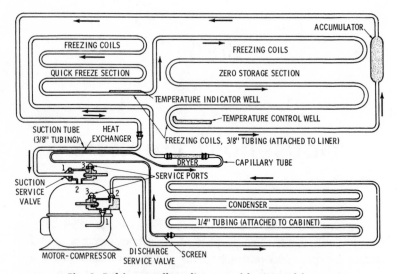

Fig. 1. Refrigerant-flow diagram of horizontal freezer.

ant evaporates, absorbing heat in the process, thus cooling the evaporator. The vapor is drawn through the suction line by the compressor, which compresses the refrigerant gas and forces it into the condenser under high pressure. The compression of the vapor causes the temperature to rise permitting the condenser to transfer the heat to the cabinet shell and into the air surrounding the cabinet as shown in Fig. 2. As the compressed vapor gives up its heat, it condenses to a liquid in the condenser.

The capillary tube is made small in diameter in order to control the amount of liquid refrigerant forced through it from the condenser to the evaporator. For a short period of time after the motor-compressor shuts off, the pressure in the condenser continues to force refrigerant through the capillary tube until the pressure is substantially equalized throughout the system. If the

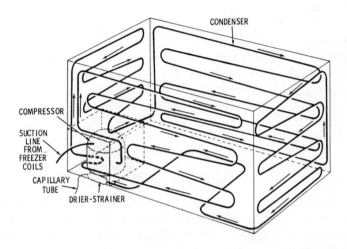

Fig. 2. *The routing of the tubing in a typical horizontal freezer.*

motor-compressor attempts to start immediately after it shuts off (before equalizing has occurred), the motor-compressor may stall and trip the overload protector, thereby breaking the electrical circuit. This prevents the motor windings from burning out.

CHARACTERISTICS OF A CAPILLARY-TUBE SYSTEM

A refrigeration system that uses a *capillary tube* as the refrigerant control has certain characteristics and advantages. A capillary tube allows the liquid refrigerant to continue its flow from the condenser into the evaporator after the temperature control has shut off the motor-compressor. This effects a reduction in the condenser pressure during the *off* cycle, and permits the motor-compressor to start easily against a relatively low pressure when refrigeration is again required.

The amount of refrigerant in a capillary-tube system is small but critical. There should be just enough refrigerant so that, during normal operation, evaporation will take place for the entire length of the freezing coil, but not beyond. If there is *too little* refrigerant, there will be insufficient cooling of the freezing coils. If there is *too much* refrigerant, the excess liquid will flow into the suction line. Refrigerant in this line will cause it to frost during the *on* cycle, and the frost will melt and drip off during the *off* cycle.

ELECTRICAL SYSTEM

The hermetically sealed motor-compressor requires a 60-cycle, 115-volt AC current, and has a capacity of from 1/4 to 1/3 hp, depending on the size of the total food-storing capacity of the freezer cabinet.

Fan Motor

The fan for cooling the motor-compressor in some models is mounted on the compressor housing. It is connected directly across the power supply to the motor-compressor after the temperature control and before the overload protector, as shown in Fig. 3. Connected in this manner, the fan will continue to cool the motor-compressor even if the overload protector has opened because of overheating. The fan will stop only when the temperature controls cut out.

Temperature Control and Signal Light

The temperature control, in addition to its conventional function, also controls the operation of the signal light, as noted in Fig. 3. The temperature control is an electrical switch controlled by the temperature of the control feeler tube. As the feeler tube

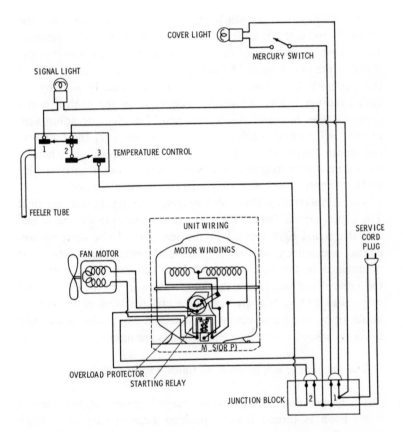

COVER LIGHT
MERCURY SWITCH
SIGNAL LIGHT
TEMPERATURE CONTROL
1 2 3
FEELER TUBE
SERVICE
CORD
PLUG
UNIT WIRING
MOTOR WINDINGS
FAN MOTOR
M_S(OR P)
OVERLOAD PROTECTOR
STARTING RELAY
JUNCTION BLOCK   2   1

Fig. 3. Wiring diagram of electrical connections in a horizontal freezer.

gets warmer the temperature control switches on and the motor-compressor starts. When the temperature of the feeler tube has been brought down to a predetermined temperature, the switch contacts open and the motor-compressor stops.

The temperature at which the control opens (turns off the motor-compressor) is called the *cut-out point,* and the temperaature at which the control closes (turns on the motor-compressor) is called the *cut-in point.* Adjusting the temperature control knob changes both the *cut-in* and *cut-out* temperatures, by varying the spring tension against which the diaphragm of the control exerts pressure. The design of the control provides adequate adjustment to meet all normal requirements. For average use, the temperature control knob should be set to the normal position, which is the warmest operating position. Since there is no *off* position, this makes it impossible to shut off the freezer accidentally.

The temperature control also operates the signal warning light The signal circuit (inside the temperature control) will be closed and the signal light located in the top part of the temperature-control escutcheon will be *on* when safe temperatures are being maintained in the food compartment. The expanding action of the control bellows (when the temperature in the food compart-ment rises 15° F. or more above the cut-in setting of the control knob) opens the signal-circuit contacts and causes the signal light to go out when food-storage temperatures are unsafe.

The signal light will be *on* at all times, except as follows:

1. *Temperature control knob turned colder.* If the control knob is turned from a position near normal to a much colder position, so that the cut-in point of the new control knob position is 15° F. or more below the temperature at the control feeler tube, the signal light will go out. When the temperature is reduced to less than 15° F. above the cut-in temperature of the new position, the signal light will come on.

2. *Large amounts of warm food in freezer.* If a large amount of warm food is put in the freezer, the light may go out. It is best to freeze smaller amounts of food at one time.
3. *Freezer door left open too long.* The signal light will go out if the freezer door is left open for an extended length of time.
4. *Blown fuse.* A blown fuse in the electrical supply (house circuit) will cause the signal light to go out.
5. *Service cord disconnected from wall outlet.* The signal light will go out if the service cord plug is disconnected from the wall outlet.
6. Bulb (signal light) burned out.
7. Loose wire connections at the control terminals.
8. *Defective operation of refrigeration system.* If defective operation of the refrigeration system causes the temperature in the food compartment to rise 15° F. or more above the cut-in point of the control-knob position, the signal light will go out.

To obtain a clearer understanding of the temperature control which regulates the operation of the motor-compressor and signal light, refer to Figs. 4, 5, and 6. During a normal *off* cycle of the motor-compressor, the feeler tube of the temperature control is cold and the bellows is contracted, allowing the spring to pull the control arm down, as illustrated in Fig. 4. Contacts A and B are open and the motor-compressor is idle. Contacts C and D are closed and the signal light is on, indicating a safe food-storage temperature.

During a normal *on* cycle of the motor-compressor, the bellows, control arm, and spring are in an intermediate position, as shown in Fig. 5. In this position, contacts A and B are closed, and power is supplied to the motor-compressor. Contacts C and

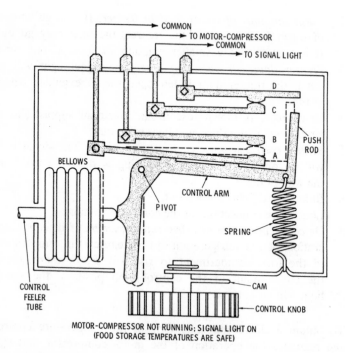

COMMON
TO MOTOR-COMPRESSOR
COMMON
TO SIGNAL LIGHT

D
C
B
A

PUSH ROD

BELLOWS

CONTROL ARM

PIVOT

SPRING

CONTROL FEELER TUBE

CAM

CONTROL KNOB

MOTOR-COMPRESSOR NOT RUNNING; SIGNAL LIGHT ON
(FOOD STORAGE TEMPERATURES ARE SAFE)

Fig. 4. Cutaway view of temperature control during normal off cycle.

D are also closed, so that the signal light is on and a safe food-storage temperature is indicated. If, for some reason, the temperature in the food compartment is 15° F. or more above the cut-in temperature of the control, the bellows is expanded to a point that forces the right-hand end of the control arm upward, as shown in Fig. 6. Contacts *A* and *B* are closed, supplying power to the motor-compressor, but the push rod breaks contact at *C* and *D* and causes the signal circuit to open. The signal light will stay off, indicating an unsafe food-storage temperature, until the

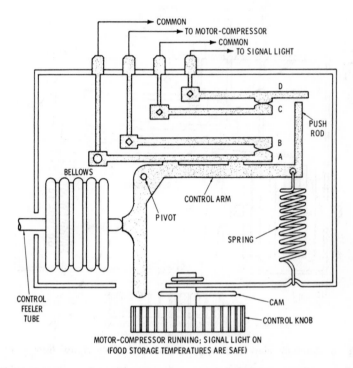

COMMON
TO MOTOR-COMPRESSOR
COMMON
TO SIGNAL LIGHT

D
C

PUSH
ROD

B
A

BELLOWS

CONTROL ARM

PIVOT

SPRING

CONTROL
FEELER
TUBE

CAM

CONTROL KNOB

MOTOR-COMPRESSOR RUNNING; SIGNAL LIGHT ON
(FOOD STORAGE TEMPERATURES ARE SAFE)

Fig. 5. Cutaway view of temperature control during normal on cycle.

motor-compressor restores proper temperature in the food compartment. The bellows will then contract, and the signal-circuit contacts *C* and *D*, will close.

UPRIGHT FREEZERS

One basic refrigeration system is used on practically all upright freezers, the only major variation being the use of a fan-cooled

215

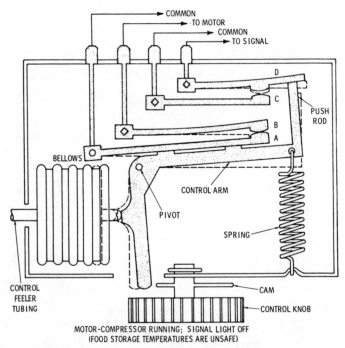

Fig. 6. Cutaway view of temperature control when signal light is off.

condenser (Fig. 7) located beneath the cabinet on a few models. Other upright freezers use a static condenser (Fig. 8) located on the back of the cabinet. All units are of the conventional hermetically sealed design. For service purposes, the compressor is considered as one part, and the freezer shelf and heat-exchanger assembly as another and completely separate part.

The Refrigeration System

The first few passes of the condenser tubing (static type Fig. 8) form the oil-cooler loops that carry the partially cooled refriger-

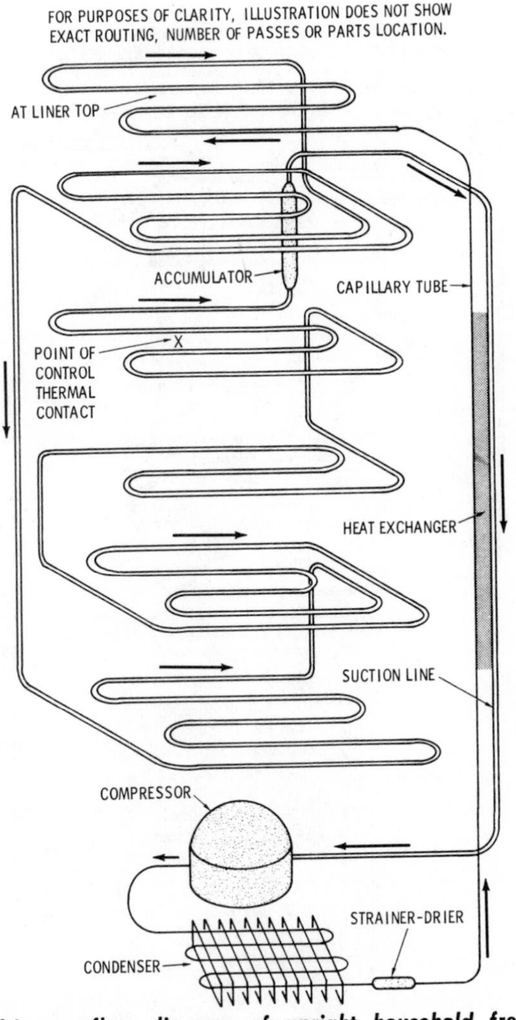

FOR PURPOSES OF CLARITY, ILLUSTRATION DOES NOT SHOW
EXACT ROUTING, NUMBER OF PASSES OR PARTS LOCATION.

AT LINER TOP

ACCUMULATOR

CAPILLARY TUBE

POINT OF
CONTROL
THERMAL
CONTACT

X

HEAT EXCHANGER

SUCTION LINE

COMPRESSOR

STRAINER-DRIER

CONDENSER

*Fig. 7. Refrigerant-flow diagram of upright household freezer with
fan-cooled condenser.*

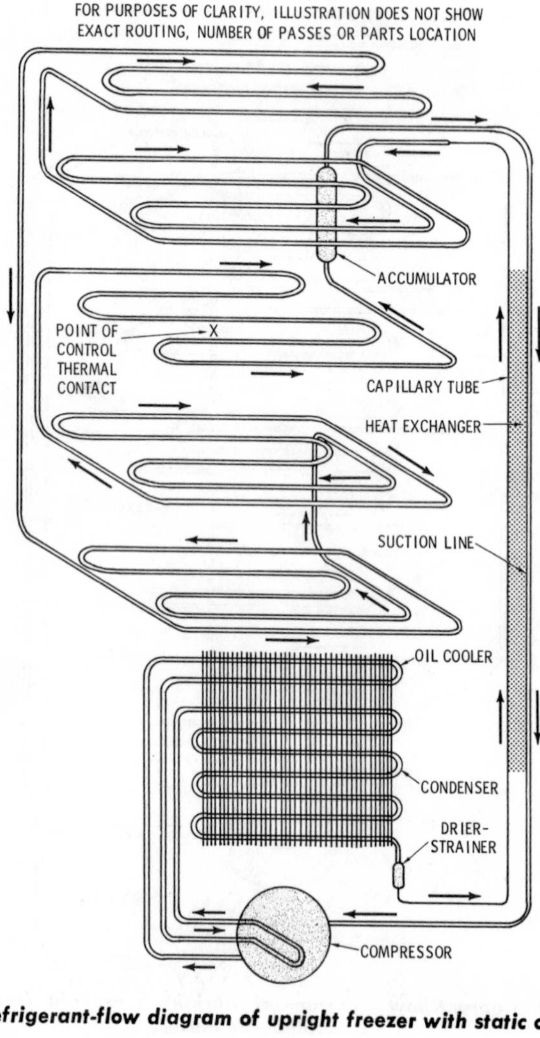

FOR PURPOSES OF CLARITY, ILLUSTRATION DOES NOT SHOW
EXACT ROUTING, NUMBER OF PASSES OR PARTS LOCATION

ACCUMULATOR

POINT OF
CONTROL
THERMAL
CONTACT

X

CAPILLARY TUBE

HEAT EXCHANGER

SUCTION LINE

OIL COOLER

CONDENSER

DRIER-
STRAINER

COMPRESSOR

Fig. 8. Refrigerant-flow diagram of upright freezer with static condenser.

ant gas back through the compressor. This lowers the operating temperature of the compressor and results in increased efficiency for the unit. The condenser releases the heat absorbed by the refrigerant and changes the hot gaseous refrigerant into a cool liquid refrigerant.

The capillary tube controls the flow of refrigerant to the freezer shelves. Part of the capillary tube is soldered to the suction line to form a heat exchanger. The heat from the capillary tube is transferred to the suction line, and the cold suction line further cools the liquid refrigerant in the capillary tube. When the refrigerant leaves the capillary tube and enters the larger tubing of the freezer shelves, the sudden increase in tubing diameter forms a low-pressure area, and the temperature of the refrigerant drops rapidly as it changes to a mixture of liquid and gas. This cold mixture passes through the top shelf (or top freezer plate in some models) then to the bottom shelf, ascending through each additional shelf until it reaches the accumulator.

In the process of passing through the shelf tubing, the refrigerant absorbs heat from the storage area and is gradually changed from a liquid and gas mixture to a gas. The accumulator traps and evaporates any small amount of liquid refrigerant remaining in the low side, thereby preventing the liquid from entering the suction line to the compressor.

The refrigerant gas passes through the suction line to the compressor to be compressed and then repeats the cycle. The temperature-control and signal-light circuits are basically the same as those previously discussed in the section on horizontal freezers.

CHEST-TYPE FREEZERS

Ice-cream freezers are similar in most respects to chest-type household freezers, except for interior design. The insulation usually consists of approximately 4″ of corkboard on the sides, ends, and bottom, supported by steel framework. This insulation in a well designed cabinet is encased in a steel shell and sealed against infiltration of moisture by a seal of asphalt compound.

The lids are generally hinged and have a soft rubber lip on the outer edge, which forms a tight seal against the soft rubber insulating collar at the top of each compartment. A typical ice-cream cabinet is illustrated in Fig. 9. The freezers usually are of 1, 2-1/2, or 5 gallon capacity per batch and are usually built integral with hardening and storage space for 40, 60, or 80 gallons, depending upon individual requirements.

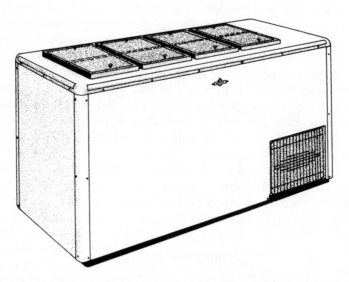

Fig. 9. Exterior view of portable ice cream cabinet. Note grill work for condensing unit located in lower right hand corner.

Supply Handling

In the combination plant setup, the hardening space is provided as an integral part of the unit. It is often necessary to supply one or two extra hardening cabinets for additional storage space. The load can be figured on these individual units exactly as in the large plants and summed up to give the total hardening load.

Machine Requirements

As a general rule, counter freezers are applicable for use only with methyl chloride or *Freon-12* refrigerants. Fig. 10 illustrates a right- and left-side view of a typical air-cooled condensing unit used in ice-cream cabinets. There are, however, some of the old ammonia type brine counter freezers still in use.

Although condensing unit sizes may vary, Table 1 shows the approximate compressor size requirements for various freezers.

Table 1. Freezer Requirements

Freezer	Hardening Space	Gal/Hr.	Daily Capacity	Approx.* Comp. Size
2½ Gal.	None	12½	Continuous	1 H.P.
2½ Gal.	40 Gal.	12½	40 Gal.	1 H.P.
2½ Gal.	60 Gal.	12½	60 Gal.	1½ H.P.
5 Gal.	None	20	Continuous	1½ H.P.
5 Gal.	40 Gal.	20	40 Gal.	1½ H.P.
5 Gal.	60 Gal.	25	60 Gal.	2 H.P.

*NOTE.—Compressors are to run at —20° suction and 100° condensing pressure on hardening cabinets.

It must be understood that the foregoing table gives approximate values only and is offered only as an example. Different freezer and cabinet construction may result in slightly different machine recommendations. In most household freezers there is a direct relationship between troubles, causes, and their remedy.

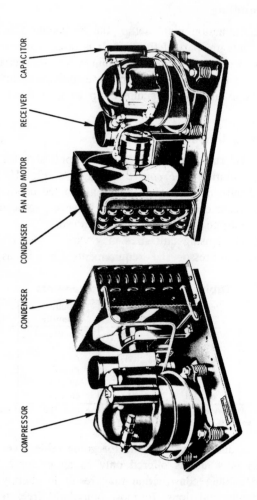

Fig. 10. An air-cooled condensing unit as employed in ice-cream cabinets.

Service instruction charts have been worked out which will be of help in locating and repairing faults likely to be encountered in day-to-day service work.

HOUSEHOLD FREEZER TROUBLE CHART

Compressor Does Not Run

Possible Cause	Possible Remedy
Low voltage	Check with voltmeter. Voltage should be within 10% of that stamped on the compressor-motor.
Defective compressor, relay or overload protector	Test the compressor. To test the compressor without any cabinet wiring in the circuit, unplug the compressor lead cord from the junction assembly and connect it directly to the electrical outlet (use a short extension cord if necessary). If the compressor starts, the trouble is not in the compressor, starting relay or overload protector. Plug the lead cord into junction assembly and check the temperature control and all cabinet wiring for defects or poor connections. If the compressor does not start, check the overload protector, starting relay and motor windings. To check an overload protector short across its terminals. If the compressor starts, replace the overload with one having the same part number. If the compressor does not start, look for other trouble (low line voltage, defective starting relay, defective compressor). To check a starting relay, pull it off of the compressor terminals. Remove the line cord lead from the terminal on the relay and connect it directly to the run terminal of the compressor. Plug the line cord into wall outlet, and at the same time, momentarily short between the run terminal and the start terminal. If the compressor starts, the relay is defective and must be replaced. If the compressor does not start, it is defective and must be replaced.

Signal Light Off

Possible Cause

Burned out bulb.
Line cord unplugged.
Loose wire connection
at control.

Possible Remedy

Replace.
Plug in to proper outlet.
Reconnect loose wire at control.

Compressor Cycle On Overload Protection

Possible Cause

Low voltage.
Defective starting relay or
overload protector.
Poor air circulation around
freezer.
Overcharged or restricted
system.

Possible Remedy

See previous note in this section on low voltage.
See previous note in this section for proper check.

Defective freezer or compressor-motor fan. Check
and replace if necessary.
An overcharged system may have a frostback condition on the suction line. Trouble of this kind is
usually recognized by water drippings when the
compressor stops. Excessively long running time, a
warmer than normal freezer compartment are
other signs of an overcharged system. If a system
is seriously overcharged, it must be evacuated and
recharged.

Compressor Runs But Freezer Is Too Warm Or Too Cold

Possible Cause

Improperly calibrated control.

Poor gasket seal.

Possible Remedy

The temperature control may be re-calibrated by
varying the cut-in and cut-out temperature. Turn
the calibration screw right to "raise" and left to
"lower" the cut-in or cut-out temperature.
Check and repair as required.

Compressor Runs Too Much Or All Of The Time

Possible Cause

Incorrect control knob setting.
Defective or improperly
calibrated control.
Poor gasket seal.

Possible Remedy

Adjust temperature control calibration screw.
Replace defective control. Recalibrate control as
noted in the foregoing.
Repair or replace as required.

Compressor Runs But Freezer Is Too Warm Or Too Cold, Or The Compressor Runs Too Much Or All Of The Time

Possible Cause	*Possible Remedy*
Undercharged or partially restricted system.	If the system is undercharged the freezer will be colder than normal. An undercharged system must be purged, evacuated, and recharged with the proper amount of Freon. Before recharging, however, test for refrigerant leaks as instructed elsewhere in this book. Bent tubing, foreign matter or moisture in the system may cause a partial restriction in the low side tubing. This is usually indicated by frost-free tubing between the restriction and the capillary tube and by frost-covered tubing between the restriction and the suction line. The restriction acts like a second capillary tube, increasing the pressure behind it (warming) and decreasing the pressure beyond it (cooling). Replace the component part if there is a partial restriction in the refrigerant tubing.
Compressor not pumping adequately.	A compressor which is not pumping adequately will produce very little cooling effect. All cooling surfaces may be covered with a thin film of frost, but the temperature will not descend to the cut-out temperature of the control, even with continuous running of the compressor. Place hand on the accumulator surface for 2 or 3 seconds, then examine the surface. If all frost is melted where touched, install gauges and check operating pressures. If high side pressures are lower than normal, and low side pressures are higher than normal, suspicions of defective compressors will be confirmed and the compressors must be replaced.

Noisy Operation

Possible Cause	*Possible Remedy*
Tubing vibrating against compressor cabinet.	Adjust or fasten tubing.

Household Freezers

Loose compressor mounting.
Unlevel cabinet or weak floor.

Fasten compressor securely.
Make sure the freezer is level by checking, both from front to rear, and from side to side, with a carpenter's level. An adjustable leveler is provided at each corner of the cabinet. Always level the freezer and check the gasket seal whenever the freezer is installed, and again if the freezer is moved.

CHAPTER 9

Operation and Service

In order to enable the serviceman to render intelligent and efficient service, it is necessary that he understand the full operation of the different parts that make up a complete refrigeration system. While some service problems can be detected and eliminated in a few minutes, others may require considerable work before being properly diagnosed and corrected. The importance of a thorough diagnosis of the faulty unit cannot be too strongly emphasized. Do not simply guess at the remedy to be applied until the actual trouble has been determined.

SEALED SYSTEM OPERATION

The correct operation of the sealed system is dependent upon the proper functioning of each part that makes up the system. If the system does not operate correctly due to abnormally long running periods, or warmer than normal interior temperatures, the trouble may be caused by one of the following conditions:

1. Restricted capillary tube.
2. Incorrect refrigerant charge.
3. Partial restriction in evaporator.
4. Defective compressor.

227

Restricted Capillary Tube

A restriction in the capillary tube may be caused by moisture in the system, kinked tubing, or foreign particles lodged in the lines. Each of these conditions will cause similar symptoms to occur. The evaporator will have little or no frost formation, and the compressor will run for an extended period of time and eventually cycle on the overload protector. Moisture in the system will usually freeze at the outlet of the capillary tube where it joins the evaporator tubing. The tubing in the immediate vicinity of the freeze-up may be heavily frosted, but the remaining evaporator tubing will be free from frost.

If, when the refrigerator is inspected, the compressor is running but the evaporator is not frosted, stop the compressor and remove the frame. Apply heat to the end of the capillary tubing; usually a match held under the tubing at this point will be sufficient. If an ice block is present, the application of heat will melt the ice and a gurgling sound can be heard as the refrigerant surges through the tubing. If, after applying heat to the capillary tube, the restriction has not been eliminated, check for kinks in the tubing or an undercharged system. In the event the application of heat melts the ice block, the drier should absorb and retain enough moisture to eliminate future freeze-ups. If the freeze-up reoccurs, the sealed system must be replaced. An illustration of the refrigerant tubing is shown in Fig. 1.

A kinked capillary tube will stop the flow of refrigerant and the evaporator will be free from frost. The compressor will run continuously and eventually cycle on the overload protector. Check the capillary tube along its entire length and, if possible, straighten the tubing enough to alleviate the difficulty. Foreign particles lodged in the capillary tube will also stop the flow of refrigerant, and the system will exhibit the same symptoms as with a kinked tube. If checks have been made to eliminate the possibility of a

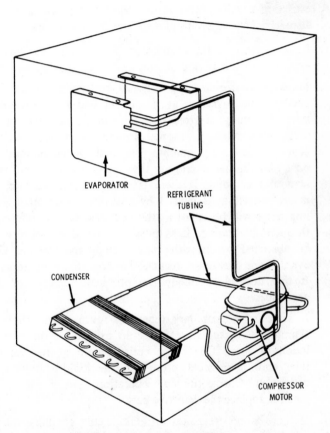

Fig. 1. Schematic diagram showing arrangement of refrigerant tubing in a typical household refrigerator.

moisture freeze-up or a kinked capillary tube, it may be assumed that a foreign particle is lodged at the entrance to the capillary tube, and the sealed system must be replaced.

A restriction usually occurs in the capillary tube because of its small diameter. The symptoms of a restricted capillary are:

1. Lack of frost on the evaporator. The compressor may operate for a short period of time and then cycle on overload.

2. Moisture freeze-up may cause a restriction in the line, and it usually occurs at the outlet end of the capillary tube. Normally, a frost buildup can be detected in this area, but insulation wrapped around the tubing may conceal or limit the amount of frost accumulation. Expose the discharge end of the capillary tube, and apply heat at this point. If there is enough head pressure, and if the restriction is caused by moisture freeze-up, a gurgling noise will be heard as the heat releases the refrigerant through the tubing. It is possible that this moisture will be absorbed by the drier and remedy the trouble. However, if the freeze-up recurs, the drier must be replaced. If this does not remedy the problem, replace the heat exchanger.

3. A kink in the capillary tube will reveal about the same symptom as a moisture freeze-up except for the accumulation of frost. Check the entire length of the capillary tube and, if possible, straighten the kink to relieve the restriction. Check the unit operation, and if the trouble persists, replace the defective part.

4. If there is no freeze-up or kink in the capillary tube, it can be assumed that a foreign particle is causing the restriction—the only remedy in this case is to replace the heat exchanger.

Incorrect Refrigerant Charge

A refrigerator system that is *undercharged* with refrigerants will produce various conditions depending upon the degree of under-charge. During normal operation, a system that is fully charged will have frost covering the entire evaporator and accumulator. Any degree of undercharge or a gradual leak of refrigerant will be noticed first by the absence of frost on the accumulator. The compressor will run for long periods of time, and the food compartment temperature may be colder than normal. As the leakage of refrigerant progresses, the last few passages in the evaporator will be free of frost. The compressor will run continually, since the temperature of the evaporator at the control contact location fails to descend to the control cut-out point.

A system that is *overcharged* will have a frostback condition on the suction line under the cabinet during the *on* period. The frost will then melt and drip on the floor during the *off* period. This situation in a slightly overcharged system may be remedied by wrapping the suction line with insulation tape or its equivalent. Should moisture continue to drip on the floor, replace the sealed system.

Overcharge—The symptoms of an overcharged refrigerator are usually as follows:

1. A frostback condition on the suction line to the extent that it can be noticed on the line back to the compressor unit.

2. If the overcharge is great enough, the control contact may not get cold enough to cut-out the compressor, resulting in long periods of operation.

3. Suction and head pressure will be high at both cut-out or when the system has stabilized.

4. An overcharged system must be evacuated and recharged with the proper amount of refrigerant.

231

Undercharge—When too little refrigerant is present in the refrigerator, the system is undercharged. This defect can be diagnosed as follows:

1. In an undercharged system the refrigerant system will be colder than normal. The freezer compartment may or may not be cold, depending upon the amount of undercharge.
2. The compressor may run continuously because the cold control contact fails to descend to the control cut-out point.
3. Suction charge will be low (possibly a vacuum) depending upon the degree of undercharge.
4. Head pressure will be lower than normal at cut-out or when the system has stabilized.
5. An undercharged system must be evacuated and recharged with the proper amount of refrigerant.

Partial Restriction in Evaporator

An accumulation of moisture or foreign particles may freeze or lodge in the evaporator tubing and cause a partial restriction at that point. This condition is usually indicated by the evaporator being heavily frosted for a few passes ahead of the restriction, and bare of frost on the first few passes behind the restriction. A restriction of this nature tends to act as a second capillary tube. Increased pressure in the evaporator line toward the high side will cause warmer temperatures; decreasing the pressure as the refrigerant passes toward the low side will cause colder temperatures. The evaporator tubing on the high side of the restriction will be free of frost, and the tubing on the low side will be heavily frosted.

If the restriction occurs on the low side of the control feeler-tube contact point, the compressor will run continuously since the control cutout point is never reached. Should the restriction occur on the high side of the control feeler-tube contact point, the compressor will cycle frequently, but running time will be short and the food compartment temperatures will be warmer than usual. A partial restriction in the evaporator tubing will require replacement of the sealed system.

Defective Compressor

A compressor which is not pumping adequately will produce very little cooling effect. The evaporator may be covered with a thin film of frost, but the evaporator temperature will not descend to the cut-out temperature of the control, even with continuous running of the compressor. Place your hand on the evaporator surface for 2 or 3 seconds, then examine the surface. If all of the frost has melted where the evaporator was touched, suspicions of a defective compressor will be confirmed and the sealed system must be replaced.

An inefficient or defective compressor will affect the operation as follows:

1. A compressor that is not pumping correctly will produce very little cooling effect. All cooling surfaces may be covered with a thin film of frost.

2. A popular checking method is to place a hand on the accumulator for two or three seconds and then examine the surface. If all of the frost is melted at the contact surface, the operating pressures should be checked.

3. If high-side pressures are lower than normal, and low-side pressures higher than normal, suspicions of a defective compressor are confirmed and the compressor unit must be replaced.

ELECTRICAL TESTING

In normal operation the compressor is actuated by the thermo-stat. When the thermostat contacts close, the motor running wind-ing and the relay coil are energized. The heavy surge of current that will be drawn by the motor attempting to start, will create an electromagnetic force strong enough to pick up the relay arma-ture and close the starting contacts of the relay, which will ener-gize the running windings. A fraction of a second later, as the motor comes up to full speed, the running current decreases to normal value and allows the relay armature to drop and open the starting contacts.

The starting winding which was needed to provide the extra torque to overcome the inertia of the compressor is now out of the circuit. The motor continues to operate on only the running winding. The overload protector has a set of bimetal contacts which are normally in the closed position, and are in series with a resistance heater. If there is difficulty in starting the motor, or if the compressor becomes too hot for any reason, the excess heat will cause the contacts to open and interrupt all electrical power to the compressor motor.

Test Lamps

When the serviceman is attempting to diagnose the reason for an inoperative unit, it is recommended that a series test lamp,

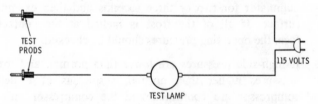

TEST
PRODS

115 VOLTS

TEST LAMP

Fig. 2. Typical test lamp arrangement.

shown in Fig. 2, be used for electrical tests. Remember to disconnect the service cord. Disconnect and insulate all of the relay leads and plug a series test lamp into a 115-volt outlet.

Starting Winding

To test the continuity of the motor starting winding, place the test lamp probes on compressor terminals *S* (starting) and *C* (common) (Fig. 3). If the test lamp does not light, the starting winding is open.

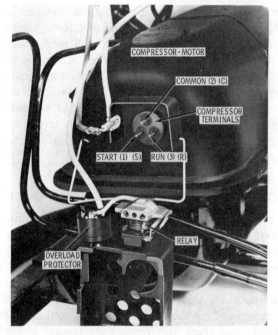

Courtesy of Hotpoint Co.

Fig. 3. Compressor motor terminal arrangement in a typical household refrigerator.

Running Winding

To test the running winding, place the test lamp probes on compressor terminals *R* (running) and *C* (common), (Fig. 3). If the test lamp fails to light, the running winding is open. If either the starting or running windings are open, the entire unit must be replaced.

Overload Protector

Before an accurate continuity check can be made on the overload protector, it must be determined that the unit has not been on overload during the past hour. If the unit is on overload, the protector contacts will be open and there will be no circuit continuity. If, however, the unit has not cycled on the overload, the continuity check will determine whether or not the overload protector is inoperative. To test the protector, place the test lamp probes on protector terminals *C* (common) and terminal 3 (or line, depending upon the wiring arrangement). If the test lamp does not light, either the overload protector or the resistance heater is open.

COMPRESSOR TESTING WITH DIRECT POWER

Before proceeding with this test, be sure the compressor is level. To test the compressor without any cabinet wiring in the circuit, disconnect the compressor lead cord from the junction block and connect it directly to the electrical wall outlet. If necessary, use a short extension cord to reach the outlet. If the compressor starts, the trouble is not in the compressor, relay, or overload protector. Plug the compressor lead cord back into the junction block, and check the temperature control and all cabinet wiring for an open circuit or poor connections. If the compressor does not start, check the overload protector.

The overload protector is mounted on the compressor under the terminal cover. The protector trips open when the compressor is overheated and/or when excessive current is drawn. Cycling on the overload may be the result of poor air circulation around the compressor and condenser. The compressor should not attempt to start until the refrigeration system has become equalized, which takes about 3 to 5 minutes after previous run. At least 100 volts are required at the compressor terminals during the starting interval. A typical compressor motor circuit is shown in Fig. 4.

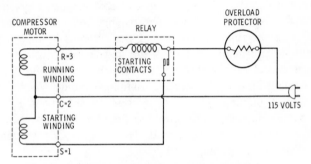

Fig. 4. Showing a schematic wiring diagram of a compressor motor.

If the compressor repeatedly starts and runs for 5 or 6 seconds and then cycles on the overload protector, the starting relay contacts may be stuck closed and the excess current is tripping the overload. Disconnect the wire from compressor terminal S, and make a momentary short between wire terminals R and S (see Figs. 3 and 4). If the compressor starts and runs without cycling on the overload protector, replace with a new complete starting relay.

To check for an open overload protector, short across the terminals (see Figs. 3 and 4). If the compressor starts after shorting the protector terminals, replace the overload with one having the same part number. If the compressor does not start, look for other trouble such as a low line voltage, defective starting relay, and defective operating protective relay, compressor. Other possibilities are blown fuse, broken service cord, inoperative thermostat, faulty capacitor, etc.

Starting Relay

The starting relay is usually mounted under the compressor terminal cover and consists essentially of a magnetically operated switch with starting contacts. The magnet coil of the relay is in series with the running winding of the compressor motor. When current is applied to the motor, the magnet coil raises the relay plunger and closes the starting contacts, thus connecting the starting winding in parallel with the running winding. As the motor approaches running speed, the current in the running winding and in the relay coil diminishes and the plunger *drops out,* which opens the starting winding circuit. The compressor then continues to operate on the running winding only.

To check for open relay starting contacts, short between the wires at the compressor terminals. If the compressor starts, the relay is defective. If the compressor does not start, check the relay magnet. To check the relay magnet coil, disconnect the power lead from the relay screw terminal. Short between the wires at the compressor terminals and, at the same time, touch the wire terminal with the disconnected power lead. This bypasses the relay and connects the line directly to the compressor, but through the overload protector. If the compressor does not start, a check for open motor windings or electrical grounds can be made with an ohmmeter. Test between compressor terminals *common* and *run*, and between *common* and *start*.

DEFROSTING HEATERS

All automatic defrosting refrigerators are provided with a combination *temperature defrost control*, a flexible defrost heater *element* and a *warming wire* wrapped around the temperature control bellows and part of the control feeler tube. When the defrost button is pushed in, the compressor circuit opens and closes the defrost circuit. The defrost heater element heats the evaporator until the temperature at the control feeler-tube contact point reaches approximately 55° (if the control is at *normal*). At this point, expansion of the control bellows opens the defrost circuit and closes the compressor circuit. Should the defrost heater element continue to heat, even after all frost is melted, check the control warmer wire.

Checking Defrost Heater Element

If the defrost heater element becomes inoperative, proceed as follows:

1. Remove the line cord from the electrical outlet and turn the temperature control to the *off* position.
2. Remove the control from the food liner.
3. Check for loose or open connections.
4. Plug the line cord into the electrical outlet and short across terminals 2 and 3 on the defrost control (Fig. 5). Maintain the short for the length of time necessary to determine by touch if the defrost element is heating. If the defrost element heats, the *control* is defective and must be replaced. If the element does not heat, replace it with a new element.

Checking Control Warmer Wire

Automatic defrost refrigerator units have a warmer wire attached to the temperature control. During the defrost cycle, this

**Fig. 5. Connection terminals on a typical combination
defrost temperature control.**

wire heats the control bellows and keeps it warmer than the contact point at the end of the feeler tube. Should the warmer wire
become defective, the control bellows may get cooler than the
feeler-tube contact, and cause the defrost heater to heat longer
than necessary. The warmer wire encircles the control bellows
twice, then folds partially over the control top and bottom, and
finally is routed along the control feeler tube for a short distance.
An illustration of a warmer wire connection is shown in Fig. 6.

If the control warmer wire does not heat when the defrost
button is pushed in, check it as follows:

1. Unplug the line cord from the electrical outlet and turn
   the temperature control to *off*.
2. Remove the temperature control from the food liner.

3. Plug the line cord into the electrical outlet and short across terminals 2 and 3 on the control (Fig. 5).

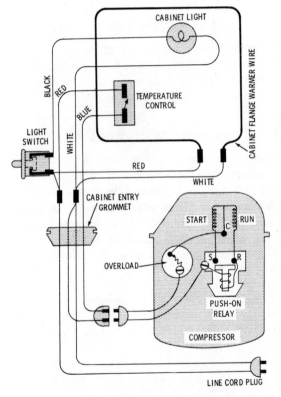

Fig. 6. Wiring diagram showing warmer wire connection in a combination defrost refrigerator.

If the control warmer wire and the defrost heater element are warm, the control is defective and must be replaced. If the

241

defrost heater element gets warm but the control warmer wire does not, the control warmer wire is defective and must be replaced.

CABINET LIGHT AND SWITCH

The cabinet light (or lights) is energized by the door-operated switch. If the cabinet light does not go on when the door is opened, it may be due to a burned out light bulb, a defective light switch or socket, or faulty wiring.

CONDENSER COOLING FAN

The condenser cooling fan (when used) is connected in parallel with the compressor. Therefore, if the compressor operates but the fan does not, the fan is either defective or disconnected. An excessive fan noise complaint may arise if one of the fan blades has been bent out of alignment. If any irregularity is noted, replace the fan blade. Another cause of excessive fan noise may be loose fan bracket mounting screws. A typical fan assembly is shown in Fig. 7.

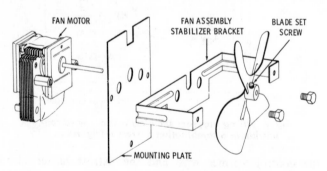

Fig. 7. Fan motor and assembly components.

If the cut-in and cut-out temperature readings obtained by the use of a remote reading thermometer are not within 1 or 2 degrees of those specified in the operating temperature chart supplied by the manufacturer, recalibrate the control.

Replacing Controls

To replace controls on most models, proceed as follows:

1. Disconnect the electrical power cord.
2. Pull the control knob off of the shaft.
3. Remove the control mounting screws and work the control out of the food liner opening.
4. Disconnect the control leads from its terminal. When installing a new control, make sure that the capillary tube is firmly clamped against the stainless steel plate. If the control capillary tube is not located correctly, the control will not be able to sense the proper temperature, and erratic refrigeration operation will result.

Calibrating Controls

The temperature control may be calibrated to vary the *cut-in* and *cut-out* temperatures by turning the range adjustment screw. This screw, shown in Fig. 8, raises and lowers these temperatures by an equal amount. The procedure is as follows:

1. Turn the range adjustment screw right to raise and left to lower the *cut-in* and *cut-out* temperatures (Fig. 8). Each 1/4 turn of the screw will raise or lower the temperatures proximately 2 degrees. *Do not turn this screw more than one full turn as erratic operation may result beyond that point.*

door gasket seal, poor air circulation in the evaporator, or an inoperative fan, defrost heater wire, or defrost timer. All dual temps use a constant *cut-in* type temperature control. Changing the control knob setting will change the *cut-out* temperature, but will not affect the *cut-in* temperature.

A constant *cut-in* simply means that the setting only determines the temperature at which the electrical contacts open, interrupting power to the compressor. The temperature which causes the contacts to close always remains constant, regardless of control setting. The constant cut-in temperature is approximately 37 degrees. Therefore, whenever the temperature in the fresh-food section causes the control contacts to open, the frost that has accumulated on the cooling coil will begin to melt and drain off. All of the frost will be dissipated since the control contacts will not close until the control capillary senses a temperature of 37 degrees, which is above the frost point. If defrosting of the cooling coil is not achieved, it is usually due to a high setting of the control dial which resulted in constant running of the compressor.

Checking Operating Temperatures

Cabinet and evaporator temperatures can be varied considerably by changing the control setting. If no change occurs, check the control *cut-in* and *cut-out* temperatures. To check control operating temperatures, proceed as follows:

1. Scrape away the frost on the inside of the evaporator adjacent to the feeler-tube thermal connection.
2. Using a few drops of water, freeze the bulb of an accurately calibrated remote reading thermometer to the evaporator.
3. Set the control at *normal*. Close the cabinet door and allow the compressor to run through 2 or 3 complete cycles.

EVAPORATOR COOLING FAN

The evaporator cooling fan (when used) is designed to blow cold air over the evaporator compartment area to maintain an even temperature throughout. The air circulation also prevents frost accumulation on food packages and freezer racks. If the fan fails to operate or runs erratically, the reduced air circulation will cause unsatisfactory temperatures in the evaporator compartment.

Most troubles of this sort are usually due to defective wiring, a faulty fan-motor switch or a bent motor shaft. The switch and fan motor may easily be checked out by means of an ohmmeter or the conventional test lamp probes. If, after making the foregoing checks, the evaporator fan fails to operate, the trouble is either in the wiring or the fan motor itself.

TEMPERATURE CONTROL SERVICE

There are generally two types of temperature control devices, and their functions depend upon:

1. Temperature standard controls serving solely as *on* and *off* switches for the compressor.
2. Temperature combination controls with automatic defrost features which govern the defrost operation as well as the compressor operation.

Most problems resulting from temperature control defects will show up in the refrigerator compartment, or in both compartments, but never in the evaporator alone. Attention given to the refrigerator compartment and control adjustments is important because the evaporator compartment will react favorably to nearly all corrective measures. Unsatisfactory temperatures in the evaporator compartment only are usually the result of a poor

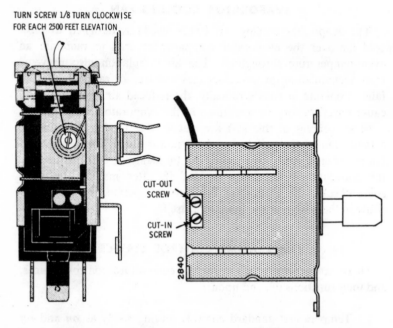

TURN SCREW 1/8 TURN CLOCKWISE
FOR EACH 2500 FEET ELEVATION

CUT-OUT
SCREW

CUT-IN
SCREW

2840

*Fig. 8. Temperature adjustment on Ranco and Cutler Hammer tempera-
ture controls respectively.*

   2. Connect the line cord and recheck for proper *cut-in* and
cut-out temperatures.

REPLACING SYSTEM COMPONENTS

   When component replacements are necessary, careful checks
must be made in order that identical parts are obtained from the
manufacturers. Before actually opening a sealed refrigeration
system, be sure that all the necessary tools are close at hand.
The system should be opened only long enough to make the

repair or component replacement. If the system is allowed to be open for an extended period of time, the motor winding in the compressor will pick up moisture, which will be very difficult to remove during compressor evacuation.

Compressor Unit Replacements

When cutting into a system for compressor replacement, proceed as follows:

1. Pinch off the suction and discharge lines as close as possible to the compressor. This will prevent excess oil spilling when cutting the lines.
2. Clean the paint from the suction line and cut the suction line close to the pinched area with a tube cutter. Place a fitting on the cabinet suction line and plug it to prevent entrance of air and dirt.
3. Clean the paint from the discharge line at the pinched area. Then cut the discharge line close to the pinched area with a tube cutter. Install a fitting on the discharge line and attach a compound gauge with a proper fitting.
4. Remove the inoperative compressor by taking out the four spring clips holding it to the cabinet cross rails. Install a replacement compressor, making sure the rubber grommets from the inoperative compressor are remounted. The replacement compressor suction, discharge, and charging lines are equipped with flare nuts and plugs.
5. With a tube cutter, cut the compressor suction and discharge tubes as close to the flare nuts as possible, and install the proper fittings. Connect the compressor suction line to the cabinet suction line. Plug the compressor discharge line. *Note: Be sure to clean the paint from the tubing before cutting any lines.*

6. **Remove the** original dryer and install a replacement drier. Compression fittings are provided for the inlet to the dryer. The output end of the drier connects directly to the capillary line and will have to be silver soldered.

7. Remove the plug from the compressor charging line and connect a test can of refrigerant to the charging line via hoses and a manifold. Be sure to purge the lines.

8. Charge the system to 10 psig (pounds per square inch gauge) as read on the condenser line gauge. Close all valves and leak test all connections.

9. Replace the test can with an exact measured charge of refrigerant.

10. Remove the plug from the compressor discharge line fitting. Apply power to the compressor and evacuate the system to at least a 25-in. vacuum (as read on the condenser gauge) for a minimum of 15 minutes. Then replace and tighten the plug on the compressor discharge line fitting and disconnect the power from the compressor.

11. Charge the unit to 2 psig as read on the condenser line gauge. This is to break the vacuum in the unit.

12. Remove the gauge from the condenser tubing and the plug from the compressor discharge tube. Then connect the fitting between the compressor discharge line and the condenser line. Make the connection immediately while the unit still contains an atmosphere of refrigerant.

13. Begin to charge the unit and apply power to the compressor. While the compressor is running, leak test the high side.

14. After the system has been charged, pinch off the charging line and insert the plug previously removed back on the charging line. *Note: Leave the pinch-off tool on the line until the plug is reinstalled.*

15. Disconnect the power, permitting the low-side pressure to equalize. Leak test once more, and recheck all joints and fittings. Repaint all tubing surfaces previously sanded.

Evaporator Replacement

To replace an evaporator in a sealed system, proceed as follows:

1. Disconnect the electrical line cord.
2. Cut off the suction line from the compressor close to the heat exchanger after the refrigerant charge is released. Place the fitting on the line and plug the line to prevent entrance of air and dirt.
3. Clean the paint from the compressor discharge line about two inches beyond the joint, and cut the tubing with a tube cutter. Install the fittings on the lines. Plug the compressor discharge line and attach a compound gauge with the proper fitting to the discharge line going to the condenser.
4. Clean the paint from the compressor charging line and, with a tube cutter, cut the line as close to the end as possible. Then install the fitting and plug on the open end of the line.
5. Remove the rear tube cover from the cabinet back to expose the heat exchanger tubing that is imbedded against the foam insulation.
6. Cut the heat exchanger line near the top of the cabinet back where it enters the liner. This will permit easier removal of the heat exchanger through the cabinet when removing the evaporator.
7. Remove the screws holding the evaporator to the top of the cabinet. Slowly pull out the evaporator and heat exchanger from the cabinet, as an assembly.

8. Take off the control cover and thermostat from the inoperative evaporator and install the new evaporator.
9. Insert the heat exchanger and evaporator through the liner opening on the cabinet until the evaporator is properly positioned. Then remount the evaporator assembly and top cover.
10. At the rear of the cabinet, carefully reposition the heat exchanger.
11. Connect the cabinet suction line to the compressor suction line.
12. Evacuate and recharge the unit as outlined in other parts of this chapter.

Drier Replacement

A new drier must be installed when any system component is replaced or whenever the system is opened. To replace the drier, proceed as follows:

1. Remove all paint and scale from the refrigerant lines for a distance of about three inches at both ends of the old drier (use steel wool or fine emery cloth).
2. Cut the lines approximately one inch from the old joints. To cut the capillary tube, score the walls with a knife or file. Make a uniform cut around the entire tube, then break it off.
3. Make an offset about one inch from the end of the capillary tube to prevent its penetrating too far into the new drier.
4. Immediately solder the new drier into place. Use silver solder and the proper flux.

Replacing Heat Exchanger

To replace the heat exchanger, proceed as follows:

1. Purge the charge by cutting the process tube on the compressor and install the service valve, leaving it open.

2. Remove the defective heat exchanger.

3. The capillary tube will have to be unsoldered from the evaporator inlet. Be careful not to restrict the evaporator inlet. Remove heat as soon as the solder liquefies.

4. Unsolder the suction line from the evaporator outlet; clean, then cut the suction line about for inches from the compressor.

5. Unsolder the drier from the condenser outlet. Hold the outlet tube down and wipe the solder off of the tube immediately after the drier is removed.

6. Swedge the compressor suction line so the replacement suction line will fit inside.

7. Install the replacement heat exchanger, making all solder joints except on the condenser outlet.

8. Install the new drier on the condenser outlet.

9. Make an offset on the end of the capillary tube and solder it in the outlet of the new drier.

10. Pull a vacuum for about twenty minutes, then add enough refrigerant to produce a pressure of 35 to 40 lbs.

11. Leak test the low side, then start the compressor and leak test the high side.

12. Purge the charge and continue with the vacuum as previously outlined.

13. Charge the system and reassemble the refrigerator, making sure to locate the system lines properly and seal where necessary.

14. Test run the refrigerator to be sure it is operating properly.

Replacing Condensers

Most refrigerant condensers are made of copper-coated steel tubing. If a leak occurs, a piece of copper tube can be spliced in place, in which case the condenser does not need to be replaced. When a condenser is in need of replacement, proceed as follows:

1. Open the sealed system at the compressor process tube first. After the refrigerant charge is released, install a service valve on the process tube, leaving the valve open.

2. Before cutting the tubing lines going to the condenser, check the ends of the replacement condenser tubing. If there is no excess tubing on the connector lines, unsolder the connector tubes from the old condenser.

3. Score and break the capillary tube about one inch from the old drier. Remove the old condenser and install the replacement. Depending on the type of condenser to be replaced (fan-cooled or static), it might be preferable to make the joints on the replacement before installing it in its place (clean all tubing before soldering the joints).

4. After all other joints are made, make an offset in the capillary tube and install the new drier. *Note: When soldering these joints, make sure to leave the service valve on the compressor process tube open.*

5. Start evacuation procedures.

6. Refer to the evacuating, purging, and charging procedures as outlined in this chapter.

7. After reassembling the refrigerator, make a test run to be sure that is is operating properly.

SERVICE VALVES

Service valves referred to in service operations are named according to their function, as:

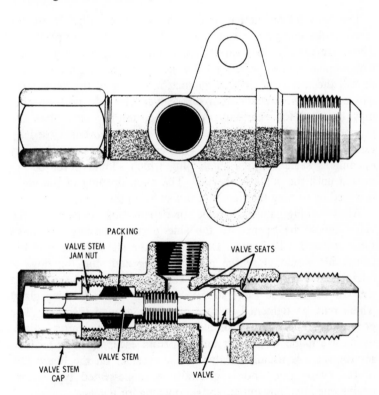

Fig. 9. Exterior and interior view of a typical compressor suction or discharge valve.

1. Compressor suction. }
2. Compressor discharge. } Service shut-off valves

3. Receiver service.
4. Evaporator liquid-line service.
5. Evaporator suction-line service, etc.

The compressor suction and discharge valves (Fig. 9) are located at the compressor inlet and outlet connection, respectively. These are usually dual valves, commonly called two-way valves, which open or close with the valve stem screwed "all the way in" or "all the way out". In this manner, a turning of the valve stem will control two outlets from one valve. The side port opening may be used for charging, dehydrating, testing, etc., after the proper connections have been made. The side port is closed by turning the valve stem, which is covered by a brass cap. The port opening is sealed with a small plug which should never be removed until the valve is checked. The main opening of the valve is closed by turning the stem all the way in (to the right).

After making gauge, charging, or dehydrating connections, the valve should be opened to the side port by turning the valve stem one and a half turns. Do not turn the stem all the way because this would close the main opening and stop the flow of refrigerant. Fig. 10 illustrates the various positions of the service shut-off valves. The valve stem is provided with a packing gland which may be tightened in case of a leak around the stem. The port plug and valve cap should always be replaced after adjustments are made to prevent any gas from escaping. The receiver service valve is usually located at the receiver on the liquid line to the evaporator, and is generally a single-seated type valve, having one inlet, one outlet, and no opening for a gauge.

The evaporator liquid- and suction-line service valves are used only on evaporators having a float-valve header. Frequently the valves are equipped with a built-in strainer to remove foreign particles before entering the evaporator, and is located at the

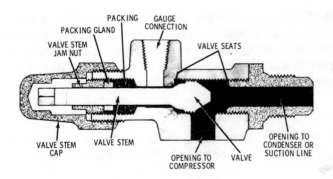

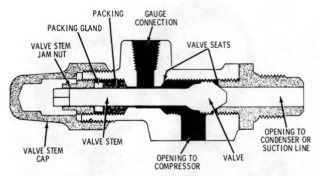

Fig. 10. Showing service shut-off valve in open and closed position.

evaporator header in the liquid-line connection between the receiver and the evaporator. The evaporator suction-line service valve is also located at the evaporator header in the suction line, and is connected between the compressor and the evaporator.

TO CRACK A VALVE

The term *crack*, as used in servicing refrigeration units, means to open slightly and close again. Thus, to *crack* the liquid-line

Operation and Service

shut-off valve, for example, open it slightly to allow a tiny spurt of liquid to flow through, and then close it. The same procedure applies to cracking any valve or valve port in the system. This is important when purging the gauge on the charging line of air, and to avoid releasing an excessive amount of refrigerant.

THE COMBINATION GAUGE SET

A test gauge set or testing manifold, (Fig. 11) consists of two tee valves built into one valve body, with the valve stems extend-

Courtesy Mueller Brass Co.

Fig. 11. Typical combination gauge set.

256

ing out on each end for wrench or hand-wheel operations. The tee valves are constructed so that the valve works only on the leg which is attached to the tee. The opening or closing of the stem only effects the one opening; the other two openings on the valve will remain open.

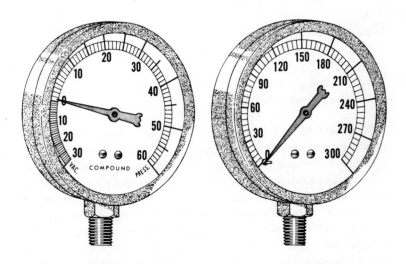

Fig. 12. Typical compound pressure and plain pressure gauge.

Importance of Gauges and Combination Gauge Set

Since most household refrigeration units are not equipped with gauges, a serviceman must insert his own for the various testing and service operations that must be dealt with in solving day-to-day problems. The number of important operations and tests that may be performed by the use of a test gauge set are numerous, the most important being:

1. Observation of operating pressure.
2. Charge refrigerant through compressor, etc.
3. Purge receiver.
4. Charge liquid into high side.
5. Build up pressure in low side for control setting or to test for leaks.
6. Charge oil through the compressor, etc.

Types of Gauges Used

The gauges used in refrigeration servicing are:

1. The low-pressure (compound) gauge.
2. The high-pressure gauge.

The standard type of low-pressure gauge is often called a compound gauge because its construction permits a reading of both pressure in pounds per square inch and vacuum in inches of mercury as shown in Fig. 12. A standard compound gauge dial is graduated to record a pressure range of from 30 inches of vacuum to 60 pounds per square inch. The high-pressure gauge is equipped with a dial for measuring pressures of from 0 to 300 pounds per square inch. Gauges used in refrigeration service should be graduated to read approximately double the actual working pressure.

SEALED SYSTEMS

The first step when charging a sealed system with refrigerants is to have the right charging and evacuating equipment. This will enable the serviceman to charge the unit with the exact amount of refrigerant required. Although there are several charging methods used the sight-glass charging cylinder is to be recom-

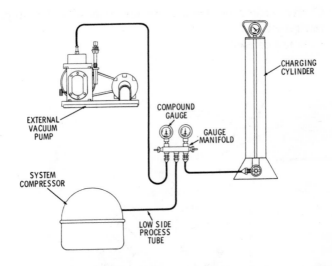

Fig. 13. Showing typical charging and evacuation arrangement when installed.

mended. This method of refrigerant charge will be accurate regardless of ambient temperature.

Evacuating and Recharging

Generally, every refrigerator unit is properly charged with refrigerant upon delivery, the main service due to refrigerant troubles usually consists in evacuation and recharging. A step-by-step procedure after the charging equipment has been installed, as shown in Fig. 13, will be as follows:

1. Discharge the system and adapt the proper replacement components.
2. Evacuate the system thoroughly.

3. Charge accurately through the low side with the proper refrigerant.
4. Leak test carefully.

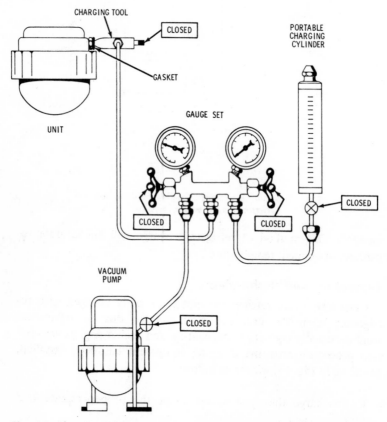

Fig. 14. Showing arrangement of charging equipment when installed ready for use with all valves in closed position.

Figs. 14 to 18 are schematic illustrations of typical external vacuum-pump and charging-cylinder connections through a gauge manifold and the compressor process tube.

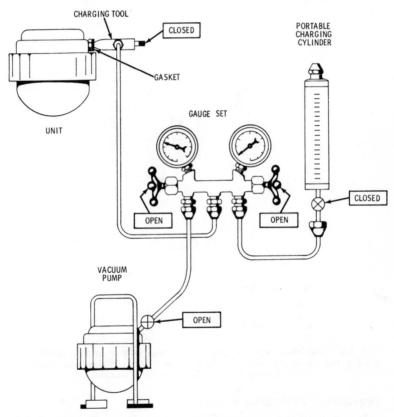

Fig. 15. *To evacuate lines, open gauge set and gauge manifold. Close vacuum pump valve and check to see that vacuum holds.*

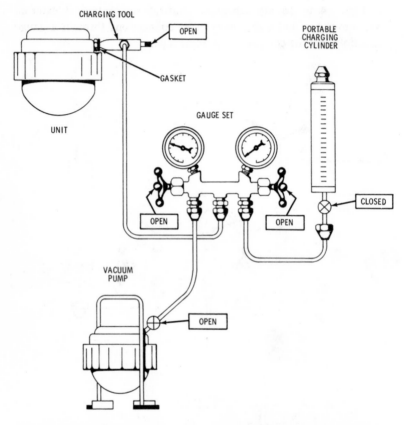

Fig. 16. Open charging tool, vacuum pump valves and evacuate assembly for about 20 minutes. Close vacuum pump valve and check to see that vacuum holds for about 5 minutes.

Evacuation of Sealed System

It is a good rule, whenever a sealed system is opened and the refrigerant charge removed, to evacuate the system and install a new service drier before recharging the system. To evacuate the refrigerator, proceed as follows:

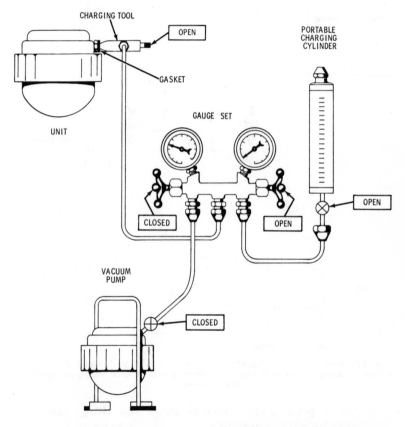

Fig. 17. *To charge unit close vacuum pump line and open charging cylinder valve; allow refrigerant to be drawn into compressor. Stop flow when refrigerant on the sight glass reaches zero.*

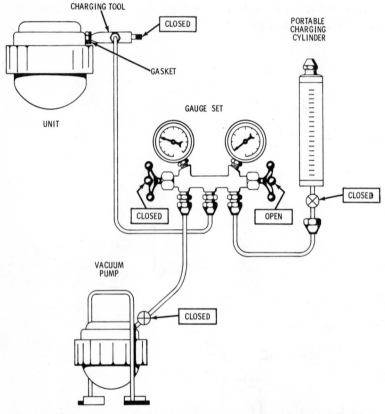

Fig. 18. After the compressor has been fully charged, close charging valve on compressor and remove charging tool. Check charging screw for tightness.

1. Use a good external vacuum pump and change the oil often for efficient operation.
2. Install a service valve on the low-side process tube of the compressor.

3. Connect the vacuum pump hose to the service valve. Leave the valve in a closed position.
4. Start the vacuum pump, open its discharge valve, and slowly open the service valve on the system compressor.
5. If an extremely efficient vacuum pump is used, crack the suction valve on the pump for the first minute, then slowly open it. This procedure will prevent the oil in the system from foaming and being sucked into the vacuum pump in large quantities.
6. Next, pull a vacuum for about 20 minutes, which should give a reading of 500 microns or 29.6 inches of mercury on the compound gauge. At the end of the 20-minute vacuum time, the vacuum pump should be valved off and the micron gauge left in the system. *It is important to observe the gauge.* If the gauge reading rises, there could be a leak in the system.
7. Close the service valve on the system compressor, then stop the vacuum pump.
8. Connect a sight-glass charging cylinder hose to the service valve (Fig. 15) and purge the charging hose. Induce a charge of refrigerant into the system until the low-pressure side reads 30 to 40 psig, then leak test the low side. After the low-side leak tests are completed, run the system compressor for a few minutes.
9. Leak test the high side of the refrigerant system.
10. After completion of the leak tests, purge this temporary refrigerant charge out of the low side. This refrigerant charge will assist in removing moisture within the system.
11. Repeat the vacuum pump procedure for another 30 minutes, which should give a reading of 500 microns or 29.6 inches of mercury. If the discharge tube of the vacuum

pump is in a container of oil, there should be bubbles in the oil after completion of the foregoing procedure.

Charging of Sealed System

The equipment for charging refrigerant is the same as that used for evacuation. The charging procedure is normally as follows:

1. The first step in charging a system is to have the proper equipment so that the refrigerant can be accurately determined within $\pm 1/4$ ounce. Although there are several methods of charging, the use of a sight-glass charging cylinder is preferred, since this method is accurate regardless of ambient temperature.
2. Always charge through the low side of the system, either through the process tube or the suction line. Charge the system with the compressor off, since most of the refrigerant will enter in liquid state. Allow about 5 minutes after the charge has entered the system before starting the compressor. The efficiency of charging can be increased by elevating the charging cylinder; however, refrigerant should always be introduced slowly.
3. Connect the charging hose of the charger to the service valve on the compressor.
4. Open the charger valve and purge the hose. As soon as the refrigerant has stabilized in the charging cylinder, check the pressure reading of the cylinder and rotate the sleeve to correct the setting for pressure and the type of refrigerant being used. Control the flow of refrigerant with the service valve, not the charger valve.
5. When charging the refrigeration system, some bubbles may appear in the charging cylinder. These can be elimi-

nated by closing the service valve and tipping the charging cylinder upside-down momentarily. Then continue with charging until the correct charge has entered the system.

6. If, at any time, it is required to raise the internal pressure of a charging cylinder, use a bucket of warm water (not over 125° F.) and place the cylinder in the bucket. *Caution: Never place a flame on any refrigerant cylinder.* This can cause hydrostatic pressure to build up to dangerous levels and, in extreme cases, cause the cylinder to rupture like a bomb. Extreme care should always be taken when handling refrigerant cylinders.

7. When it has been ascertained that the system has the correct refrigerant charge, use the pinch-off tool and make the final joint. If possible, leave enough round tubing between the compressor and the pinch-off crimp in order that the process tube may be used at a later date.

EXPANSION VALVE UNITS

Because numerous serviceable refrigerators are equipped with expansion valves for refrigerant control, the more common service operations on these units are described in the following paragraphs:

Use of Combination Gauge Set to Add Oil

With reference to Fig. 19, oil may be added to the compressor as follows:

Connect a piece of 1/4" copper tubing between the oil supply and valve *E*. Pour the refrigeration oil into a clean dry bottle. Put the compound gauge on the suction line valve and close the liquid line at the receiver. When a sufficient amount

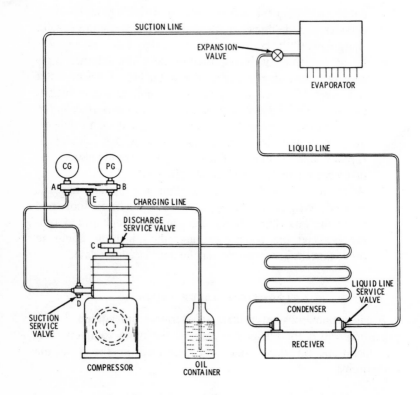

Fig. 19. Schematic diagram illustrating the connections for adding oil to compressor.

of oil has been added, close the valve at point *A* and open valve *D*. The compressor may now be put into normal operation. *Caution: Make sure that the end of the oil-supply tubing is kept submerged below the oil level in the container, so that air will not be drawn into the system during the operation.*

To Charge Refrigerant Through Low Side

With reference to Fig. 20, refrigerant may be added as follows:

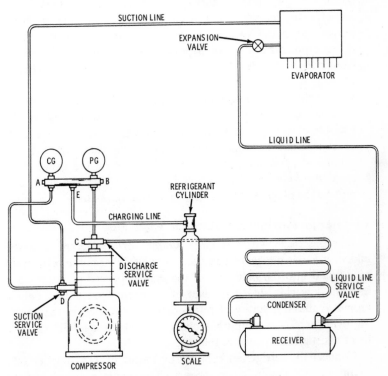

Fig. 20. Schematic diagram illustrating connections for adding refrigerant through low side.

Connect the suction-line valve port and the refrigerant tank with a piece of 1/4″ copper tubing with gauges connected as shown. The cylinder should be placed on a suitable scale in an upright position, with the scale reading noted. The 1/4″ tube between the manifold and the charging drum must be long enough so as not to affect the scale reading. Purge the air out of the charging line by turning on the gas at the tank valve and cracking the valve unit at valve B. When the line has been purged, open the suction-line valve and start the compressor. A back pressure of about 5 pounds is maintained in charging with sulfur dioxide (SO_2) and about 10 pounds for *Freon* (*F*-12).

If the cylinder is cold, apply heat to the gas cylinder by means of a hot cloth or a pail of hot water; this will assist in the transfer of refrigerant to the unit. When the required amount of refrigerant has been added, close the valve on the gas drum and allow the pressure to fall to zero on the gauge, then close the valve at the suction line. Disconnect the lines and replace the plugs. Put the unit into normal operation.

To Charge Refrigerant Through High Side

In some cases where a large amount of refrigerant is to be added, it is advantageous and time saving to charge the refrigerant as a liquid into the high side of the system instead of pumping it into the low side. In such cases, it is recommended that only a known required quantity of refrigerant be contained in the charging cylinder. To accomplish a charge, a reference to Fig. 21 will be of assistance. Proceed as follows:

Connect the refrigerant cylinder by means of 1/4″ copper tubing to the manifold, as shown. The compressor should be stopped and the condenser allowed to cool to room temperature. The charging line should be purged in the manner previously described. The refrigerant cylinder should be heated, inverted, and securely fastened, after which the cylinder valve is opened. While the cylinder is being discharged, it may be

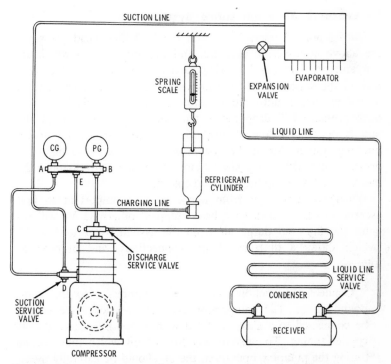

SUCTION LINE

SPRING SCALE

EXPANSION VALVE

EVAPORATOR

LIQUID LINE

CG   PG

A   B

E

REFRIGERANT CYLINDER

CHARGING LINE

C

DISCHARGE SERVICE VALVE

LIQUID LINE SERVICE VALVE

CONDENSER

SUCTION SERVICE VALVE

D

RECEIVER

COMPRESSOR

Fig. 21. Schematic diagram illustrating connections for adding refrigerant through high side.

necessary to supply additional heat to maintain the flow of refrigerant to the unit. When the required amount of gas has been added, close both the valve on the gas container and valve *A*. Valve *B* should be opened to by-pass the pressure from the charging line to the low side. Finally, after the charging line records zero, valve *B* should be closed, after which the manifold connection to the service drum is capped and the unit put into operation.

To Evacuate Air From Entire System

During normal operations, both the back and head pressures are above atmospheric pressure, and the only way in which air can enter the system is during service operations or due to a leak in the system. When the high side of the system has a leak, it will expel gas until atmospheric pressure is reached and the back pressure will drop below atmospheric pressure. When the unit is operated below atmospheric pressure, air will be drawn into the system. Air in the system will cause excessive high-side pressure and will nearly always stop the unit by overloading the motor, which will trip the overload cutout.

When evacuating air from a system, it is important to first ascertain that all leaks have been stopped, otherwise air will re-enter the line. To purge air from the system, refer to Fig. 22 (which shows a diagram of the connections) and proceed as follows:

Connect the suction side of the compressor to the compound gauge. The compressor discharge service valve should be connected to a glass jar filled with water, by mans of 1/4" copper tubing. To prevent any loss of oil which may escape during the pumping operation, the oil should be carefully measured and returned to the compressor after the purging operation. Check the compressor discharge-valve port to make sure it is closed, after which the compressor suction-valve ports should be opened to both the gauge set and the evaporator. The receiver liquid line should be checked to make sure it is opened, and the compressor should be put under intermittent operation until a maximum amount of vacuum is being obtained, as registered by the compound gauge.

If, after the unit has been stopped for a period of four or five minutes without any change in the gauge reading, the

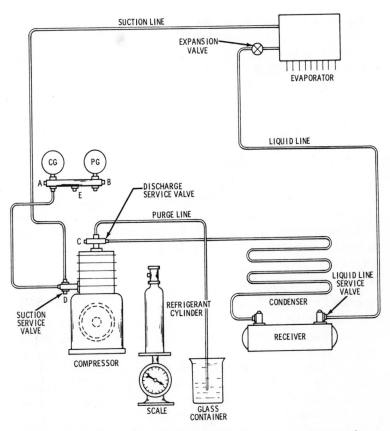

Fig. 22. Schematic diagram showing connections for purging air from entire system.

unit is free from air, and the glass jar end of the copper tubing should be connected to the middle leg of the manifold. At this time, a charged refrigerant gas drum should be connected to the manifold at valve *B*, and the line connection from the

273

gas drum purged. When the gas-drum valve and manifold valve are opened, the gas charge enters the system and the pressure is built up to a positive value of about 10 pounds. When the required amount of refrigerant has been added, close the valve on the gas drum and add any oil which may have escaped during the purging operation. After this operation, a final check for leaks should be made and the unit put back into normal operation.

Purging Air From Condenser

Air in the condenser will cause excessive high-side pressure resulting in long operating periods, with an accompanying waste of power. The unit should be shut down during this test and during the purging operation. Allow the condenser to cool down to room temperature. With reference to the diagram, proceed as follows:

Attach a purging line (1/4″ copper tubing) to the service connection valve *E* on the manifold, as shown in Fig. 23. If the refrigerant is sulfur dioxide (SO_2), place the end of the tubing into the bottom of a container in which 1-1/2 pounds of concentrated lye (NaOH) has been dissolved in a gallon of water. Then crack valve *B* (loosen and immediately tighten) and purge slowly for several minutes. Observe the pressure drop registered on the pressure gauge, and when it has returned to normal, the purging should be discontinued, valve *B* should be tightened, the purging line removed, and the unit returned to normal operation.

Evacuating the Entire Refrigerant Charge

When it becomes necessary to remove the entire refrigerant charge from the unit (as in the case when an exchange of the compressor or any other component of the condensing unit is

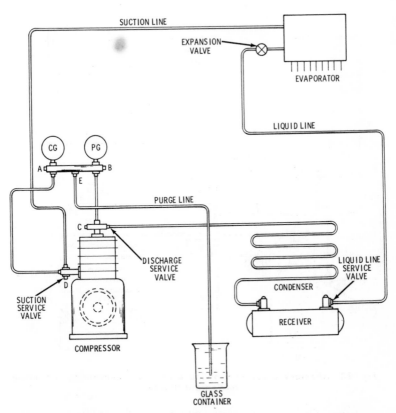

Fig. 23. Schematic diagram showing the connections for purging air from the condenser.

necessary), it is often desirable to salvage the refrigerant by evacuating (pumping) it into an empty service drum. With reference to Fig. 24, the procedure is as follows:

To pump the gas into an empty cylinder or drum, put the cylinder in a bucket of cold water (preferably ice water), as

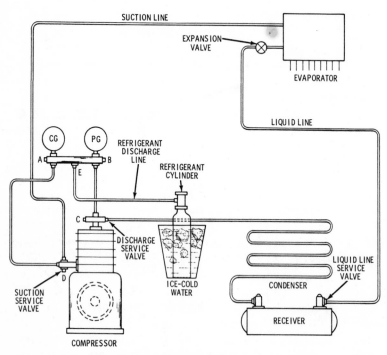

Fig. 24. *Schematic diagram showing connections evacuating the entire refrigerant charge.*

shown. Connect the empty cylinder to the middle leg of the manifold by means of 1/4″ copper tubing. The compressor discharge service valve should be closed, and valve *B* should be opened; the valve on the cylinder should also be open. After the compressor suction-line service valve and the receiver liquid-line valve are opened, the compressor is put into operation. keep the cylinder as cold as possible until the operation is complete. The compound gauge attached to the suction shut-off valve will show when the charge has been completely removed. If, during this pumping operation, the pressure gauge indicates an abnormally high pressure, the unit should be stopped, allowing the compressor to cool down. An indication of a complete evacuation of the system will be obtained by closing the cylinder valve. If an observation of the gauge indicates a constant high vacuum for any length of time, the evacuation is complete and the service attachments, including the gas cylinder, may be removed from the unit.

LEAK TESTING

The old soap-bubble and oil method of detecting leaks in refrigerators using modern refrigerants is, at best, only a makeshift one to be used only in the absence of proper detectors. There are several types of leak detectors available, such as the *halide torches,* or an *electronic* type which is presently manufactured by the General Electric Company (Fig. 25). The halide type, however, is probably the most widely employed and is sufficiently sensitive for household refrigeration systems.

Leaks in a refrigeration system will usually result in an undercharge of refrigerant. To add refrigerant would only be a temporary solution without first locating and repairing the leak, since adding refrigerant will not permanently correct the difficulty. The leak must be located and repaired, if possible, after which the entire system must be evacuated and recharged with the proper amount of refrigerant. Whenever a new charge of refrigerant is added, it is necessary to install a new drier. Any leak, regardless of its size, must be located before a determination can be made of the operative status of the system components. Do not replace a component because the system is short of gas unless a nonrepairable leak is found.

Fig. 25. General Electric type H-5 electronic portable type leak detector unit with tiny hand-held proportioning probe.

If the analysis indicates a leak, find it before opening the system. It is better to locate the leak before discharging than if the surrounding air is contaminated with refrigerant from a newly opened system. The presence of oil around a tubing joint usually indicates a leak, but do not let this be the determining factor. Always check the area with a leak detector to make sure.

The Soap-Bubble Method

Soap bubbles can be used to detect small leaks in the following manner:

Brush liquid detergent over the suspected area and watch for the formation of bubbles as the gas escapes. Sometimes, if the leak is of a slight intensity, several minutes must elapse for a bubble to appear. *Caution: Use the bubble method only when it is certain that the system has positive pressure.* Using it where a vacuum is present could pull moisture or soap bubbles into the system. A joint which is suspected of leaking can be enclosed in an envelope of cellophane film. Tightly tape both ends and any openings to make it gas-tight. After about an hour, pierce one end of the film for the probe and pierce the other end for air to enter. If a response is obtained, the joint should be repaired.

The Halide Leak Detector

When testing with the halide torch, make sure the room is free from refrigerant vapors. Watch the flame for the slightest change in color. A very faint *green* color indicates a small leak. The flame will be unmistakably *green* to *purple* when large leaks are encountered. To simplify the leak detection, keep the system pressurized to a minimum of 75 psi. This is easily accomplished for the high side by merely running the compressor. To pressurize the low side, allow the entire system to warm up to room temperature.

The halide leak detector method has been used for many years by air-conditioning and refrigeration servicemen, and consists of a combustible gas supply with a small burner on top. A tube from the bottom of this burner forms the probe. When this probe is moved near a large leak, the refrigerant going into the tube combines with the flame to cause perceptible change in the flame color. Disadvantages of using the halide torch include the following:

1. It is slow and relatively insensitive.
2. In a brightly lighted area, it is almost impossible to locate leaks smaller than about six ounces per year.
3. If the area is darkened, a smaller leak can be located; however, the change in the color of the flame is difficult

to interpret because other gases and dust cause the flame to change color.

The Electronic Type Leak Detector

Although leak testing with a halide torch is considered satisfactory in most instances, a more reliable test is made by means of the electronic type tester illustrated in Fig. 25. This easy to use instrument reduces the guesswork from leak testing because it is more sensitive, faster responding, and is capable of detecting a leak even though the surrounding air may be contaminated. The electronic detector contains an internal pump which draws air and leaking halogen tracer gas (halogen gases are chlorine, bromine, fluorine, and iodine, or any of their compounds) through a probe and hose as the probe is passed over leaking joints, gaskets, welds, etc. The air-gas mixture is drawn between two electrodes in the control unit—the ion-emitter and collector.

The presence of halogen gas in the interelectrode space causes an increase in interelectrode conductance that is proportional to the amount of halogen gas present, which results in greater positive-ion current. In the electronic detector, this emission current is electronically amplified and the amplifier output causes the leak indicating lamp to flash. A knob on the control unit permits the user to adjust the sensitivity to detect leaks in the range from 0.5 ounce per year to approximately 10 ounces per year.

The leak detector is specifically designed for use in atmospheres containing a relatively high concentration of halogen gas (up to 1000 ppm). Operation in such an atmosphere is made possible by the proportioning valve on the tip of the sending probe. This proportioning valve permits the user to regulate the ratio of contaminated atmospheric air and pure air (drawn in through an activated charcoal filter located within the control unit) that passes over the sensitive element. In this fashion, the concentration of halogen in the atmosphere is reduced to a tolerable level without affecting the sensitivity of the leak detector.

The leak detector contains an automatic balance circuit so that a constant or slowly changing contamination in the atmosphere will not cause the lamp to flash. Refrigerant gas will cause the lamp to flash only when there is an abrupt increase in the amount of gas going into the tip of the probe, such as when the probe tip passes near a leak.

To make a leak probe by means of the electronic detector, proceed as follows:

1. Plug the test detector into a 110-volt *AC* outlet.
2. Turn the sensitivity knob to the right and allow a 1-minute warm up.
3. Check the operation by turning the sensitivity knob quickly from one position to another. This should light the probe lamp.
4. Probe for leaks, starting with maximum sensitivity.
5. If the probe lamp lights twice for each leak, reduce the sensitivity.
6. Recheck the suspected leaks for confirmation.

After replacing a component in the refrigerating system, always test leak all joints before recharging. The extra time it takes is negligible compared to the loss of a charge due to a faulty connection. Be sure to clean the excess soldering flux (if used) from the new joints before leak testing, since it could seal off pinhole leaks that would show up later.

Service instruction charts have been worked out which will be of help in locating and repairing faults likely to be encountered in day-to-day service work.

REFRIGERATION TROUBLE CHART

Unit Dead, Will Not Run

Possible Cause	Possible Remedy
Blown fuse.	Check and replace if defective.
Rating of power source too low.	Check source with voltmeter. Should check within 10% of 115 volts.
Broken service cord.	Check voltage at relay. If no voltage at relay, but voltage indicated at outlet, replace service cord or plug on cord.
Inoperative thermostat.	Insert jumper across terminals of thermostat. If unit runs and connections are all tight, replace thermostat.
Faulty capacitor	Check capacitor using test cord and 150 watt light bulb. If bad or shows signs of leakage, replace capacitor.
Inoperative relay.	Use starter cord and check unit. If unit runs with normal wattage and above conditions are correct, replace relay.
Stalled Unit.	Use starter cord and check unit. If unit runs with normal wattage and above conditions are correct, replace relay.
Broken lead to compressor, timer or thermostat.	Replace or repair broken leads.

Compressor Cycles on Overload Protector

Possible Cause	Possible Remedy
Voltage too high or too low.	Check line voltage. Must be within 10% of name-plate rating. Connect refrigerator to proper power source.
Relay or overload protector inoperative.	Check continuity and replace if inoperative.
Motor winding open.	Check continuity of motor windings. If open, unit must be replaced.
Lead broken or connections loose.	Check for broken leads and loose terminal connections. Make necessary corrections.

Unit Hums and Shuts Off

Possible Cause	Possible Remedy
Low voltage.	Check electrical source with volt-wattmeter. Under

a load, voltage should be 115 volts ±10%. Check for possible use of extremely long extension cord, or several appliances on same circuit.

Faulty capacitor.	Replace capacitor.
Inoperative relay.	Replace relay.
Stalled compressor.	Check with test cord if compressor will not start—replace.

Unit Runs Excessively

Possible Cause	*Possible Remedy*
Frequent door openings.	Advise user on proper location and use of refrigerator.
High ambient temperature and humidity.	
Poor door seal.	Check to see if cabinet is level. Make necessary front and rear adjustments.
Gasket not sealing	Check door gasket. Realign door and when indicated, replace door gasket.
Interior light burns constantly.	Check light switch operation. If light does not go out when door is closed, replace the light switch.
Insufficient air circulation.	Check position of refrigerator. The rear and sides must be several inches away from walls. Locate in correct position.
Gas leaking from unit.	Check unit for gas leak. If a leak is found, replace the unit.
Loose connection of thermostat bulb to cooling coil.	Check connection and make necessary adjustment.
Faulty thermostat.	Turn thermostat to "off" position. If unit continues to run, replace the thermostat.
Refrigerant charge.	Too much or too little gas. Discharge, evacuate and recharge with proper charge.
Restriction or moisture.	Replace component where restriction is located. If moisture is suspected replace drier-filter.
Placing sudden load on unit.	Explain to user that heavy loading will cause long running time until temperatures are maintained. This running period may be several hours after heavy loading of the cabinet.

High Noise Level

Possible Cause	*Possible Remedy*
Loose compressor mounting bolts.	Replace mounts. This type noise usually occurs during starting or stopping of the unit.

Blower motor.	Check for motor wheel rubbing against housing. Readjust. Replace motor if noise is excessive.
Vibrating unit tubing.	Run the hands over various lines. This can often help determine the location of the vibration. Gently reform tubing to eliminate vibration problem. Check discharge line from compressor to top of condenser to eliminate possible rubbing of line against condenser.
Cabinet not level.	Check level, and if necessary, make the appropriate side-to-side and front-to-rear adjustments to level the cabinet.
Location of cabinet.	An out-of-level floor may be a factor in causing noise. Also certain types of flooring transmit vibration more readily than others. Investigate type of floor construction where cabinet is located.
Compressor	Only after all external sources have been checked should the compressor be changed for noise.

Food Compartment Temperatures Too Warm

Possible Cause	*Possible Remedy*
Inoperative thermostat.	Determine product temperatures. If slightly high, adjust control for longer running time. If control is discharged, broken or if recording indicates switch settings are off, replace switch.
Poor door seal.	Level cabinet. Adjust door seal. Adjust tie rods in door.
Repeated door openings or overloading of shelves in food compartment.	Instruct user regarding blocking normal air circulation in the cabinet.
Inoperative fan switch.	Check leads and control. Replace if discharged, broken or if other conditions would warrant replacing the control.
Inoperative fan motors.	Replace motor.
Lights stay on.	Adjust door to engage plunger. If switch is faulty, replace switch.
Food compartment air flow control.	Check for obstruction in the passage from the freezer to the food compartment. Check for proper sealing around the control and the bellows.
Conventional refrigerator needs defrosting.	Excessive frost accumulation on freezer slows down heat transfer to refrigerant in the freezer. Excessive frost also resists normal air flow around

Improper bulb spacer.	the freezer. Suggest that user defrost more often. Check for proper bulb spacer, use thicker spacer to lower switch cut-off point and lower cabinet temperature by increasing the running time.
Seasonal control when used in closed position, or drip tray all the way back.	Change seasonal control or drip tray to the open position to allow more air circulation around the freezer.

Food Compartment Temperature Too Cold

Possible Cause	*Possible Remedy*
Inoperative or erratic thermostat.	Turn control dial to highest setting and by-pass thermostat. If unit starts and temperature goes down to normal level, replace the thermostat. Do not condemn the control until other factors are considered. If control does cycle the product regularly but foods are too cold, adjust the control warmer. If the unit does not cycle, replace the control.
Very cold ambient temperature.	If in an extremely cold room, the freezer temperature and cabinet temperature tend to equalize causing cabinet temperature to be below 32°, refrigerator should be moved to a warmer location.
Improper bulb space.	Use thinner bulb spacer to raise the effective switch cut-off point and raise cabinet temperatures by reducing running time.

Freezing Compartment Too Warm (Automatic Defrosting)

Possible Cause	*Possible Remedy*
Inoperative thermostat.	Note running time and freezer package temperatures, adjust control for longer running time. If control is broken or discharged, replace control.
Poor door seal.	Level cabinet. Adjust door hinge wings. Check for interference from packages or foot pedal.
Light Stays on.	Adjust door to engage plunger. If switch is inoperative, replace switch.
Blower motor inoperative.	Check to see that the blower motor is free. Check voltage to motor. Replace if inoperative.
Inoperative timer.	Timer may not allow unit to go into defrost causing ice to build up on coil. This cuts down on

Coil iced up.

the air flow. Replace timer if inoperative.
Check drain heater, defrost heater, limiter switch, and timer. These items could cause the coil to ice up.

Water On Floor, Suction Lines Frosted

Possible Cause	*Possible Remedy*
Overcharge of refrigerant.	This frost back should stop after first couple of cycles. Purge slightly from high side charging port. If too much has been purged, evacuate and recharge system.
Freezer blower motor (when used) inoperative.	Check for voltage supply to motor. If none, check wiring. Remember this motor only runs when the compressor runs.

Oil On the Floor

Possible Cause	*Possible Remedy*
Terminal stud leak.	Check with leak detector. Tighten stud. Evacuate and recharge with proper charge.
Charging screw loose.	Check with leak detector. Tighten screw. Evacuate and recharge.
Broken line.	Replace component or repair wtih line connector, if possible. Evacuate and recharge.

Frost in Freezer (Automatic Defrosting)

Possible Cause	*Possible Remedy*
Water spilled when ice cube trays are placed in the freezer.	Caution user that water spilled will not readily be removed. Tap bottom of cold storage liner and ice will break loose.
Poor door seal.	Level cabinet. Adjust door hinge. Check for interference from packages or door opening pedal.
Improper loading.	Packages should not block the air flow at the top in back of the cold storage liner.
Inoperative freezer blower motor (when used).	Check to see that the blower wheel is free. Check voltage to motor. Replace if defective.

Excessive Moisture Inside Food Compartment (Temperature Normal)

Possible Cause	*Possible Remedy*
Poor door seal.	Level cabinet. Adjust door hinges. Adjust tie rods in door.
Normal operation.	During humid weather, moisture will accumulate on cold surfaces within refrigerator, just as it accumulates on a glass containing iced drink on a hot summer day. This is perfectly normal and is particularly noticeable when the refrigerator door is open frequently.

CHAPTER 10

Food Arrangement

The proper arrangement of food is of the utmost importance if the best result of refrigeration is to be obtained. Generally, foods should be stored according to the delicacy of flavor, as well as to their keeping qualities. Reference to Fig. 1 will indicate the proper food arrangement in a single-door refrigerator. The same relative arrangement should be maintained in a two-door refrigerator (Fig. 2). Food arrangement in apartment-type refrigerators is shown in Figs. 3 and 4. As noted in the illustrations, modern refrigerating units include a storage bin in the base of the cabinet to be used for dry vegetables which do not require refrigeration, such as potatoes, squash, dry onions, and turnips. The inner door panel is used for the storage of eggs, bottled foods, liquids, etc.

In this connection it should be noted that good air circulation is vital to the efficient refrigeration and preservation of food. If the air is restricted from circulating to all parts of the cabinet, the food in the lower area will not be refrigerated sufficiently. It is therefore important that packages and other items of food be placed in the refrigerator in such a way as to allow sufficient air circulation. Large bulky items, especially square packages that

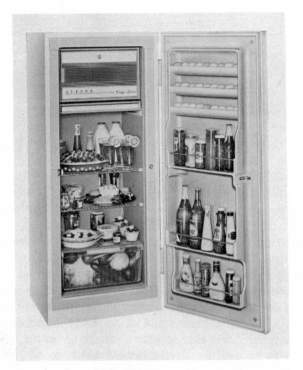

Courtesy Gibson Refrigerator Corporation.

**Fig. 1. Food arrangement in a typical one-door
type refrigerator.**

are pushed against the rear wall of the cabinet, prevent the cold air from circulating downward to the lower shelves and vegetable drawers. Space should be left between packages, and nothing should be placed too close to the cabinet walls. It is especially important that the refrigerator cabinet never be overloaded.

Placing hot foods or hot liquids in the refrigerator imposes an excessive load on the unit. Foods and liquids should be cooled at

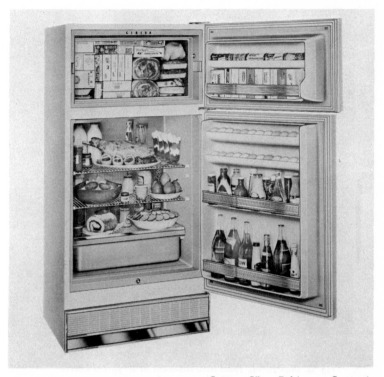

Courtesy Gibson Refrigerator Corporation.

Fig. 2. Food arrangement in a typical two-door refrigerator with special freezer compartment.

room temperature before they are placed in the refrigerator. Doing this will reduce the operating time of the unit.

DOOR OPENINGS

The user should be instructed that door openings should be kept at an absolute minimum. One way to do this is to remove

Fig. 3. Illustrating food arrangement in a typical hotel-apartment single-door refrigerator.

all of the items from the refrigerator at one time when a meal is being prepared, instead of opening the door each time something is needed. Hot, humid weather imposes a greater load on the refrigerator unit. During humid weather, moisture will accumulate on the cold inner walls of the refrigerator cabinet. This is quite normal, and is similar to the formation of moisture on the outside of a glass which is filled with a cold liquid. Although this condition is normal during periods of high humidity, it is annoying, and can be minimized by opening the refrigerator door less frequently.

Courtesy Gibson Refrigerator Corporation.

Fig. 4. Food arrangement in typical hotel-apartment refrigerator installation with an independent freezer unit.

WARM WEATHER EFFECT

Warm weather operation, particularly during the summer months and in locations where air contains a considerable amount of moisture, will impose an additional effect on the refrigeration unit, known as *sweating*. When the warm moisture-laden air comes in contact with the cold surfaces of the refrigerator, the moisture condenses. The result of this is a condition which affects the inside surfaces of the refrigerator cabinet. This is a completely normal condition during warm, humid weather. The extent to which this sweating condition will take place is contingent upon the number of door openings, the length of time which the door is left open, the temperature of the air outside the refrigerator, and the relative humidity.

A loose door seal will allow warm air to leak into the cabinet, and cause excessive sweating during warm weather. If the door seal is good, the user must be informed that a certain amount of sweating is normal. Also, he should be told that the condition can be kept to a minimum by following these recommended procedures:

1. Keep all liquids and moist food covered. This will prevent the moisture from evaporating and settling on the interior surfaces of the cabinet.
2. Keep the number of door openings to a minimum—*this is extremely important.*
3. Defrost often. On models which do not have the automatic defrosting mechanism, it might be necessary to defrost as often as twice a week during warm, humid weather.

COOLING COIL FROSTING

The refrigerator unit will run longer during very hot humid weather, and will cycle more frequently than in cooler weather. If the control knob is set *too high* under these conditions, the *off* cycle (on automatic defrost units) may not be long enough to allow the cooling coil to defrost completely. In this event, the entire cooling coil will become heavily frosted within a very short period of time. This condition is a result of the inability of heat from the heating wires to penetrate the thick frost surface. This will tend to increase the temperature in the fresh-food area.

The solution to this problem is to turn the thermostat to a low setting for a period of 12 hours, or until the cooling coil has defrosted completely. Then the control knob should be kept at a lower setting to allow the cooling coil to defrost completely during any *off* cycle that might occur. Because each *on* cycle will begin with a cooling coil free from frost, better fresh-food temperatures will be obtained.

CLEANING

Regular cleaning of the refrigerator interior is of the utmost importance. A warm baking-soda solution is very good for cleaning the interior and will keep it fresh and sweet smelling. In the absence of baking soda, warm sudsy water may be used. Plastic interior pans should also be cleaned in order to keep the food fresh and free from odors. Use only mild sudsy water (the same as that used for hand dishwashing) or a baking-soda solution. Exteriors should be washed regularly with clean sudsy water.

ODOR PREVENTION

In addition to the regular cleaning, prompt attention to spill-overs (especially milk), or an orange or lemon that has been overlooked, is most important to maintaining a sweet smelling refrigerator. When cleaning both the refrigerator and freezer sections, pay particular attention to the underside of the shelves and the moisture pan, and examine the crevices in the door seal, especially in humid climates.

Package any foods to be frozen in moisture-and vapor proof wrapping paper. This is especially important in case of fish, onions, and foods containing garlic. It is also a good idea to rinse the hands in lemon water after handling fish and before handling the outside wrappings of fish packages. Charcoal canisters (available from hardware and department stores) can be placed in the refrigerator or food freezer to help in odor removal. Whenever a refrigerator is to be turned off for a few weeks (or when it is to be moved), it is important that it be thoroughly cleaned and dried. The door should be left ajar for air circulation, except during the actual move. A closed-up odor takes time to disappear after the refrigerator is cooled down and in use again. Swinging the door wide each time it is opened will permit a greater change of air inside the refrigerator, and will help speed up this process.

CHAPTER 11

Cabinet Maintenance And Repairs

Proper fit of the door is of the utmost importance in any refrigerator. The door seal should always be tested before a refrigerator is placed in operation or when servicing a refrigerator in the home. A poor door seal usually results in cabinet sweating inside, excessive frosting of the cooling unit, high percentage of running time, high power consumption, slow ice freezing, high cabinet air temperature, and possible sweating on the outside front of the cabinet. A typical door construction and seal assembly is illustrated in Fig. 1.

A good method of testing the tightness of a door seal is to place a light inside the cabinet; this should be a strong flashlight. The light will be visible at any point where the door gasket does not make sufficient contact with the cabinet. Another method to locate imperfect door seals is by the use of a 0.003-in thick metal feeler. Locate the point of a poor seal by inserting the feeler at various points around the door between the gasket and the cabinet front with the door closed. A magnet-enclosed gasket seal is shown in Fig. 2.

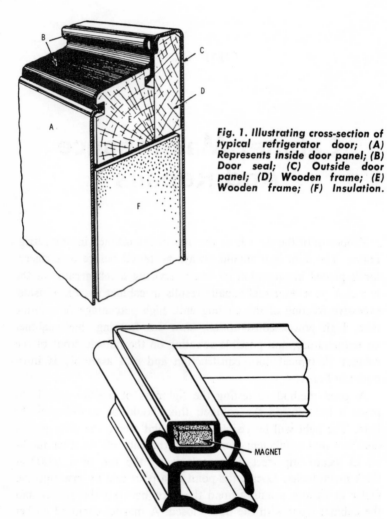

Fig. 1. Illustrating cross-section of typical refrigerator door; (A) Represents inside door panel; (B) Door seal; (C) Outside door panel; (D) Wooden frame; (E) Wooden frame; (F) Insulation.

MAGNET

Fig. 2. Cross-section of a typical magnetic door gasket.

If a poor seal is located, check the gasket first to see that it is not excessively worn. Check the hardware to see that it is not sprung or worn, and that the screws are tight. A poor seal can be corrected by rehanging the door, by replacing the gasket, or by properly adjusting or replacing the hardware. If, however, a poor seal is caused by the door being sprung out of line or by the front of the cabinet being out of line, the poor seal can be corrected as follows:

1. If the leak is on the hinge side of the door, open the door and hold with the left hand. Then with the heel of the right hand strike all along the hinge edge until the door is sprung in sufficiently to tighten the seal.
2. If leakage is on the top-latch side, spring the door in at the top until contact is made along this side by opening the door, holding it at the bottom, and pushing in at the top. Reverse this process if the leakage is at the bottom on the latch side.
3. To stop a leakage at the top or bottom of the door, spring the door in at the top or bottom by opening the door, holding one end, and pushing on the end to be sprung in.
4. Place friction tape in back of the door gasket at any point where the gasket does not make a tight fit after the above procedure has been followed. Be sure to fold the tape so that it does not show above the gasket.

DOOR REPLACEMENT

Doors are obviously replaceable by removing the hardware and transferring it to the new door, as shown in Fig. 3. Carefully center the door in the opening and draw the hinge screws tight in rotation so that unequal pressure of the screws will not throw the door out of line, as shown in Fig. 4.

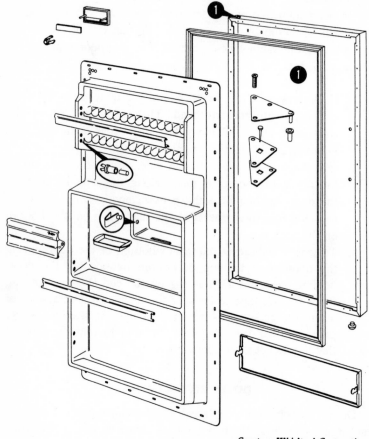

Courtesy Whirlpool Corporation.

Fig. 3. Exploded view of typical door parts.

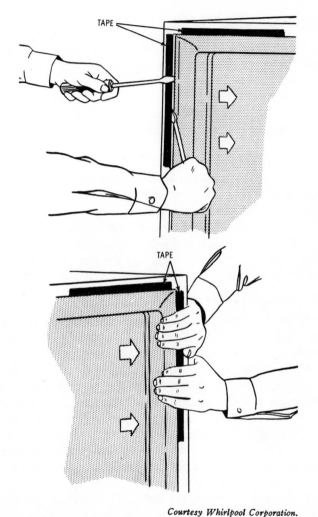

TAPE

TAPE

Courtesy Whirlpool Corporation.

Fig. 4. Replacement of food liner in a typical refrigeration door.

301

Hinge Replacement

Hinges usually have a metal cover that conceals the screws. To remove this cover, insert a knife blade in the slot and pry out. The screws are now exposed and can be removed; the hinge can now be replaced. The hinge screws are embedded in heavy screw plates attached to the inside of the steel case. This prevents any sagging or distortion of the cabinet.

Latch Replacement

First remove the escutcheon that usually encloses the base of the handle by inserting a small screwdriver in the slot under the handle at the bottom of the escutcheon. Pry it off at the bottom, then lift it up and off. One type of escutcheon is removed by squeezing it in the middle of its plate to elongate it, then simply slipping it off. The defective latch can now be removed and replaced with a new one.

Latch Strike Adjustment

Three latch-tongue adjustments may be made to obtain the correct door closure and gasket seal. To make *up and down* adjustments, pencil a line on the cabinet flange just opposite the front edge of the latch mechanism nylon well (Fig. 5). Loosen the mounting screws and adjust the latch tongue up or down until the lower point of the tongue is approximately $1/16''$ above the penciled line. To make *in and out* adjustments, slowly close the door until a slight resistance is felt as the latch tongue contacts the rear edge of the mechanism nylon well. The distance between the door gasket and the cabinet flange should be approximately $1/4''$ when the tongue touches the well.

Only one distinct resistance should be noted as the door is closed. If two contacts occur, the latch tongue is positioned too low on the door. Shims may be added to or removed from the

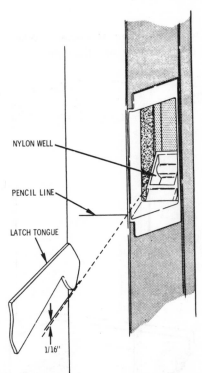

Fig. 5. Typical latch tongue adjustment.

NYLON WELL

PENCIL LINE

LATCH TONGUE

1/16″

latch tongue for in and out adjustments. *To make sideways adjustments,* hold the door in a partially open position and measure the distance between the cabinet flange and the side of the latch tongue. Loosen the mounting screws and adjust the tongue sideways until this distance is approximately 1/4″.

Interior Light Arrangement

Refrigerators are equipped with an automatic interior electric light, as shown in Fig. 6. The switch is operated by the door and is designed and wired to complete the lamp circuit and light the

303

lamp when the door is opened. When the door is closed, the switch contacts open, and the light is extinguished.

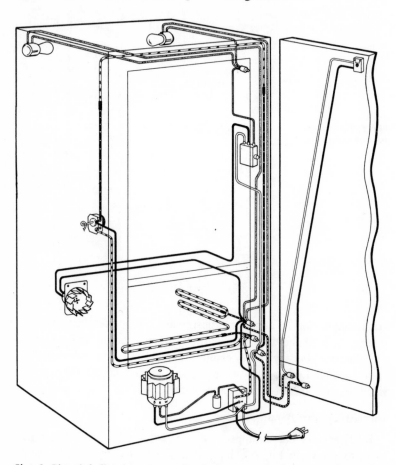

Fig. 6. Pictorial diagram of an electrical system including interior light arrangement in a typical refrigerator.

Due to careful design of the switch and simplicity of the circuit, service complaints dealing with this part of the refrigerator are very infrequent. Trouble is most often found to be a burned-out lamp. Thus, if the lamp will not light, check for a burned-out or loosened lamp. If no trouble is found here, check the light-switch plunger; it may be loose or stuck. Check all terminals of the light circuit for loose connections. Sometimes a broken wire may be responsible for the failure, although this is a rather remote possibility.

CHAPTER 12

Installation Methods

The success or failure of any refrigerating system depends largely on correct installation. Therefore, when completing an installation, be certain that everything is absolutely correct before checking out the unit. Since a large percentage of service calls are caused by improperly installed equipment, the importance of a thorough installation cannot be too strongly emphasized.

CLASSIFICATION

Refrigerators can be divided into two general classes, according to the location of the condensing unit:

1. Self-contained.
2. Remote.

A *self-contained* refrigerator is one in which the condensing unit is located in the box, whereas a remote installation is one in which the condensing unit is installed in a separate location, with the necessary refrigerant conductors connecting the condensing unit with the box itself. Years ago, when mechanical refrigeration was first adapted for household use, a great percentage of installations was accomplished by converting the existing ice box into a mechanical refrigerator. To make this possible, as no space was availabe in the box, the condensing unit was placed in a remote location and the brine tank or cooling coil, together with the liquid control valve and thermostat, were located in the box itself.

With the introduction of the self-contained refrigerator, however, no such problems as drilling holes through the floor, installation of tubing, etc., are encountered. All that is required is to place and level the cabinet, remove the shipping bolts, test for leaks, and put the unit into service. The service is complete when the temperature control dial is set in the desired position.

A method practiced by numerous distributors of household refrigerators is to uncrate the cabinet at the service shop. This is an excellent plan to follow, inasmuch as it permits the unit to be operated and checked through its cycle. It permits the delivery of a tested unit and also eliminates uncrating, with the accompanying disorder on the customer's premises. However, when this method is impractical, the following procedure is recommended:

1. Determine where the customer wants to locate the refrigerator, then make an inspection with the customer, bearing in mind the following important factors that are necessary for an efficient and smoothly running refrigerator.
2. Perform the uncrating operations carefully so that the finish of the cabinet will not be scratched or marred.
3. Remove the shipping bolts and wood blocks that hold the condensing unit secure during shipment. Some cabinets are shipped with mounting springs or suspension parts in a separate package, usually accompanied by de-

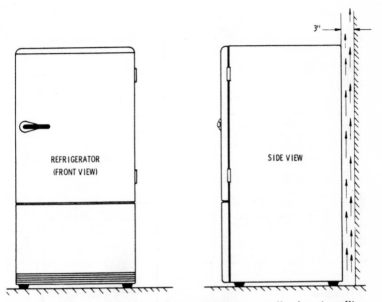

3"

REFRIGERATOR
(FRONT VIEW)

SIDE VIEW

Fig. 1. Installation showing minimum distance to wall when installing self-contained refrigerator.

tailed instructions for this part of the installation. Regardless of the style of mounting, be certain that the unit floats freely on the spring or suspension mounting so it will be able to absorb any vibration caused by the operation. Unpack and install the shelves and defrosting trays.

4. The back of the cabinet should be at least 3″ from the wall, as illustrated in Fig. 1.

5. If the refrigerator is to be placed in a recessed wall or built-in cupboard, there must be an opening of at least 3″ at the top and sides of the cabinet for proper ventilation, as shown in Fig. 2.

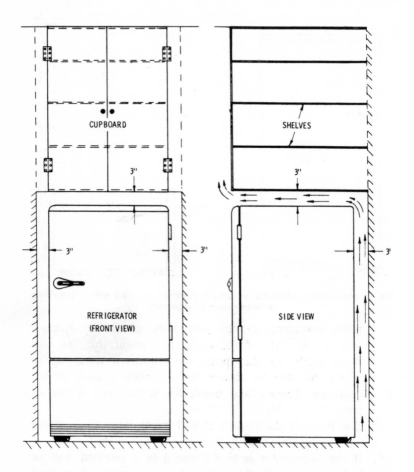

Fig. 2. Illustrating method of placing self-contained refrigerator in recessed wall space underneath a built-in cupboard. Dimensions shown are minimum for proper ventilation.

6. Be sure that the floor is solid. If not, it may be necessary to brace the floor directly beneath where the refrigerator is to be located.

Leak Test

As a general rule, most self-contained units are shipped with the refrigerant confined in the condenser or liquid receiver. During shipment, however, it is quite possible that, due to strains at one or several joints, a leak is caused. It is therefore quite essential to test for leaks.

REMOTE CONDENSING-UNIT INSTALLATIONS

A remotely installed refrigerator is one in which the condensing unit is located separately, usually in the basement or other suitable location. When making an installation of this kind, the serviceman is confronted with the problem of running the necessary copper tubing (suction and liquid lines) which are connected to the condensing unit in the cabinet.

Location of Condensing Unit

The most satisfactory remote installation for the condensing unit is in the basement. When choosing a location for this unit, the following should be adhered to:

1. The condensing unit should be located in a level, cool, dry, clean, and well-ventilated place, no farther from the cabinet than is necessary. It should be completely covered or boxed in.
2. When placing the condensing unit, accessibility for the serviceman should be considered.
3. It should be so placed that no water will be splashed on it, and should be built on a solid base and raised from

311

the floor to prevent the possibility of its being flooded if water should enter the basement.

4. It should not be located directly underneath a bedroom where operation might be noticeable in the still hours of the night.

5. It should not be placed where the temperature will be high, such as in closets or small rooms without adequate air circulation, or near furnaces or steam pipes.

6. It should not be placed where the temperature will be low (below 30° in winter) such as on porches, or in cold basements.

7. Never place a condensing unit on a platform or base that is connected to rafters or uprights. It should always be located on the basement floor or on a platform that rests on the floor, as shown in Fig. 3.

Caution. It is advisable to place a guard over the flywheel and fan if the chassis is installed where any person might accidently come in contact with the mechanism.

Size of Suction and Liquid Lines

After determining the location of the condensing unit and the cabinet, cut a 1-1/2" hole in the floor directly in line with the hole in the back of the cabinet. The hole should be drilled as close to the wall as possible. Run a suction line (3/8" average size) from the cooling unit suction-line connection to the compressor suction service valve and a liquid line (1/4" average size) from the liquid receiver outlet service valve to the cooling unit liquid-line connection, as shown in Fig. 4.

The installation procedure is as follows:

1. Run the 3/8" suction-line tubing and the 1/4" liquid-line tubing up through the hole in the floor. Hold the end

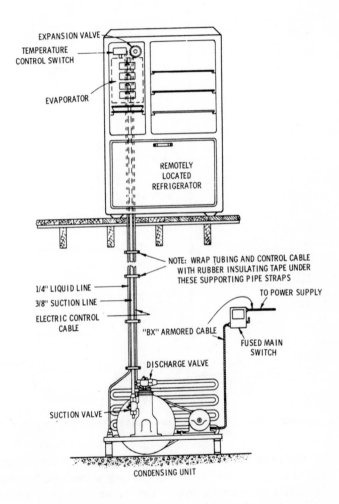

EXPANSION VALVE

TEMPERATURE
CONTROL SWITCH

EVAPORATOR

REMOTELY
LOCATED
REFRIGERATOR

NOTE: WRAP TUBING AND CONTROL CABLE
WITH RUBBER INSULATING TAPE UNDER
THESE SUPPORTING PIPE STRAPS

1/4" LIQUID LINE

3/8" SUCTION LINE

ELECTRIC CONTROL
CABLE

TO POWER SUPPLY

"BX" ARMORED CABLE

FUSED MAIN
SWITCH

DISCHARGE VALVE

SUCTION VALVE

CONDENSING UNIT

Fig. 3. Showing method of installation with separate condensing unit.

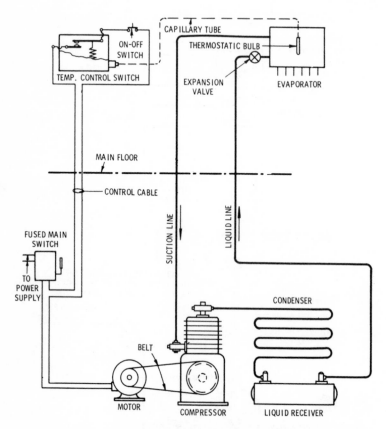

Fig. 4. Schematic diagram showing connection details for remotely installed condensing unit.

of the tubing down and cut it off square. When cutting the tubing, use the flare block, sawing a line close against the block to insure a square cut. When using the file, be sure that the tubing is filed straight. Remove any filings by tapping, and remove the rough edges within the tubing with the handle end of a small file or other instrument that will do the job. Slip a flare nut over the tubing and make a flare with a wide and thick shoulder that can be drawn down firmly to prevent leaks.

2. Always keep the end of the tubing slanted downward. Connect the 3/8″ suction line to the end of the original suction line with a 3/8″union. Connect the 1/4″ liquid line to the original liquid line with a 1/4″ union. The tubing should be neatly installed with as few bends as possible. It should be run in straight vertical and horizontal lines, and not diagonally across a wall or ceiling. This will give the installation a neat appearance. Avoid sharp bends and traps as much as possible. Allow plenty of slack at the chassis and evaporator to absorb vibration and permit the removal of parts.

3. Wherever tubing is exposed to damage, it is necessary to provide adequate shielding, which consists of suitable metal conduit.

Electric Wiring

In some cases, it may be required to run a special line from the meter to the compressor motor. Some local and state ordinances require this work to be done by a licensed electrician. In such localities, the serviceman must have a license or have the work performed by a licensed electrician. Inspect the motor and make certain that the voltage and frequency of the electric supply conform with those stamped on the motor nameplate. A special line of No. 12 or 14 *AWG* wire should be connected from the service panel to the compressor motor and temperature control.

The hot side of the line should be connected to the temperature control. The hot side can readily be determined by using a test lamp, touching one wire from the test lamp to the line and the other to the ground. When the lamp lights, the hot wire is found. It is important that all electrical work be done in conformance with the National Electric Code and all state and local ordinances.

Removing Air from the System

When removing air from the system, the first thing to do is to loosen the flare nut at the suction valve on the compressor. *Do not open the suction valve*. Then *crack* the liquid valve so that a sufficient supply of refrigerant gas can escape from the loosened flare nut at the suction valve of the compressor. Then immediately tighten the liquid valve. The air must be allowed to escape at the loosened flare nut and not through the gauge port at the suction valve. Next, open the suction and high-side valves by backing the valve stems all the way out until they seat firmly. Install compound and pressure gauges and turn the valve stems of the suction and high-side valves *in* one complete turn to register pressure. Crack the flare nut at the compound gauge to purge the gauge tubing, then tighten the nut firmly. Test all connections for leaks.

If no leaks are found, open the liquid valve by backing the valve stem out, and start the motor. Be sure to replace the liquid valve-stem cap and gasket immediately after opening this valve. Turn the temperature control switch to an average temperature position, and allow the unit to operate continuously. Adjust the automatic expansion valve for the proper setting. Make certain the suction and discharge valve stems are backed all the way out until firmly seated. Remove the gauges, replace the gauge plugs, and test around all valves and tubing connections for refrigerant leaks. On high-side float-valve (flooded) systems, it is necessary to purge air from the liquid line, since it cannot be pumped out unless the float chamber is equipped with a service valve.

To purge the air from the liquid line, attach a refrigerant cylinder by means of tubing and fittings to the gauge opening of the discharge service valve. Crack the valve to a point where it is about half open. Loosen the flare nut of the liquid entrance connection at the top of the float chamber. Next open the valve on the top of the refrigerant cylinder; allow the refrigerant to purge the air or vapor out of the condenser and liquid line to the float chamber.

Any air that might remain in the float chamber will collect in the top of the chamber and can be purged out by first stopping the condensing unit after it has run for about twenty minutes. Then carefully loosen the flare nut at the top of the float chamber and allow the vapor to escape for a few seconds. The air, mixed with some refrigerant, will escape. When the air has been purged out, retighten the flare nut.

Start the motor, and when a 20-in vacuum is obtained, run the motor intermittently until a 28-in vacuum is reached. This procedure will usually prevent the compressor from pumping oil. If the compressor, however, does pump oil, stop the motor and turn the compressor slowly by hand for a few revolutions.

When testing for leaks, stop the motor and screw a pressure gauge into the compressor discharge service-valve gauge opening. Open the valve completely, then close it one turn for a gauge reading.

Open the liquid receiver service valve slightly until the vacuum is displaced with a pressure of 3 pounds per square inch. Test all joints and other possible points of stress for leaks. If no leaks are found at this pressure, open the liquid receiver outlet service again until a pressure of 15 to 20 pounds per square inch is indicated on the gauge, then retest for leaks. If no leaks are found, open the liquid receiver outlet service valve completely and put the unit into operation.

MULTIPLE-UNIT INSTALLATIONS

Other installations having the condensing unit or units installed remotely from the evaporator or chilling units are stores and markets, soda fountains, florist shops, apartment buildings, locker plants, etc. The refrigerant is usually circulated from a common source to two or more cabinets, each containing one or more evaporators or chilling units.

There are two general classes of these systems, namely:

1. Brine piping system.
2. Vapor piping system.

The brine piping system consists of one or more commercial compressors placed in a machinery room that is usually located in the basement of the building to be served. A cold brine solution, at a temperature of about 9° F., is pumped through heavily insulated pipes into the refrigerator cabinet of each unit.

The vapor piping system consists of one or more commercial compressors installed in the basement, and a cabinet containing one or more chilling units located in the box where the refrigeration is desired. Copper tubing and piping are used to connect the machine in the basement with the remotely located chilling coils. The refrigerant liquid is circulated through these tubes into the cooling coils of each cabinet, and the refrigerant gas is returned to the compressor in the basement.

There are two general methods of piping used in connecting the compressor with the chilling units. They are:

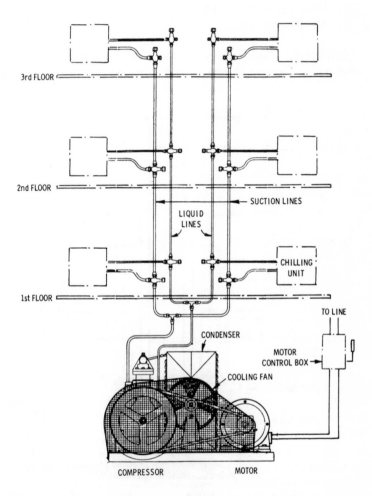

Fig. 5. Multiple refrigerator installation with the header and riser piping system.

1. Header and riser system.
2. Manifold system.

Refrigeration applications in which these piping methods are employed are shown in Figs. 5 and 6. In the installations shown,

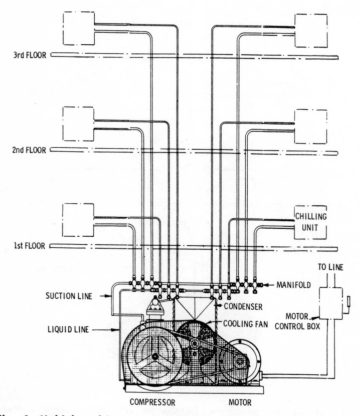

Fig. 6. Multiple refrigerator installation using the manifold system.

each machine has one suction and one liquid connection. All of the liquid lines connected to the chilling units must be connected somewhere to the single liquid outlet on the compressor.

Header and Riser System

It may simplify the matter for some students if this system of refrigerant distribution is compared to the problem of the water and drainage connections of a multiple dwelling. The water supply comes from the city main in one large supply line. This line is run laterally and vertically through the building and has valved branches tapped off for each apartment. The supply line entering the building will be comparatively large, but will gradually reduce in size as it passes through the building, since the demand decreases toward the end. The branch lines taken off will be just large enough to supply the particular outlets involved. This system compares with the liquid supply of a multiple refrigerating system. It must be remembered, however, that when a vertical rise is involved, the pressure of the liquid at the top is less than that at the bottom in proportion to the height. This effect can usually be ignored up to a height of about 75 ft., but above this height difficulties will be encountered unless the head pressures are adjusted above normal.

To return to the water-system analogy, let us consider the drain lines as compared to our suction lines. A small line runs from each apartment and is tapped into a larger line serving a number of apartments, and these lines finally run into a large trunk sewer and out of the building. All of these drain lines are vertical or have a slight slope toward the final outlet.

The suction lines on the refrigerating system are handled in the same way. Small lines (5/16" or 3/8") run out of each chilling unit and tap the risers of larger diameter (3/8" or 1/2"), and these risers pass down to the basement and tap into laterals of still larger diameter (1/2" or 5/8") which connect to the suction side of the compressor. It can be ascertained that the same rules are followed for drainage systems; the tube diameter should be increased often enough to carry the return gas without undue drop in pressure, and since some oil flows back to the compressor by gravity, all suction lines should be given a small pitch angle to assist the gas flow.

Manifolding Method of Connection

Another method is to run one liquid line and one suction line from the basement to each cabinet, and to locate the shut-off valves at one point in the basement or near the cabinet. This scheme is known as *manifolding* and works very well, although it is more expensive than the header and riser method. With the manifolding ideas in mind, the following rules can be followed for tubing sizes:

Liquid Lines 1/4" on all applications.
Suction Lines For one cabinet, 5/16" or 3/8" tubing; for two cabinets, 3/8" tubing; for three cabinets, 3/8" tubing; for four to seven cabinets, 1/2" tubing; for eight cabinets and over, 5/8" tubing.

A liquid line of 1/4" tubing runs from the machine across the basement, and to convenient points under all refrigerator cabinets. This tubing is branched by means of tees to run risers up past the cabinets. Tee valves near each cabinet serve to branch the risers and permit shutting down one chilling unit without disturbing the remainder of the system. A suction line runs parallel to the liquid line across the basement. The size of the risers taken off of this header must be governed by the number of refrigerators on each riser.

Valves

As in the liquid line, tee valves should be installed near each cabinet. These should preferably be of the reducing type. For instance, if the risers for six refrigerators are 1/2" past the first three, and 3/8" beyond, the size of the valves will be as follows: *1st Floor:* 1/2" × 1/2" × 5/16"; *2nd Floor:* 1/2" × 1/2" × 5/16"; *3rd Floor:* 1/2" × 3/8" × 5/16"; *4th Floor:* 3/8" × 3/8" × 5/16"; *5th Floor:* 3/8" × 3/8" × 5/16". These risers should be run in a rigid conduit. The steel cabinets that house the valves should be 8" × 12" to allow convenient space for making connections.

These valves should be located on the same level as the chilling units, or slightly below wherever possible, and in no instance should they be located more than one foot higher than the chilling units. After connecting these lines, run the 1/4" liquid lines and the 5/16" suction from the valves to the chilling units. Avoid looping or trapping these lines. They should be carried level or sloping down slightly from the cabinet to the tee valves on each unit.

Caution: Be very careful to make up the flare connections so they will be positively tight. The very fact that there may be as many as a hundred flare joints in a single system makes it necessary that each one be absolutely gas tight.

Leak Test

After the lines and valves are all connected, open all valves wide except those on the compressor. Attach a compound gauge and a refrigerant drum to the suction shut-off valve on the receiver and allow a few pounds of refrigerant to enter the system. If there are no large leaks, the pressure will build up in the suction gauge. Allow it to reach 30 or 40 pounds per square inch, and then close the receiver suction shut-off valve again. Thoroughly test all joints and fittings for leaks. When no leaks can be found, and the pressure on the gauge holds constant for half an hour or more, remove the plug from the discharge shut-off valve and allow the entrapped refrigerant in the low side to blow out through the compressor. The chilling units can now be put in operation.

INSTALLATION OF ABSORPTION-TYPE REFRIGERATORS

Household refrigerators employing the absorption cycle do not differ in any important respect (with regard to location of units) from that of the previously discussed units in which the compression method of refrigeration was used. All units of this type require heat energy instead of mechanical energy to make the change in condition required in the refrigeration cycle. The heat energy required is usually obtained from a gas flame, with the gas piped from a convenient place (usually in the basement of the building).

There are two principal types of units used, namely:

1. Water-cooled units.
2. Air-cooled units.

A typical refrigerator employing water-cooled condensers is shown in Fig. 7. This type of unit usually necessitates tapping the water system of the house or apartment in which the installation is to be made. Although this is a rather simple problem, it should be done with care and in accordance with the Underwriter's Code or any local rules that affect such work. In addition, a pipe must be installed from the gas supply line; in most locations this will require a permit from the gas company.

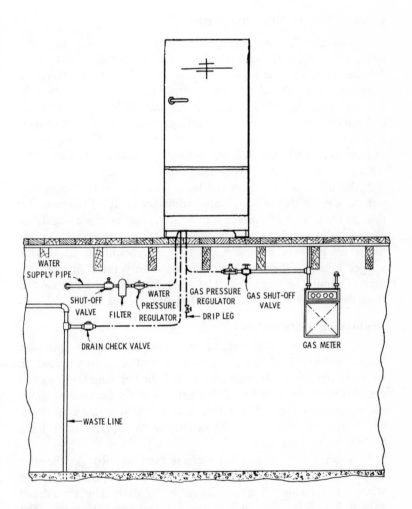

Fig. 7. Illustrating method of connection for water cooled refrigerator.

Cooling Water Line Installation

The purpose of the cooling water line is to furnish an uninterrupted supply of cool water to the condenser. After it is determined where the customer wants to locate the refrigerator, ascertain by means of a careful inspection that the location is suitable with respect to ventilation, accessibility, maintenance, and repairs, etc., then proceed. Make certain that the connections to the unit are made at a point in the water supply line where full pessrure and flow will be constantly maintained. Close the main valve in the water supply line.

Make the extension from the house line with a 1/2" diameter pipe to a point that is within approximately 10 ft. of the unit. At this point, a shut-off valve, water filter, and pressure regulator should be installed, as shown in Fig. 7. The connection between the water pressure regulator and the unit should be made with copper tubing. When securing the lines, only brass fittings and nipples should be employed. The water line should be separated from the gas line to prevent condensation in the gas line.

Drain Line Installation

The drain line is that part of the piping required to drain the heated water out of the condenser so that a constant flow of water in the system is maintained. This line is connected to the water control valve outlet of the unit and to a convenient drain outlet, or waste line. When this latter method is used, a check valve must be installed in the drain line to prevent water from backing up into the unit.

It is customary to install all connections as close to the unit as possible; this facilitates the inspection and adjustment of the water control valve. Vertical drops in the drain line should not exceed 5 to 6 ft., since it may result in a partial vacuum in the water control and increases water consumption. An elimination of this tendency is sometimes accomplished by the installation of a larger pipe (1/2″ or 5/8″) instead of the 3/8″ standard tubing.

Gas Line Installation

When installing a gas line, first turn off the main valve at the gas meter. The gas in the line is consumed by lighting a gas burner connected to the line. It is considered good practice to tap the refrigeration service main directly after the meter and ahead of any other gas appliances to ensure a steady and uninterrupted supply of gas.

The gas line usually consists of 1/2″ black-iron pipe; this pipe should be extended to within approximately 10 ft. of the unit, at which point the gas shut-off valve is installed in a closed position, and the main gas valve is opened at the meter. All pilot lights that became extinguished when the gas was shut off should be lighted, and the gas jets that were opened to exhaust the gas from the line should be closed.

Gas Pressure Regulator

The gas regulator is now installed in the line next to the gas shut-off valve as shown in Fig. 8. The function of this gas regulator is to automatically regulate the gas so it will maintain a constant burner pressure independent of any gas-line pressure fluctuations, thus ensuring a uniform rate of gas supply to the burner. The gas regulator should be installed at least one foot from the gas thermostat in a horizontal position and with the arrow on the regulator pointing in the direction of gas flow. The installation of the gas line is completed with copper tubing connected to the thermostatic gas control on the unit.

Traps in the line should be avoided, since they have a tendency to become filled with condensation, thus interfering with

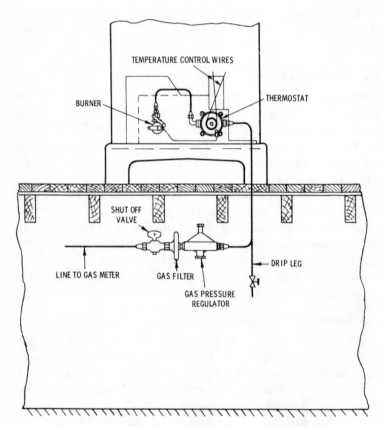

TEMPERATURE CONTROL WIRES

BURNER

THERMOSTAT

SHUT OFF
VALVE

LINE TO GAS METER

GAS FILTER

GAS PRESSURE
REGULATOR

DRIP LEG

Fig. 8. Method of connection for air cooled refrigerator.

the free flow of gas. The gas line should be insulated wherever it is in direct contact with cold walls or where it runs through cold rooms or refrigerated compartments. Before the installation is completed, a careful check for gas leaks as well as a thorough inspection of all joints should be made.

CHAPTER 13

Service Tools

A careless repair job is dangerous and has no place in refrigeration service work. Properly chosen tools will not only save time but will, in addition, insure a neat, dependable, and satisfactory job which will result in mutual benefits to the serviceman and customer alike.

There are many types of tools on the market. Some of them are so poorly constructed that they are expensive at any price. A good tool warrants a fair price, because it is properly designed and will stand up under service. A list of special tools is given in this chapter.

TEST GAUGE SET

One of the handiest aids in servicing small machines is the test gauge. Most small units are not equipped with gauges; the serviceman must apply his own so that the pressures existing in the high and low sides can be determined. A test gauge set consists essentially of two *tee* valves and a special *tee* as shown in Fig. 1. The tee valves are constructed so that the valve stem works only on the leg attached to the tee. Therefore, opening or closing the stem affects only this one opening; the other two openings of the

COMBINATION TESTING OUTFIT

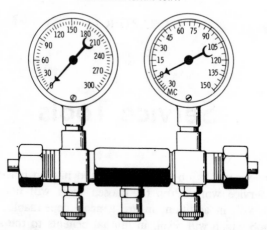

Fig. 1. Combination gauge set. High-pressure side gauges are usually scaled for pressures up to 300 pounds per square inch. The low-pressure gauge is of the compound type and is used to measure inches of vacuum and pressure in pounds per square inch.

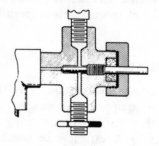

Fig. 2. A sectional view of a refrigerator tee valve.

valve remain open at all times. This fact is plainly shown in the sectional view of the valve in Fig. 2. This unit can be used to obtain pressure readings on both high and low sides when adding oil, adding or recharging the refrigerant, purging off an excess of refrigerant or air, or when pumping the refrigerant from one side to the other.

DENTAL MIRRORS

Magnifying mirrors are used by many servicemen for observing leaks in refrigerating machines where soap and water or oil is used as a leak detector. The long handles permit these mirrors to be used in difficult or cramped quarters. Some compressor assemblies are designed so that these mirrors offer the only means of seeing certain bolts, inserting other pins, or aligning parts.

PIPE CUTTERS

Pipe can be cut in two ways—by hack saw or by pipe cutter. The former method is often slow and laborious. Pipe cut by a hack saw is not beaded or provided with a thickened lip, as is the case when pipe cutters are used. If a three-wheel cutter is used, as shown in Fig. 3, the outer edge of the pipe must be filed down before a die can be applied to the pipe. When a single cutter wheel is used in conjunction with two rollers, the outside

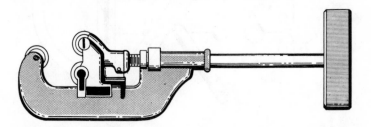

Fig. 3. An adjustable three-wheel pipe cutter for use on ⅛" to ¼" pipe.

of the pipe stays close to its original diameter, but the inside of the pipe is given a lip or burr that must be removed with a pipe reamer. If this burr is allowed to remain, it will decrease the free internal diameter and will offer a resistance to the passage of the fluid that is to flow through the pipe. Such burrs collect dirt and often result in subsequent binding or clogging at such obstructions.

Pipes severed with a hack saw do not require reaming, and the die can be applied without the necessity of filing the outer edge. In effecting a cut with a hack saw, it is important that a square cut be made. If an angular cut is made, the die will not cut straight threads. When such a threaded end is screwed into a fitting, the pipe will point out at an angle, and it will be difficult to

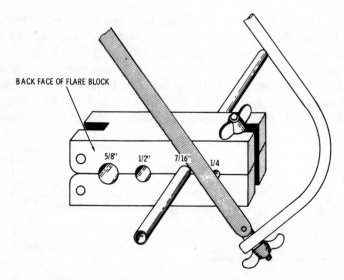

Fig. 4. Method of cutting tubing with hack saw in a flaring block.

assemble a run of pipe with such threads, especially close or short lengths. Pipe cutters offer the quickest severance and, if properly applied, result in a square cut so that the die will follow the pipe without trouble.

TUBE CUTTERS

The larger installations make use of steel or iron pipe for connections, but the smaller machines utilize copper tubing. Copper tubing can be easily installed, because it can be bent around obstructions and eliminates many elbows. Since tubing is made in fairly long lengths, most small installations can be completed by the use of a single length of tubing. For instance, the evaporator can be connected to the receiver by means of a 1/4" tube in one single piece, even when the two units are separated by a distance of 100 feet. Therefore, sharp bends are eliminated, and all changes of clogging at constrictions or bends are eliminated, while the friction factor is greatly reduced.

Copper tubing can be cut by means of a saw and flaring block, as shown in Fig. 4. The tube is held in the flaring block for the purpose of securing a square end. It is important to secure a square end, otherwise the operator will be obliged to make careful use of a file. A much easier and quicker method is to use a tubing cutter, as shown in Fig. 5. This tool is a small version of the pipe cutter shown previously.

BENDING TOOLS

Where accurate bends of a specified radius must be made, a bending tool should be used. This bending tool, shown in Fig. 6, consists of a stationary arm on which is located the radius guide. The radius guide is usually provided with a pin, so that the bending

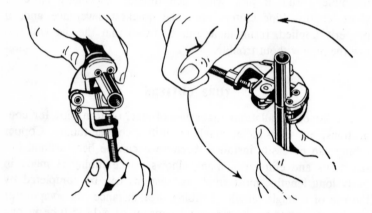

Fig. 5. Illustrating the use of a tube cutter to cut tubing.

arm can be attached and used to make the bend. The bending shoe is also grooved and is furnished as a shoe block or a grooved wheel. The tool makes a perfect bend without crimping or flattening the tube.

PINCH-OFF TOOLS

Most of the larger apparatus is equipped with sufficient valves to enable any portion or section to be closed off and worked on without loss of the refrigerant charge. Some of the smaller and simpler systems have only a few valves. This is an economy measure so that the cost of the apparatus can be kept to a minimum. While the elimination of valves makes a simpler, lower priced piece of equipment, it makes servicing somewhat harder for the serviceman. Where there are only a few or no valves in a system, the pinch-off tool offers a means of closing the copper line so that the defective or worn part can be removed and replaced.

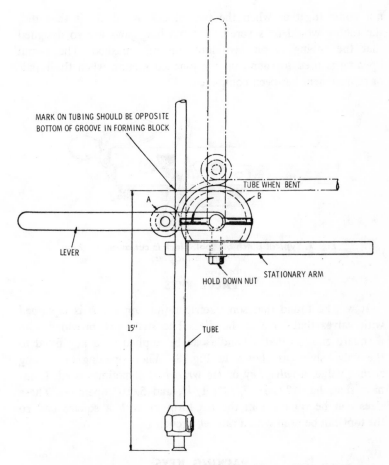

MARK ON TUBING SHOULD BE OPPOSITE
BOTTOM OF GROOVE IN FORMING BLOCK

TUBE WHEN BENT

A

B

LEVER

HOLD DOWN NUT

STATIONARY ARM

15"

TUBE

Fig. 6. Bending tubing by means of a specially designed bending tool.

A simple pinch-off tool is shown in Fig. 7. Notice the jaws for the purpose of pinching or squeezing a tube shut. These jaws do not come together when the two blocks are flush; if they did, the tubing would be severed. The pinching jaws are so designed that the tubing is pinched shut but not mashed. The round opening is used to round up the pinched section when the repair or replacement has been completed.

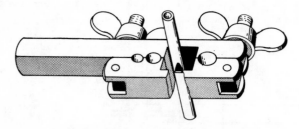

Fig. 7. Typical pinch-off tool. Block is cut away to show working principles.

VALVE KEYS

It will be found that some refrigeration apparatus is equipped with valves that have no handles. The stems are provided with a square end, so that a handle can be applied or a key fitted to the valve stem, as shown in Fig. 8. When opening or closing such a valve, a *valve key* or *tee wrench* is sometimes used. Common sizes have 3/16″, 7/32″, 1/4″, and 5/16″ openings. These sizes can be obtained in the *tee* form or with a square end so the tool can be used with a ratchet wrench.

PACKING KEYS

Some valves are packed with a resilient material that serves as a seal to prevent the refrigerant from escaping around the stem. A packing nut can be tightened by means of a wrench.

When tightening external packing nuts, use a 12-point wrench if one is available, or make use of the proper open-end wrench.

The packing nut is generally the internal type and is provided with a slot across its face for tightening. Unfortunately, the stem of the valve projects through this nut and makes it necessary to use a special gland or packing-nut key, such as shown in Fig. 9. This key is hollow in the center, permitting the valve stem to extend through the tool, and is provided with two teeth that engage the slot in the packing nut.

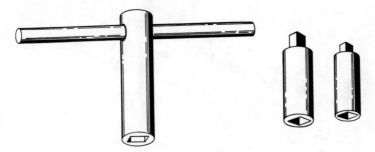

Fig. 8. Various valve keys.

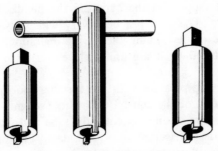

Fig. 9. Typical packing keys.

FLARING TOOLS

A typical flaring tool is shown in Fig. 10. It consists of two bars held together by a wing nut and bolt; the bars are provided with holes for the various sizes of tubing. A yoke containing the

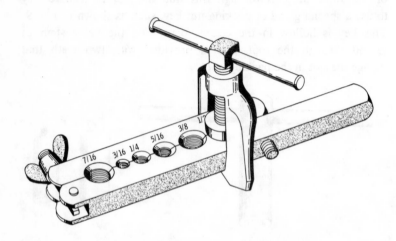

Fig. 10. Flaring tool for use on various tube diameters.

forming die is slipped on the bars and the handle is rotated to produce a flare. This tool has been very widely used due to its simplicity, ease of performing the flaring operation, and because the flares produced by it are uniformly excellent in producing a tight seal.

Before applying pressure with the forming tool, place a drop of oil on the end of the tube. Be sure to use only refrigeration oil. Any other type of oil may enter the tube and give trouble by reacting with the refrigerant at a later date. The proper use of the flaring tool is illustrated in Fig. 11.

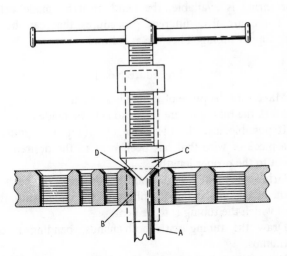

Fig. 11. Proper use of flaring tool; (A) Shows tubing in place; (B) Teeth in the die, holding tubing securely; (C) Indicates compressor making a perfect flare; (D) Black section shows flare formed at top of tubing.

GASKET TACKING MACHINE

The serviceman should notice the condition of the packing around ducts and cabinet doors. If it is worn or collapsed so that air is permitted to pass, the packing strips should be renewed or replaced. One of the best labor saving devices is the use of a tacking or stapling machine when a wooden door or strip is provided for the attachment of the gasket material.

MAKING A HAND BEND

Occasionally a serviceman will find it necessary to remove a battered, leaking, plugged, or defective piece of tubing and replace it with a new piece or section. If no mechanical bending tool or spring is available, the bend must be made entirely by hand. There are five different procedures that can be used in bending copper tubing. They are as follows:

Procedure No. 1

1. Make sure the piece of tubing is straight.
2. Mark the tubing where the bend is to be made.
3. If possible, use the old piece of tubing as a guide, or use a piece of wire that has been bent to the desired form and cut to the proper length.
4. Grip the tubing with both hands, one on each side of the mark; place the thumbs directly underneath the point at which the tubing is to be bent.
5. Draw the tubing with both hands, bending it over the thumbs.
6. Bend slowly and watch for indications of buckling or kinking.
7. Keep moving thumbs and bend slowly so that the curve takes shape evenly.
8. Never attempt to make a very close bend with the hands.

Fig. 12 shows three types of bends used in refrigeration.

Precautions

If the bend to be replaced is a close one, use iron or any stiff wire to measure off a wide swing for the replacement; a close bend cannot be made by hand and should not be attempted.

Inside and Outside Springs

An inside spring can be used for making a bend in the tubing. The inside spring can only be used where the bend is to be or near the end of the tubing. If a bend is to be made in the mid-

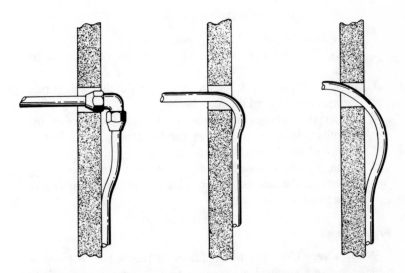

Fig. 12. Three types of bends as required in refrigeration service.

dle or at any distance from the end, an outside spring or bending tool must be employed.

A No. 4 screen-door spring with the paint removed can be used for an inside bending tool. The spring is prone to gather dust, dirt, and grime between its coils, and this can result in dirt being introduced into a system. Make sure the spring is clean before using it. One end of the spring should be enlarged or a ring of heavy wire attached to one end, so it can be removed from the tubing. An inside spring will give a closer bend than an outside spring. An inside spring can only be used successfully on 1/2″ or larger sizes of tubing because an inside spring is much harder to remove when the diameter is less than 1/2″ in size. A tool kit can be purchased that will include not only the proper tube cutter and reamer, but will also include the tube bending springs.

341

Procedure No. 2

1. Straighten the piece of tubing. Ream the end.
2. Mark the tubing at the point where the bend is to be made.
3. Insert a clean, oiled spring, making sure that the spring extends well beyond the bend point.
4. Grasp the tubing with both hands, and bend over the thumbs. Move the thumbs as the bend progresses, so that a bend of the desired degree is obtained.
5. Bend a little beyond the degree desired, and then bring it back to the desired radius. This will loosen the spring so it can be removed.

Precautions

When a very close bend is required at the end of a piece of tubing, and no mechanical bending tool is available, use both inside and outside springs at the same time. Be sure that the spring is clean. Do not drop it on the floor, or place the spring where it can gather dirt between its convolutions. This dirt will drop out in the copper tubing and be introduced into the refrigerant system, where it will cause operating defects. Do not attempt too close a bend. Move the thumbs after each slight bend and examine the bend.

When a bend collapses or flattens, and the spring cannot be removed easily, tap the tube round with a hammer. This will release the spring. If done carefully, the tube bend will not be badly battered and can be placed in use if it is not subjected to machine vibration. Use a flat piece of iron or wood between the hammer and tube so it will not be dented or battered. Oil the spring with refrigeration oil. Do not use any other type of oil. If no refrigeration oil is on hand, use the spring dry. Oil makes the spring somewhat easier to remove and the bend somewhat less strenuous to form.

Outside bending springs are made in all sizes for use on standard tubing. Servicemen have more or less adopted the outside tube spring. A miniature pipe bender is used on production jobs where a great number of the same sized bends are required, but this tool is not used to any great extent in the field. Outside springs should be used to acquire practice in the forming of bends, as shown in Fig. 13.

Procedure No. 3

1. Mark the tubing where the bend is desired.
2. Make another mark on the tubing equal to one half the length of the spring.
3. Slide the outside spring up to the second mark. The first mark (where the bend is desired) will be covered, but it is known to be at the center of the bending spring.

Precautions

Determine the size of the bend required, and make the bend in one smooth motion. If bent too much or too little at a time, the repeated working will harden the tubing and make bending difficult. Such a bend can crystallize and break the tubing if subjected to vibration in use. Some springs have plain ends, while others are provided with a flare or funnel-shaped end so that the spring can be easily slipped on and off the tube. When pulling the spring off the tube, grasp the spring and pull on the flared end. Springs will slip on and off much easier if they are slightly oiled. Wipe each tube after bending to remove any oil squeezed from between the convolutions of the spring. Use the springs with care or they will become sprung and kinked. A spring should last for years with proper care.

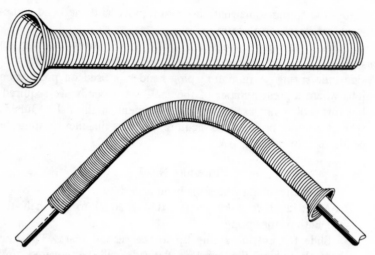

Fig. 13. Typical outside spring and method of application to tubing.

MAKING A RELIEVED BEND

This procedure is for making a bend that will hug the corners of a wall when rounding a corner, as shown in Fig. 14. Notice that any ordinary 90° bend will not touch the walls and is likely to be dislodged by any moving object coming into contact with it. The relieved bend will hug the wall tightly and permit proper attachment. Use this type of bend for a neat, satisfactory jog.

Procedure No. 4

1. Make a 90° bend as outlined in the previous procedure.
2. Move the spring to one leg and make a relieved bend.
3. Do the same with the other leg.
4. With both legs relieved, try the bend on a corner and determine whether it hugs both walls properly.

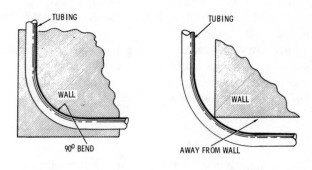

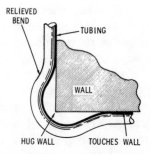

Fig. 14. Use of relief bend when close application to a wall is desirable.

USE OF RESEATING TOOLS

The reseating tool is used for resurfacing the ends of flared fittings which, due to excessive use or abuse, would otherwise have to be replaced with new fittings. Some fittings are specially designed. Through continued use, or more often through abuse, the flared end or *nose* becomes rounded, scored, or grooved to the extent that it cannot be made gas tight. Through the use of a reseating tool, these special (as well as ordinary) fittings can be re-conditioned and used again with the assurance that they are as good as new, so far as the flare nose is concerned.

There are several types of reseating tools on the market. One type is equipped with a cutter guide, removable bushings, cutter feed, and automatic tension, and is an excellent tool for use in the shop where considerable resurfacing is done, such as in the case of general overhauling work.

Procedure No. 5

1. Insert the damaged fitting in an adapter of proper size. Screw the fitting into the adapter from the rear and allow it to run in until the fitting seats on the shoulder. Use a 12-point wrench where a hex shoulder is available. Do not damage the threads on other parts of the fittings.
2. Place a drop or two of refrigeration oil on the reamer body and insert the reamer in the proper adapter.
3. With a firm, light pressure, rotate the reamer clockwise so that the end of the fitting is smooth.
4. If the fitting nose is badly scored or ridged, it may take several minutes to cut a clean, smooth face.
5. Remove the reamer and inspect the face at regular intervals, When a perfect seat is obtained, do not cut away any metal.
6. When the face is smooth, remove the reamer and take the fitting out of the adapter.
7. If the end is clean and satisfactory, proceed with the operation; if not, make further use of the reseating tool.
8. With the flare nose clean and smooth, run a strip of cloth through the fitting to remove metal shavings. Do not blow through the fitting to clear it of shavings. Moisture in the breath can condense in the fitting.

Precautions

When using a reamer, a light, steady pressure must be applied. If too heavy a cut is attempted, or if the tool is applied too lightly, the reamer may skip or chatter and produce a wavy surface almost impossible to remove by subsequent treatment with hand tools. A lathe can be employed to obtain a true, smooth surface, but this course is only open to the man in the repair shop and not to the serviceman. Bear in mind that an *SAE* flared fitting must have a projecting nose. If the operation continues to cut away an excessive amount of metal, the connection will not be air tight and a new flare must be made.

COPPER TUBING

It is necessary, especially in smaller systems, to use dehydrated tubing that is factory sealed. This prevents moisture entering the system at the time of installation. Never permit unused tubing to remain unsealed in stock. A safe procedure is to seal the ends immediately after cutting, or flatten the tube end while the stock is not in use.

A table showing the sizes and dimensions of various copper tubing used in the refrigeration industry is shown below:

Sizes (O.D.)	Stubs (Gauge)	Wall Thickness (in.)	Weight (lbs. per 1,000 ft.)	Approx. No. ft. per lb.
1/8	20	0.035	38	25.4
3/16	20	0.035	65	15.4
1/4	20	0.035	92	11.0
5/16	20	0.035	119	8.5
3/8	20	0.035	145	7.0
7/16	20	0.035	171	6.0
1/2	20	0.035	198	5.0
5/8	20	0.035	251	4.0
3/4	19	0.042	362	2.8

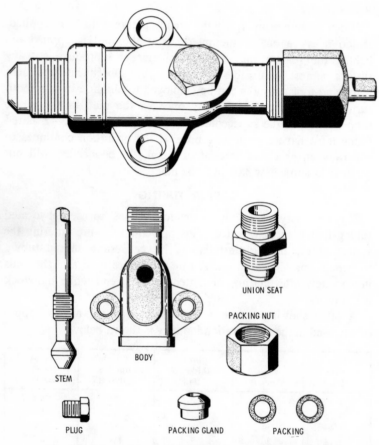

Fig. 15. A forged brass valve showing assembly and parts.

The most popular type of fittings used to make the connections on copper tubing installations is the flared type. This is due to the ease of assembly, maintenance of tight joints, and the fact that such a fitting can be taken apart and used several times without requiring replacement. Valves are made in a variety of forms. For the small unit, packed and bellows-sealed valves are employed; for larger units the packed variety is used almost exclusively because of the larger sizes employed.

A valve formed of forged brass is shown in Fig. 15, and serves to illustrate the manner of construction employed in small valve design. A comparison of the two types of valves is illustrated by examining the two angle valves shown in Fig. 16. One employs the usual packing and the other makes use of the corrugated sheet-seal metal or sylphon bellows. Both valves are back-seating, so that when fully opened, the valve itself is sealed against any possible leakage. New safety-code specifica-

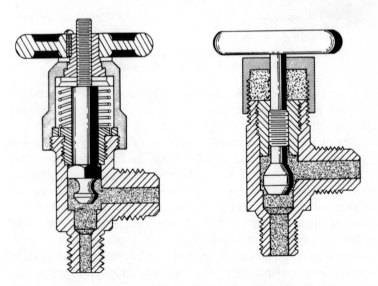

Fig. 16. Sectional views of two types of valves.

tions, which are being adopted in almost every city, require that fittings, fastenings, valves, and safety devices conform to certain standards. One of the requirements in flare-tube fittings is that intermediate bushings are used.

Two types of safety devices are illustrated in Fig. 17; one is rupturable, and the other depends on heat to effect a pressure release. The rupture devices usually utilize a thin silver disc

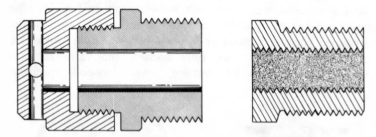

Fig. 17. Rupturable safety devices to relieve excessive pressure. The plugs melt at excessive temperatures.

of a certain diameter and thickness which, in the event of high pressure being generated due to any cause in the system, will rupture and release the refrigerant, leaving the unit without any chance of its being destroyed or strained in any way. The fusible type of safety device is usually made in the form of a plug intended to be screwed into a boss or fitting, and is operative only by heat. Regulations require the use of such plugs on refrigerant storage or charging drums, receivers, and isolated portions of apparatus that are filled with refrigerant. In the event of fire, the gas will be released without danger of explosion.

One type of connector developed and adopted by the trade is the capillary-soldered type. It is lighter, simpler, stronger, and more economical than the screwed types. These special fittings are made in the shapes and sizes familiar to the trade, and differ only in the method of joining the tubing. The tubing is inserted into the fitting until it rests against a shoulder. Then wire solder is applied through a small feed hole in the fitting under heat from a blowtorch. The solder is drawn into the fitting and evenly distributed by capillary attraction and results in a firm joint. The method of effecting a joint is illustrated in Fig. 18, which shows the wire solder being fed into the hole in the side of the fitting (a *tee* in this instance) while a blowtorch heats the fitting. A sectional view of the completed joint indicates the capillary channel holes and shoulder; it also shows the larger surface between the fitting and tube joined by the solder.

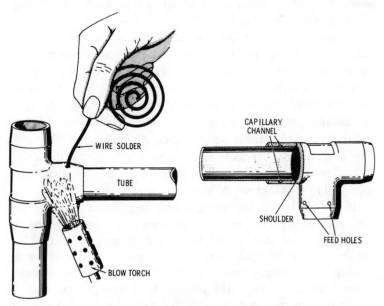

Fig. 18. Soldering a fitting in place.

SILVER BRAZING

The use of high melting point alloys has increased considerably in recent years, particularly in supermarkets, locker plants, air conditioning, or wherever a large number of joints is used. The inherent mechanical strength of the joint and the reduction of leak possibilities have made this a desirable type. In addition, code requirements in some areas have forced the use of these alloys. In order for brazing alloys to melt and flow properly, red heat (1150-1450°F.) is required. Copper will react with the oxygen in the air at these temperatures to form a scale of copper oxide on the inner walls of the tubing and fittings. The scale is broken off into flakes by the turbulence of flowing liquid refrigerant. The flakes quickly break up into a fine powder which plugs driers, strainers, and capillary tubes.

Copper oxide is so finely divided that a filter bed of other materials is usually required in driers before the filtration system in the drier can remove it, thus accounting for the approximately forty-eight hours needed to remove this material. Driers are sometimes returned as defective because they have shown an undesirable pressure drop on a new system. In conjunction with other dirt, a substantial accumulation of copper oxide is often the explanation. Chemical analysis readily confirms the condition. The drier is not defective. It has done exactly what it was designed to do—take out the dirt.

If the air in the line being brazed is replaced with an inert gas, such as dry nitrogen, the formation of copper oxide can be eliminated. The line should be purged thoroughly and a slow steady flow of nitrogen maintained by means of a pressure reducing valve. High-pressure gases (nitrogen or carbon dioxide) should never be connected directly to a system, but must be metered through a pressure reducing valve for the protection of the user. Too high a rate of flow is undesirable because of the cooling effect of the gas. The inert gas method will keep the inside of the copper lines and fittings clean and bright. When it is not completely successful, the trouble is usually attributed to applying heat before all of the air has been displaced.

On large copper pipe, the end of the tubing should be covered with some type of elastic material, such as a rubber balloon, and a small slit made in the material to provide an escape valve. In this manner, the line can be kept full of nitrogen without use of excessive quantities. The inert gas method, wherever practical, is recommended for repair work. The nitrogen clears the line of refrigerant vapor preventing acid formation due to refrigerant breakdown as well as preventing copper oxide formation.

Many servicemen find it impractical to transport heavy nitrogen cylinders in and out of buildings and have solved the problem by permanently mounting the cylinder on their service truck. The cylinder is equipped with a pressure reduction valve and flexible lines long enough to reach most of their jobs. Purge hose or a similar type of material is satisfactory for the flexible line. The line pressure is held to an absolute minimum, with the gas flow just high enough to maintain the required slow, steady rate.

CHAPTER 14

Dairy Refrigeration

Although dairy refrigeration equipment is not considered a household appliance it is used in private dairy farms all over the country. This equipment is necessary in large dairy farms to protect the milk while in storage awaiting transfer to processing plants.

Sanitary and health code requirements have resulted in an increasing application of refrigerating equipment in the dairy industry. In many sections of the country, the health codes specify that the milk must be chilled to below 50° F. within two hours after having been drawn from the cow. In most locations the milk is graded according to the method handled and the bacteria count; consequently, grade "A" milk obtains a premium over other grades.

TEMPERATURE AND BACTERIA GROWTH

Milk, as drawn from the cow, is practically free from bacteria and the present dairy farm practice in conjunction with periodic tuberculin testing of cattle has raised the average health of dairy herds and materially increased the production of healthful milk. Warm milk, however, is an ideal medium for propagation of bacteria and, although the milk is practically free from bacteria when leaving the cow, the quantity of bacteria absorbed from the air, containers, etc., and general milking operations, reproduce the bacteria rapidly as long as milk is at a temperature above 50° F.

Between 50° and 130° F., the rate of propagation of bacteria is in almost direct proportion to the temperature of the milk. Propagation, therefore, can be reduced by either cooling the milk to a point below 50° F., or by heating the milk to a point above 130° F. At the low temperature, the propagation decreases to a great extent, but the existing bacteria are practically unharmed. At a temperature above 130° to 145° F., the bacteria are destroyed in a period of 20 to 30 minutes.

From the foregoing, it is obvious that the ideal method of handling milk is to destroy the bacteria immediately after milking and to cool the milk to a point below 50° F., and to hold it at this temperature until used in order to prevent propagation of additional bacteria. The heating of milk in order to destroy bacteria is termed *pasteurization* and is obtained by heating the milk to a temperature of approximately 145° F., and holding it at this temperature for 30 minutes, followed by rapid cooling to below 50° F., and holding it at that temperature until used.

Milk Cooling Methods

The machinery used in dairy refrigeration depends largely upon the amount of milk and milk products to be handled. In a large fully equipped market milk plant, for example, the requirements may be classified as:

1. Cooling of raw milk.
2. Cooling of pasteurized milk.
3. Cooling of refrigerator boxes.
4. Cooling of by-products.

5. Ice making.
6. Air conditioning.

Smaller dairy refrigeration plants requiring less equipment are the retail dairies and dairies where milk is sold wholesale to other distributing agencies.

There are three general methods of cooling milk on the farm, such as:

1. The *aerator* or atmospheric type milk cooler.
2. The vat type of pasteurizer.
3. The tube cooler.

Aeration is the cooling of milk by allowing it to flow over a surface cooler through which either cold water or brine is pumped to reduce the temperature, as shown in Fig. 1. In the illustration,

> A represents liquid line from the condensing unit, B dehydrator, C solenoid valve, D liquid indicator, E thermal expansion valve, F inlet connection on tank, G thermal expansion valve bulb, H suction connection to tank, J suction line from tank to condensing unit, K to liquid line connection on condensing unit, L to suction connection on condensing unit, M vibration eliminator.

Principally, the cooler consists of a series of tubes located one above the other so that the milk can be distributed over the top tube and be allowed to drip from one tube to the other and be cooled by surface contact. Usually, this aerator is in two general sections—the top section which uses water for a cooling medium, and the bottom section usually supplied with the proper refrigeration.

In most localities, water between 70° and 80° F. may be obtained from city mains or from a cooling tower and used to cool

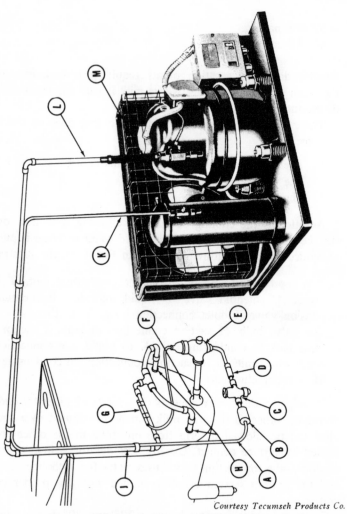

Courtesy Tecumseh Products Co.

Fig. 1. A typical externally mounted condensing unit showing the refrigerant connections.

the pasteurized milk from an initial temperature of 145° F. down to some point between 75° and 80° F., depending entirely on the temperature and quantity of water available. Milk then enters the bottom section of the aerator, which is supplied with refrigeration either directly in the direct expansion type of refrigerator, or the indirect type of refrigerator which uses brine or sweetwater as the cooling medium.

The vat type of pasteurizer and cooler combined consists of a large porcelain or glass-lined vat containing a helical coil which is submerged and rotates during the processing. During pasteurizing, hot water is generally circulated through this coil to supply the heat necessary to pasteurize the milk. Immediately after the pasteurizing is accomplished, tap water is circulated through the coil to bring the milk down to a point between 75° and 85° F., and then chilled brine or fresh water is circulated to furnish further reduction down to 40° or 45° F. This type of equipment has an advantage in that the milk is handled only once. There is no need to put it through a separate pasteurizer, pre-cooler and, finally, aerator. The chief disadvantage with this type of equipment is in its high initial cost, and the difficulty sometimes experienced in cleaning it. The calculation of the refrigeration loads for the direct or indirect refrigeration systems are practically identical.

The third type of cooling equipment consists of a concentric-tube cooler wherein the milk passes through a center tube, while water for precooling and final chilling is passed through the angular space around the center tube within the outside tube. Here again, the refrigerator load calculations are identical to those previously described. To illustrate the amount of refrigeration necessary for a typical milk cooling plant, the following step by step procedure is furnished along with actual examples to show the method of calculation.

SIMPLE LOAD CALCULATIONS

Assume that a dairy handles 800 gallons of milk daily. To cool the milk from a pasteurizing temperature of 145° F. to 40° F., the following assumptions are made:

Specific gravity of milk is 1.03; weight of milk is 8.6 pounds per gallon; weight of water is 8.34 pounds per gallon; specific heat of milk is 0.95. The equation for heat load is:

$$H = WS \ (t_1 - t_2)$$

Where

$W =$ weight of fluid being cooled.
$S =$ specific heat Btu per pound degree.
$t_1 =$ higher temperature.
$t_2 =$ lower temperature.

Substituting values in equation (1) we obtain:

$$H = 800 \times 8.6 \times 0.95(145 - 40) = 686,280 \text{ Btu.}$$

If it is assumed that ample water is available, it is entirely feasible to cool the milk with water to 80° F. The heat to be removed by water consequently is:

$$H = \frac{686,280 \times 65}{105} = 424,840 \text{ Btu.}$$

If the water used for cooling is allowed to raise 10° F., the amount of water necessary is:

$$\frac{424,840}{10 \times 8.34} = 5,094 \text{ gallons}$$

If a four hour period is allowed for the cooling, the amount of water necessary per hour is 5.094/4 or 1,274 gallons. If 25% of water is allowed for losses, the gpm requirements of water finally is:

$$\frac{1,274 \times 1.25}{60} = 26.5 \text{ gallons per minute (approximately).}$$

To cool milk from 80 to 40 F°., the amount of heat to be removed is:

$$H = 686,280 - 424,840 = 261,440 \text{ Btu.}$$

The cooling substance is usually brine. The brine for this purpose should enter the cooling coil at an initial temperature of about 18° F., and leave at about 28° F. The specific heat of brine is dependent upon the amount of salt in it, but 0.86 is a reasonable value. The weight of brine required to remove 261,440 Btu of heat can be obtained if equation (1) is solved with respect to W. That is:

$$W = \frac{H}{S(t_1 - t_2)} \qquad \frac{261,440}{0.86(28 - 18)} = 30,400 \text{ lbs.}$$

If the weight per gallon of brine is assumed to be 9.1, we can obtain the number of gallons of brine required as 30,400/9.1 or 3,340 approximately.

Again, if a four hour period is allowed for the cooling, the requirements of brine in gpm is 3,340/4 × 60 or 13.9 gallons per minute. Allowing for heat losses, a pump having a minimum capacity of 15 gpm should be provided.

COOLING SURFACE REQUIRED

If it is desired to calculate the cooling surface required for the water and brine cooler, the procedure is as follows:

For that part of the cooler in which water is the cooling medium, the amount of heat to be removed per hour is 424, 840/4 or 106,210 Btu assuming a four hour cooling period. If 20% is added to provide for losses, the additional heat to be removed is 1.2 × 106,210 or 127,450 Btu approximately. The milk comes to the cooler at 145° F., and leaves the water cooled section at 80° F. If the counter-flow principle is employed, the milk enters the top of the cooler and leaves at the bottom, while the water enters the cooler at the bottom and leaves at the top. The temperature difference at the warm end is 145° − 70° = 75° F., and at the cold end it is 80° − 60° = 20° F. The formula for computation of cooling surface is:

$$H = KAT_d$$

Where

H = heat transfer in Btu per hour.

K = co-efficient of heat transfer = 60.

A = surface area in square feet.

T_d = mean temperature difference.

If formula ($H = KAT_d$) is solved with respect to (A) and numerical values substituted, we obtain:

$$\frac{KT_d}{A = H} = \frac{127,450}{\dfrac{60\,(75 + 20)}{2}} = 44.7 \text{ sq. ft. (approximately)}$$

The amount of surface required for the brine cooler may be calculated in a similar manner. The heat to be removed by the brine is 261,440 Btu. Allowing 20% additional heat losses, the total is $261,440 \times 1.2 = 313,700$ Btu (approximately). If it is assumed that the compressor is operating eight hours per day, and that during the cooling period, the evaporating ammonia will remove half of the 313,700 Btu and the other half is absorbed by the brine to be removed by the evaporating ammonia later, then by applying the equation below we have:

$$H = WS(t_1 - t_2)$$

Where

      $H =$ heat to be absorbed by brine.

      $W =$ weight of brine in system.

      $S =$ specific heat of brine $= 0.86$.

      $t_1 =$ temperature of brine at end of milk cooling period.

      $t_2 =$ temperature of brine at beginning of milk cooling period.

Allowing the brine to warm 5° F., during the cooling period $t_1 - t_2 = 5$, and

$$W = \frac{H}{S(t_1 - t_2)} = \frac{313,700}{2 \times 0.86 \times 5} = 36,500 \text{ lbs. (Approx.)}$$

At 9.1 pounds per gallon this is 36,500/9.1 or about 4,000 gallons of brine. On the basis of eight hours operating time, the refrigerating equipment must remove heat at the rate of 313,-700/8 or 39,200 Btu per hour (Approximately). In this particular case therefore, the tonnage capacity of the compressor must be 39,200/12,000 or 3.27 tons.

The evaporating surface area in the brine tank may be calculated from equation (H=KATd). With the average brine temperature of 28° F., and the temperature of the evaporating ammonia at 5 F°., and an assumed co-efficient of heat transfer at 15, we obtain:

$$A = \frac{H}{K \times T_d} = \frac{39,200}{15(28-5)} = 114 \text{ sq. ft. (Approx.)}$$

It has been found by experience that it requires 2.3 lineal feet of 1-1/4" pipe to furnish one square foot of surface. Since the number of square feet in this particular case is 114, the pipe requirement consequently is 2.3 × 114 or 262 lineal feet.

MILK STORAGE

Most dairies have a walk-in cooler type for storage of the milk after aerating, in addition to storage of other products such as cream and butter. Usually immediately after aerating, the milk is bottled, cased and stored. During the process of bottling, the milk usually rises two or three degrees due to contact with the warm bottles. The amount of refrigeration required for such storage varies within a rather large range, depending upon such factors as insulation, amount of products to be stored, etc. Experience, however, has shown that if a certain amount of refrigeration is provided per cubic foot of room space, satisfactory conditions can be maintained.

If a room having dimensions of 18 × 12 × 10 ft. or approximately 2,200 cubic feet, and the temperature is to be held at 35° F., about one ton of refrigeration should be provided. For a room 10 × 10 × 10 or 1,000 cubic feet of space about 0.6 ton of refrigeration should be provided. A brine tank is often located in the milk storage room. It should be located near the ceiling. The refrigeration stored in it during the time the machine is in operation will help to hold the room at the proper temperature during the shut down period and the fact that it is an insulated room eliminates the necessity of insulating the tank itself.

If it cannot be placed near the ceiling, it should not be placed in the room at all because it occupies valuable space, and does not help to hold the room temperature. In a dairy manufacturing plant, two compressors, each operating at a different suction pressure, are often desirable. The machine which cools the brine for freezing and cools the hardening room can be operated with an evaporating temperature of $-20°$ F., which corresponds to a pressure of 18.3 pounds absolute or 3.6 pounds gauge. The machine which serves the milk storage room, the brine tank for milk cooling, and the mix holding vat should have an evaporating temperature of about $5°$ F., which requires a suction pressure of 34.3 pounds pressure or 19.6 pounds gauge. If ice is made the ice tank should also be connected to this machine.

CHAPTER 15

Air and Its Properties

Climate no longer needs to have the slightest effect on indoor conditions, since it is now possible to bring fresh, clean air indoors. Air can be heated or cooled; moisture can be added or subtracted to produce the exact temperature and humidity required in each individual instance. The ideal temperature and humidity vary greatly, depending on the service. For human comfort in auditoriums or theaters, the temperature should be around 70 F°., and the humidity should be between 50% and 60%. More moisture than this makes the cooled area uncomfortable and damp; less moisture makes it dry and chilly.

HUMIDITY CONTROL

Air will support or absorb moisture very easily. A simple spray will make it moist. The extraction of moisture from the air is a simple operation, but some means of cooling must be provided. Moisture can be removed by hygroscopic chemicals, such as calcium chloride, sulphuric acid and caustic potash, but the handling of these compounds is disagreeable and dangerous. Because of the labor and danger involved, the refrigeration machine is employed, so that moisture can be condensed and drawn off.

The humidity is very carefully controlled by a humidistat. This device, either directly or through a relay, operates proper dampers and motors so that the humidity is maintained within very close limits.

This is of special importance where the food is to be held for long periods of time. It is necessary that the storage rooms be properly designed and cooled, so that an even temperature and, more important, an even humidity is maintained in all parts of the room. If a stagnant pocket is allowed, the humidity will rise and result in the formation of mold. Low temperatures are required in cold storage rooms, and water cannot be used in the air washers to cool the air. The desired effect therefore is produced by blowing air over the cooling coils.

Air conditioning has been introduced to the public through theater attendance, but in this case a different set of conditions is encountered. People dress very lightly in warm weather and do not require a very cool room to feel comfortable. The important point concerning air conditioning installations is to make people feel comfortable, not cool. For this reason a large temperature drop or humidity differential should not be maintained. In residences a temperature of 72° to 78° during the day is agreeable. At night, depending on individual preferences, a slightly lower temperature may be used. Bedrooms only need air conditioning in the early evening to prepare them for proper comfort conditions.

Air conditioned rooms should be kept closed. All of the fresh air should be brought in with a fan, so that it can be cooled, washed, humidified or dried, and distributed properly. The refrigeration load is due to the entrance of air, radiation from the sun, radiation from the walls, internal heat in the enclosure, heat from the occupants, lights, and motors, heat from the cooking stove, hot plates, toasters, coffee urns, etc., and moisture from the entering air, people's breath, clothing, etc. This is somewhat different from the refrigerating load on a cold-storage plant, where the heat load coming through the walls and the heat contained in the stored material form the major portion of the load.

If fresh air is cooled to 32° F., nearly all of the moisture will be removed. As a matter of fact, only two grains of water per cubic foot of air will be retained. If this dry air is blown into a closed and empty room with a temperature of 70° F., the fresh air will gradually replace the existing air in the room. When this results there will be only two grains of moisture per cubic foot of air in the room provided that the air cannot absorb moisture from some other source. Air at 70° F., is capable of supporting eight grains of moisture per cubic foot of air, hence the relative humidity would be: 2÷8 or 25%. By cooling the incoming air to 0° F., it would be able to support only one grain per cubic foot, so that humidity in a room supplied with this air would be 1 ÷ 8 or 12.5%. Taking this as a means of control, any humidity desired can be secured through the medium of controlling the temperature of the incoming air.

Air will leak into an enclosure if it is not held slightly above atmospheric pressure. If the air in a room is 75° F., and it is desired to hold the humidity at 50%, the air will have 4.7 grains per cubic foot. If one half grain is carried into the room with the incoming air, the cool air furnished must not contain over 4.2 grains. This is the quantity of moisture that the air will hold at a 51° F. temperature when saturated. Therefore, to remove the excess moisture, so that the delivered air will have only 4.2 grains, the cooling equipment must lower the temperature of the incoming air to 51° F.

The human body radiates a considerable amount of heat. In rooms that range from 60° to 90° F., a man can get cold and radiate more heat. He then works or exercises harder to burn more fuel. This oxidizes more of his tissues and raises the heat emissivity to about 550 Btu. If he is clothed warmly, so that the radiation of heat from his body is hindered, he will perspire; the evaporation will cool him off and warm the room. About 24% of a man's heat energy is required to evaporate the moisture that he emits. This moisture must be condensed out of the air in the room by the refrigerating apparatus. The moisture involved amounts to about 1-1/2 pounds per day and requires about 1,450 Btu per day, or 1 Btu per minute. A one-ton refrigeration unit will extract 200 Btu per minute; therefore it will require a one-ton machine just to condense the moisture emitted by 200 people. In a small size auditorium or theater, it will require a 10-ton machine to condense the moisture produced by people breathing.

Assuming that there were 2,000 people in a theater and that each person breathed out 10,500 grains of moisture per day, or 7 grains per minute, then the 2,000 people would add 14,000 grains of moisture per mintue to the air. If the fan circulates 50,000 cubic feet per minute, this air, containing 4.5 grains per cubic foot, will be quickly absorbed and will result in an increase of the moisture content to 4.78 grains per cubic foot. When the temperature and humidity are correctly balanced, people enjoy equal comfort over a considerable range. This range is called the *comfort zone*. For instance, if the room is very dry, evaporation from the skin is rapid and produces a greater cooling effect. Consequently, such air should be warmed slightly to counteract the cool feeling resulting from the lack of moisture in such air.

By raising the humidity to slow down evaporation, the room can be cooled slightly and still feel comfortable. As a specific example, assume the outside air is 95° F., and the wet bulb indicates 80° F. This 15° differential corresponds to a 51.5% humidity and indicates that the air contains 8.8 grains per cubic foot. For a comfortable interior the temperature would be held at 80° F., and the humidity held at 50%. These conditions would therefore be:

Outside air .... 95°
Wet bulb temperature .... 80°
Depression wet bulb .... 15°
Outside humidity 51.5%
Grains moisture per cu. ft. 8.8
Room temperature .... 80°
Desired humidity 50%
Moisture in grains 5.4

In order to hold the air in the room at 50% with 5.4 grains, the air entering the room must be slightly drier, about 5 grains of moisture per cubic foot. This corresponds to a saturated temperature of 56° F. Since the outside air contains 8.8 grains, it is necessary to extract 3.8 grains of moisture per cubic foot before admitting it to the room. If the quantity of fresh air required for ventilation, which is cooled to 56° F., is not sufficient to hold the room at the proper temperature (80° F.), then some of the air within the enclosure must be recirculated, thus cooling it to a degree at which it will hold the desired temperature. The amount of recirculated air may vary with the load because the heat due to human occupancy, electric lights, etc., varies.

Table 1 presents data based on the air picking up 0.5 grain of moisture per cubic foot when passing through a room, the amount of moisture per cubic foot, and the temperature to which the air must be cooled before admitting it to the enclosure.

DIFFUSION OF MOISTURE

If the air is 51° F., and a moisture content of 4.2 grains is forced into an enclosure held at 75° F., and the humidity is held

Table 1. Comfort Table

Temp. in room	Room humidity %	Grains of moisture in room per cu. ft.	Grains of moisture per cu. ft. leaving air cooler	Temp. to which air must be cooled in air cooler
80	60	6.5	6.0	60
80	50	5.5	5.0	56
75	60	5.6	5.1	56.5
75	55	5.1	4.6	53.5
75	50	4.7	4.2	51
70	60	4.6	4.3	51.5
70	55	4.4	3.9	49
70	50	4.0	3.5	46

at 50% (4.7 grains of moisture per cubic foot) there will be a difference in vapor pressures. The vapor pressure in the enclosure is 0.417 inches of mercury, while the pressure of the incoming vapor is only 0.373, or 0.044 inches of mercury difference in pressure. This equals about 1/15 of a pound difference in pressure. The moisture in the enclosure forces itself into the vapor in the entering air.

This action generates heat, which warms the air so rapidly that an equilibrium is almost immediately established. The rapidity of this action is apparent when it is pointed out that the incoming air usually assumes very nearly the temperature of the room within 2 or 3 feet after leaving the orifice. A large volume of vapor contained in the enclosure gives up a slight amount of heat to the incoming air, and a small amount of moisture evaporates in the room and replaces that which flowed into the incoming air.

LOADS ON APPARATUS

The rating of a refrigerating machine is the amount of work that it can perform in 24 hours as compared to the refrigerating effect produced by the melting of ice. A one-ton machine operating for 24 hours will produce the same cooling effect in Btu as one ton of ice melting to water at 32 F., in 24 hours. In cold-storage work a one-ton unit will cool about 10,000 cubic feet of space and hold it at 32° F. Once the sensible heat is removed from the stored materials, the entire refrigerating load will consist of the heat that is filtered through the walls, plus a small quantity caused by infiltration, opening of doors, and electric lights.

Refrigerated warehouses and large refrigerators are insulated with cork or some other nonconducting material to retard the transfer of exterior heat to the refrigerated space. A one-ton unit in theater work will take care of about 15 seats, at a cost that ranges from 1 to 2 cents per seat. A theater with a seating capacity of 1,500 seats, requires a refrigerating machine of about 100 tons. The volume of such a theater is approximately 800,000 cubic feet; it is apparent that a one-ton unit will be required for each 8,000 cubic feet. This may seem strange since the cubical contents are much less than that which a one-ton unit will take care of in cold-storage work. In theater work the temperature averages about 75° F. If it is found convenient, insulation will greatly reduce the refrigerating load.

In residences and offices a one-ton unit will usually take care of 5,000 to 7,000 cubic feet, depending on the number of occupants. An approximation of the refrigerating loads imposed by various applications is indicated in the following list, which gives the work that a *one-ton unit* will accomplish when employed in different lines of work:

10,000 cu. ft. of cold-storage space at 32°.
Cool 8,000 cu. ft. or 15 seats in a theater to 75°.
Cool from 5,000 to 8,000 cu. ft. in a residence to 75°.

Cool from 3,000 to 5,000 cu. ft. of store space to 75°.
Cool from 3,000 to 5,000 cu. ft. in a dining room to 75°.
Cool from 3,000 to 8,000 cu. ft. in a candy factory to 68°.
Cool 3/4 gals. of drinking water per min. to 40°.
Freeze about 0.6 ton of ice per day.
Freeze about 0.75 ton of fish per day.

The conduction of heat through the walls of a theater is generally 0.3 Btu per hour per square foot per degree difference in temperature. If the sun shines on the roof or sides this figure will change to approximately 3 Btu. Cold-storage warehouses are insulated with 4 to 8 inches of sheet cork, but theaters, candy factories, and homes are not so insulated. Where possible, a great deal of the heat load can be offset by the use of tight windows of double glass. It has been the general practice to supply 30 cu. ft. of air per minute per person in theater work, this has been cut down to 25 cu. ft. and, in some cases, satisfactory results have been achieved with 20 cu. ft.

VENTILATION DATA

Practically all rooms and buildings in which man lives have a certain amount of natural ventilation, termed infiltration. Air seeps through cracks in the floors and walls, around windows and door frames, and amounts to a surprising number of cubic feet of air per hour. Although considerable data is available concerning air leakage, or infiltration, through walls and windows, most of this data refers to rooms that do not have a mechanical air supply, since the data was compiled for use with heating plants.

Tables of infiltration intended for use with air-conditioning apparatus involve recognition of the fact that conditioned rooms are maintained at a lower pressure than the outside conditions, and that the air leakage will be greater. The most practical method of estimating infiltration is to base it on the cubical contents of the room. For the average home, office, and small shop where only a limited number of persons gather, natural ventilation is generally satisfactory. Table 2 gives the natural changes that can be expected for normal construction. The structure should be examined so that some idea of the amount of infiltration can be determined.

Table 2. Infiltration

Exposure of room	No. of changes per hour
One side	1/2 to 1
Two sides	3/4 to 1-1/2
Three sides	1 to 2
Four sides	1 to 2
Inside room	11/2 to 3/4

At the present time the most satisfactory method for estimating infiltration appears to be based on the size of the room or space to be conditioned.

Table 3 may be used as a guide for ordinary tight structures of average construction:

Table 3. Natural Air Changes for Rooms Under Different Exposures per Hour

Exposure	No. of changes per hour
Inside	1/2
No windows or outside doors	3/4
1 side	1
2 sides	1-1/2
3 sides	1-3/4
4 sides	2

Another fault commonly found with improperly installed apparatus, or equipment carelessly operated, is that drafts are easily detected. In drying and processing work, rapid air movement is imperative, but where human comfort is concerned, the conditioned air must be evenly and thoroughly distributed without a sign of draft.

ESTIMATING INFILTRATION

If it is desirable to estimate the sensible heat load of a room, use the following formula:

$$H_s = \frac{V(t_o - t)}{n \times 3,360}$$

Where

H_s = sensible heat in Btu per minute from infiltration.

V = volume of room in cubic feet.

t_o = outdoor dry-bulb temperature assumption.

t = indoor dry-bulb temperature.

n = number of hours required to effect one complete change.

ESTIMATING TOTAL HEAT LOAD OF INFILTRATION

The total heat load of infiltration can be computed as follows:

$$H_t = \frac{V(H_o - H_I)}{n \times 810}$$

H_t = total heat load due to infiltration in Btu per minute.

H_o = total heat per pound of air at outdoor wet-bulb temperature.

H_I = total heat per pound of air at indoor wet-bulb temperature.

If the latent heat load is to be determined, use the following formula:

LATENT HEAT OF INFILTRATION

$$H_I = H_t - H_s$$

Where

H_I = latent heat load.

H_t = total heat load.

H_s = total sensible heat load.

REFRIGERATION DEMAND FOR COOLING AIR

Table 4 can be used for the calculation of the refrigeration requirements for the cooling of air and condensation of excess moisture.

Table 4. Refrigeration Load for Air Cooling

Relative Humidity	Temperature Reduction Increments, °F										
%	5°	6°	7°	8°	9°	10°	11°	12°	13°	14°	15°
40	0.045	0.085	0.120	0.155	0.195	0.235	0.280	0.320	0.365	0.415	0.460
45	0.123	0.165	0.205	0.245	0.290	0.335	0.383	0.428	0.482	0.530	0.580
50	0.200	0.245	0.290	0.335	0.385	0.435	0.485	0.535	0.590	0.645	0.700
55	0.280	0.352	0.377	0.425	0.480	0.528	0.585	0.642	0.703	0.765	0.825
60	0.360	0.410	0.465	0.515	0.575	0.630	0.685	0.750	0.815	0.885	0.950
65	0.438	0.488	0.543	0.598	0.663	0.720	0.783	0.850	0.918	0.990	1.170
70	0.515	0.565	0.620	0.680	0.745	0.810	0.875	0.950	1.020	1.095	1.175
75	0.587	0.648	0.703	0.763	0.833	0.895	0.968	1.055	1.125	1.202	1.295

Note. The above load, expressed in Btu per cubic foot of air cooled, is the refrigeration demand for air cooling and moisture condensation.

Table 3 lists a number of air changes dependent upon the exposure. For very excellent construction, the minimum infiltration figure can be employed, and for poor or old construction the greater or maximum factor should be used. This table can also be used for estimating the cooling and condensation load by using the number of changes of the room in accordance with its exposure; multiply this factor by the volume of the room, and then multiply by the factor given in table 4, which gives the refrigerating effect required per cubic foot. Taking the cubic feet required per hour and multiplying it by the factor in the table provides a very convenient method of determining the total load for any room.

Moist or properly humidified air serves to maintain paper, wood, plaster, rugs and cloth with the correct moisture balance, so that such materials are kept in proper condition. Dehydration increases the fragility of all products and, in many cases, causes a change in texture and color. Under ordinary conditions, when the outdoor temperature makes it imperative to use the heating system, materials in the home and office give up their moisture to the air. This fact can be shown by the condensation on windows during the frosty days of the heating season. During this season rugs, plaster and wood give up a certain portion of their moisture content. In buildings provided solely with heating equipment, a slow acting dry-kiln effect is created.

When humidification apparatus is operated toward the end of the heating season, it will be observed that it is difficult to maintain the proper humidity because the wood, plaster, paper, rugs, concrete, etc. tend to absorb the moisture lost during the dehydrating period. Just as soon as the humidity is raised to the proper level, the materials balance, and they will neither absorb nor give off moisture.

MOISTURE REGAIN

The absorption and especially the reabsorption of moisture by materials is known as the *moisture regain*. This is important to the manufacturers of certain products. A great deal of experimental work and study has been devoted to moisture in the air. Regain curves have been developed, especially in the rayon, silk, wool, paper and cotton trades.

CONDENSATION ON WINDOWS

When the proper indoor relative humidity is maintained in the winter months, condensation or frosting will occur on the windows. If the condensation occurs in appreciable amounts over extended periods, it will destroy the wall or frame finish and create rust or rot. Usually the putty is also impaired and may require attention every season. Condensation can be prevented by maintaining lower relative humidity, but this is one of the objectives of the air-conditioning system. In manufacturing, moisture is one of the prime essentials in the production of the finished material. In homes and offices, health and comfort require a higher relative humidity. Condensation and the load on the system can be cut down or eliminated by the use of double or triple windows.

The formation of moisture on windows is the same manifestation of the dew point shown by a pitcher of ice water. The surface of the glass in each case is at the temperature that the air coming into contact with it is cooled below the dew-point temperature, and the air deposits its excess moisture on the surface. In the

379

case of single-glass windows, the condensation appears like drops of dew, just as it does on the pitcher of ice water. If however, the outdoor temperature is below the freezing point, the condensate will freeze and result in a frosted condition.

DOUBLE AND TRIPLE WINDOWS

Double glass for windows with an air space between the panes (thermopane) maintains the inner glass at a higher surface temperature than when a single glass is employed, so that no condensation occurs under normal conditions. In industrial applications, where high humidities must be maintained, triple glass is used. Manufacturers of store display cases and counters have employed double and triple glass for a number of years, realizing that the display must not be hindered by condensation. These manufacturers also realized that the space between the panes must be sealed with an airtight and waterproof material, otherwise moisture would enter and precipitate in time.

Table 5. Percentage of Relative Humidity

SINGLE WINDOWS		
Outdoor temperature °F	Temperature of inner surface of glass	Relative humidity at which condensation forms on inner surface of glass
—10	13	12
0	20	18
10	28	23
20	34	30
30	42	38
40	48	48
50	55	64
60	62	80
70	69	99

The University of Illinois conducted a series of tests and evolved the data given in Tables 5 and 6, which list the temperatures of glass at which condensation takes place. Since the air within the air-conditioned room is usually in motion, the glass surface is slightly warmed by the air flowing over it, so that the temperatures and humidities given can be assumed to be the critical points beyond which condensation will occur.

Table 6. Percentage of Relative Humidity

DOUBLE WINDOWS		
Outdoor temperature °F	Temperature of inner surface of glass	Relative humidity at which condensation forms on inner surface of glass
−10	46	45
0	49	49
10	52	54
20	54	60
30	57	68
40	60	75
50	63	83
60	66	91
70	69	99

GLASS DOOR AND WINDOW COEFFICIENTS

The values of K, in Table 7 (the heat transfer coefficient) expressed in Btu per hour per degree of temperature difference per square foot, are given for all glass doors and windows not exposed to the direct rays of the sun.

EXPOSED WINDOWS AND DOORS

When windows have an eastern or western exposure, they should be provided with awnings, otherwise the direct rays of the

381

Table 7. Unexposed or Shaded Windows and Doors

Thickness of Glass	K
1	1.13
2	0.46
3	0.29
4	0.21

sun will give a very high *K* effect. In the case of exposed east or west windows without awnings, a coefficient of 160 Btu per square foot per hour per degree temperature differential should be used. For a southern exposure, windows should be given a *K* factor of 75, if not provided with awnings. When awnings are used over windows and doors, the standard glass coefficients, as given in the tables, should be used, but twice the temperature difference should be employed to calculate the heat leakage. Awnings should be used wherever possible in order to cut down the heat load imposed on the air-conditioning apparatus and to save costs in operation and the initial plant outlay. In many cases a smaller-sized unit can be employed, whereas if windows are not shaded from the direct rays of the sun, it may be necessary to employ a larger and more expensive unit to keep the area at the proper temperature and humidity.

When calculating the heat load due to solar radiation, it should be kept in mind that the sun's rays do not strike the east, south and west windows at the same time. It is a rather difficult matter to determine accurately just how many hours the sunlight will strike any particular exposure. The safest procedure is to select the side of the building or room being estimated that has the largest glass area and to use that side as the one being exposed to direct sunlight. The remaining glass areas should be estimated for heat load by the use of the factors given in Table 8 on the following page.

Table 8. Exposed Windows and Doors

Exposure	K
North	1.13
East	160.00
South	75.00
West	160.00

When windows are provided with awnings, estimate the heat load by taking the wall having the largest glass area exposed to the sunlight and double the temperature difference. The remaining glass area should be calculated for heat load by using the normal temperature difference and the coefficient given in Table 7. In many cases awnings cannot be employed due to the design of the building. In such cases light-colored shades and other light impervious materials can be used to cut down the effect of solar radiation. Where shades or screens are employed, a 50% reduction of the heat load of the exposed glass areas can be used.

All motors generate heat and, where installed or contemplated in air-conditioned rooms, must be included in estimating the total heat load.

Table 9. Motor Heat Load

H.P. Motor	Btu Generated per Hour
1/20	425
1/10	680
1/8	750
1/6	817
1/4	1020
1/3	1290
1/2	1870
3/4	2750
1	3410

ELECTRIC APPLIANCES

Electric lights dissipate approximately 3.42 Btu per hour for every rated watt; the heat load in any room is easily determined by a survey of the wattage. Electric toasters, waffle irons, hot plates, and coffee urns also dissipate considerable heat. To estimate the heat evolved through the use of these devices, the wattage ratings on each of the units should be noted and a study made of the length of time each is employed. Most of these devices will only be in constant use during the rush or peak load.

CHAPTER 16

Room Air Conditioners

A room air conditioner is generally considered to be a unit air conditioner suitable for placement in any particular room. The room in question may be a room in an office, a home or a small shop. Room air conditioners are usually classed according to their design and method of installation such as:

1. Window units.
2. Portable units.

As the name implies, window units are installed on the window sill. Portable units can be moved from one room to another as conditions and occupancy dictate. The advantages in this type of air conditioners are the relatively low cost summer cooling in the room selected and the portability and ease of installation. A typical window air conditioning unit is shown in Fig. 1.

When properly installed, sized and serviced, the room air conditioner unit gives a large measure of comfort, free from irritating exhaust that accompanies sweltering hot spells and extremely high humidity.

The window type air conditioner may be divided into three functional systems:

Fig. 1. Exterior view of a typical room air conditioner.

1. The electrical.
2. The refrigerant.
3. The air path.

The electrical system consists of the motor-compressor, unit control switch, fan and fan motor, starting and running capacitors, starting relay (when used), thermostat and necessary wiring. The refrigerant system consists of the compressor, condenser, drier strainer, capillary tube, evaporator, tubing and accumulator. In some systems the refrigerant flow is controlled by means of an automatic expansion valve instead of the conventional capillary tube method. The air path consists of an air discharge and intake grille, air filter, vent door, vent controls, etc. The component parts of a window air conditioner are shown in Fig. 2.

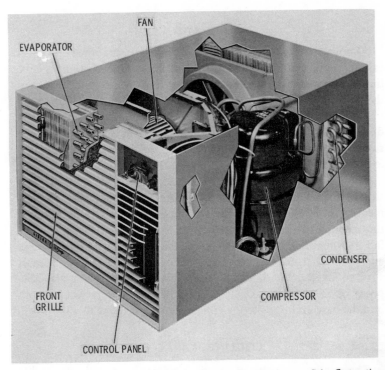

Fig. 2. Cutaway view showing the component parts of a room air conditioner.

REFRIGERATION CYCLE

Since room air conditioners operate on the same basic principles as that of household refrigerators having a similar refrigerant circuit and control methods, the reader is referred to descriptions of the refrigeration cycle given in chapters 3 thru 6 in this book.

OPERATION

Although the various types of room air conditioners vary in cabinet design as well as in the arrangement of components, they all operate on the same principle. The evaporator fan draws the recirculated air into the unit through the louvers located on the side. The air passes through the air filter evaporator and is discharged through the grille on the front of the unit into the room. The part of the unit extending into the room is insulated to reduce the transfer of heat and noise.

The condenser and compressor compartment extend outside of the room and is separated from the evaporator compartment by an insulated partition. The condenser air is drawn through the sections of the condenser coil on each side of the condenser fan housing. The air passes through the compressor compartment and is discharged through the center section of the condenser covered by the fan housing. It circulates the air and also disposes of the condensed water from the evaporator, which drops into the base and flows to the condenser end of the unit.

COOLING CAPACITY

The cooling capacity of an air conditioning unit is the ability to remove heat from a room and is usually measured in Btu per hour. The higher the Btu rating, the more heat will be removed. The capacity rating is usually given on the unit's nameplate together with such other necessary information as voltage and wattage requirements, etc. It is important that the room air conditioning units be large enough for the room or rooms to be cooled. When dealing with large units the term *ton of refrigeration is* most often used. A ton of refrigeration is equivalent to 12,000 Btu per hour. A room air conditioner rated at 10,000 Btu for example, will supply 10/12 or 0.83 ton of refrigeration.

CAPACITY REQUIREMENTS

The important variables to keep in mind when estimating the Btu requirements for a room cooling installation are:

1. Room size in square feet of floor area.
2. Wall construction, whether light or heavy.
3. Heat gain through ceiling.
4. The proportion of outside wall area that is glass.
5. The exposure to the sun of the walls of the room to be air conditioned.

Additional factors to be taken into account are: room ceiling height, number of persons using the room, miscellaneous heat loads such as wattage of lamps, radio and television sets in use in the room, etc. In order to obtain the approximate cooling capacity in Btu units, Table 1 should be used. The following steps

Table 1. Room Cooling Requirements in Btu's.

APPROX. BTU CAPACITY REQUIRED	SPACE ABOVE ROOM BEING COOLED								
	OCCUPIED ROOM			ATTIC			INSULATED FLAT ROOF		
	AREA BEING COOLED HAS EXPOSED WALLS FACING --								
	North or East	South	West	North or East	South	West	North or East	South	West
6,000	400	200	100	200	100	64	250	120	80
7,000	490	250	125	235	130	97	295	155	105
8,000	580	300	150	270	160	130	340	190	130
10,000	750	440	390	340	270	200	470	340	240
12,000	920	580	470	410	320	225	550	375	275
13,000	1000	660	550	450	350	250	600	400	300
16,000	1290	970	790	570	480	390	750	650	540

outline the procedure for using the table which shows the Btu requirements for various size rooms. In each case it is assumed that the rooms have an eight foot ceiling height. The procedure will be as follows:

1. Measure the room to be cooled for square footage (length in feet times width in feet). This determines the number of square feet in the room.
2. Determine the direction the room faces in order to determine which exposure to use.
3. Determine the condition of the space above the room to be cooled, such as occupied, attic or insulated flat roof.

Example. To determine the required amount of cooling for a room 23 feet long and 13 feet wide, a multiplication of the two figures will give 299 square feet. It is further assumed that the space above the room to be cooled is occupied and that the room has an exposed wall with windows facing south. A reference to the table indicates that the room described will require a unit having a capacity of approximately 8,000 Btu. A room of the same size and facing south having an uninsulated attic above it will require a cooling capacity of approximately 10,500 Btu.

The table indicates the approximate Btu capacity required to cool different rooms with the approximate area, and other conditions as described. The table will also permit checking an installed unit where unsatisfactory performance might be suspected as resulting from improper sizing or inadequate unit capacity.

INSTALLATION METHODS

After the unit is removed from the crate, the mounting frame should be located on the sill of the selected window. The window should be on the shady side of the room. If this is not possible, and the unit must be exposed to the sun, then some shading of the unit should be used for greater efficiency. Awnings are most effective since they shade both the unit and window at the same time, but the awning must not restrict the free flow of air to and from the unit. The awning top must be held away from the building side so that the hot air can escape. Venetian blinds or shades are a second choice to cut down a great amount of sun heat transmitted to the room through the windows.

Before installing the unit, it should first be determined if it is the correct size for the room and that the electrical power plug is correct and adequate. Whatever type of installation is used it should be made certain that the location will permit proper distribution of the cooled air throughout the room as shown in Fig. 3, and that there is no obstruction to the outside air flow that

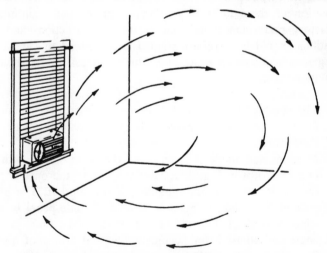

Fig. 3. Air circulation with an accompanying cooling effect provided by a typical window-mounted air-conditioning unit.

could cause restriction or recirculation of outside air back into the unit. The installation instructions provided with the unit should be studied and followed closely. The installation information included here is only general and is not intended to replace or substitute the instructions supplied with the unit. The installation should be made as neat as possible. Make certain that the unit is properly secured and that the installation is made so there is a good tight seal from the outside. It is very important that no openings are left through which rain or warm air from the outside could enter around the unit.

DOUBLE-HUNG WINDOW INSTALLATION

Most window units are manufactured for installation in sliding windows with free openings from 27″ to 40″ in width. The proper installation of these units is very important to their continued satisfactory performance and manufacturers' instructions and illustrations should be carefully studied and adhered to. The following is a step-by-step procedure which will assist in reducing installation time:

1. The depth of the unit will determine if it is to be mounted flush to the inside finished wall or at any point between these extremes.
2. Measure and mark the center of the window sill with a line as shown in Fig. 4. Extend the line to the outside sill for use in installing the mounting frame support. The purpose of the window angles is to hold the side panel in the window channel. Outside of the panel, place the window angle and adjust it for height, outline and drill pilot holes. Screw the angle firmly in place. Repeat the operation with the other angle on the opposite side of the window frame.

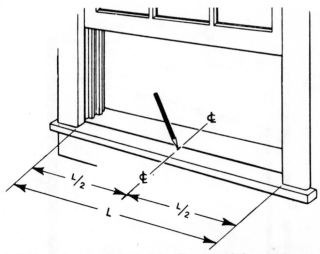

Fig. 4. Method of measuring window sill to establish mounting position of an air conditioning unit.

3. Place the mounted assembly (Fig. 5) in window, aligning center hole in lower frame with center line mark on window sill. Lower the window to the top of the frame. Extend sides of mounted assembly to full width of window, as shown by arrows. Install sash locking brackets after seating window firmly on assembly frame.

4. Break off excess filler board by pressing outward at nearest notch beyond unit opening of mounting frame as shown in Fig. 6. This operation is easier (especially for wider windows) if a pair of pliers is used.

5. Install the screws as shown in Fig. 7 if permanent installation is desired. Use of screws is recommended.

6. Install the bottom unit seal in the groove of the frame as shown in Fig. 8. Stretch the seal material to fill the groove completely.

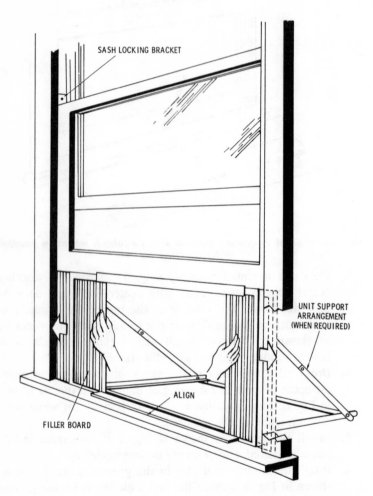

SASH LOCKING BRACKET

UNIT SUPPORT
ARRANGEMENT
(WHEN REQUIRED)

ALIGN

FILLER BOARD

Fig. 5. Method of installing unit support frame and filler boards.

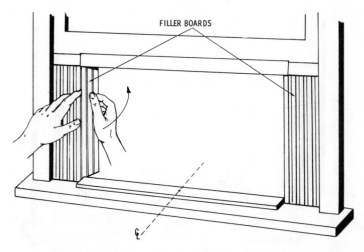

FILLER BOARDS

Fig. 6. Illustrating method of filler board installation.

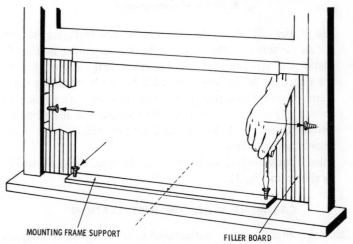

MOUNTING FRAME SUPPORT

FILLER BOARD

Fig. 7. Method of securing sill clamp to wooden window sill.

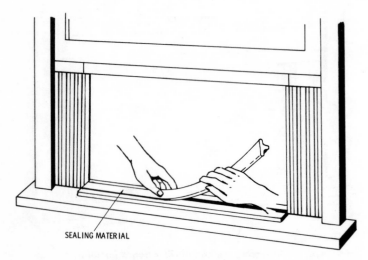

SEALING MATERIAL

Fig. 8. Unit seal arrangement.

7. Install the sill clamp in lieu of the sill fastening screws for stone sills or other such materials as shown in Fig. 9.
8. Install the top rail and seal assembly (Fig. 10) on top of the unit case in the holes provided for flush mounting only.
9. Remove unit decorative grille (Fig. 11) and install locking screws (2) on flush mount installations only. Reinstall grille.
10. Install the side seals by forcing them between the unit (filler boards and unit frame).
11. Install sash-to-glass seal, cut it to fit window glass width, as shown in Fig. 12.

CASEMENT WINDOW INSTALLATION

Casement windows are manufactured in so many different types that it will be impossible to give a single procedure to cover

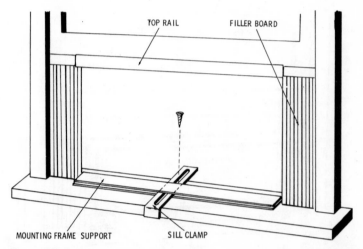

Fig. 9. Sill clamp mounting used in stone or masonry sill construction.

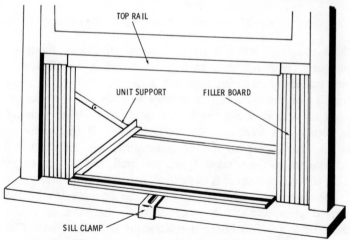

Fig. 10. Method of installing top rail and seal assembly.

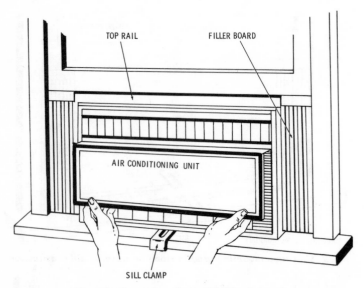

Fig. 11. Placement of air conditioning unit.

them all. Each job will require special treatment, thought, and planning. With reference to Fig. 13 A and B, installation is accomplished by removing sufficient glass and mullions to allow for passage of the unit. It is necessary to build up the window sill until the top is above the horizontal cross member forming the bottom of the frame on the metal window. If the outer cabinet is allowed to rest on this cross member, any vibration will be transmitted to the window frame and wall, and will be amplified. This starting procedure is basic to all casement windows.

Measure the height and width of the opening left by the removed glass and cut a piece of 1/4″ masonite or equivalent material to fit. This board is referred to as a filler panel. Cut out the center of the filler panel to the exact outside dimensions of

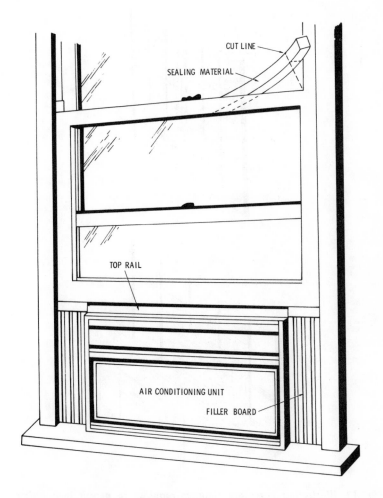

CUT LINE

SEALING MATERIAL

TOP RAIL

AIR CONDITIONING UNIT

FILLER BOARD

Fig. 12. Sealing installation arrangement.

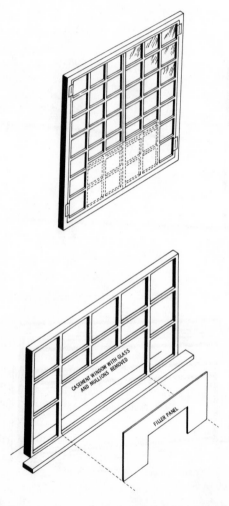

Fig. 13. Illustrating necessary changes required to permit installation of window mounted air conditioning unit in casement type window.

400

the outer cabinet. In cutting the height in the board, allow for the height of the bottom cross member on the window frame. Install the outer cabinet as described previously under "Double Hung Windows". Install the filler panel in the opening and seal the edges to the window frame with putty or caulking compound. The horizontal cross member of the supporting frame may be secured to the temporary sill by using the holes provided for this purpose, or the clamping assembly may be used if it is practical for the installation. Install chassis and inside cabinet.

Alternate Method

Measure height of opening and from this subtract height of the unit. Cut a piece of plywood, masonite or plexiglass equal in height to fit the measurement obtained as a result of the foregoing subtraction and with a width equal to the opening. Install outer cabinet in exact center of the opening and secure rigidly. Install the filler board across the top of the unit. Cement these in place at window frame. Other casement windows, where the glass panes are small, will require the cutting out of a horizontal cross member, as well as vertical mullions. In this case it may be advisable to reinstall the cross member at a height equal to the height of the outer cabinet. Cut and reinstall the glass above the cross members. The regular side panels supplied with unit may be used to fill in sides, or plexiglass may be used.

Wall Installations

In certain locations it may be desirable to cut through the existing wall and install the air conditioner in the opening thus provided. When cutting through the existing wall, carefully measure the air conditioner to be installed and cut a hole in the wall to provide for the conditioner in addition to the required framing and insulating sleeves.

Frame Construction

Fig. 14 illustrates a typical framing preparation. After inserting the cabinet into the opening, screw through the cabinet, into the framing, as shown. The existing knockouts can be used for either of the two positions; additional holes will have to be drilled along the length of the cabinet for other positions. Also screw the bottom rails to the framing, using the #14 screws. After assem-

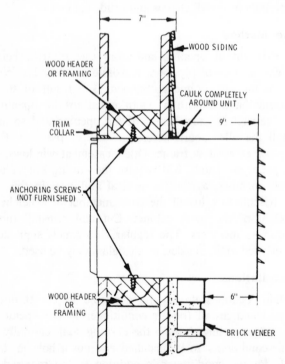

Fig. 14 Method of wood header arrangement to provide support in frame wall installation.

bling the cabinet securely, the wood trim strips can be nailed around the cabinet. Caulking and flashing should be used around the outside to provide a weather-tight seal. Rather than caulking at the bottom, a pan with side flanges and a drip rail may be used to protect the wall opening. The pan should be sloped to the rear, and must also provide a weather-tight seal.

Concrete Block or Brick Construction

To prepare the wall, remove all plaster, furring strips, etc., from the installation area. Be careful not to break plaster or exterior wall surface beyond the hole dimensions. After obtaining the proper opening, insert the cabinet and secure it with masonry nails. The existing knockouts can be used for either of the two positions; additional holes will have to be drilled along the length of the cabinet for other positions. After installation, cement the cabinet to the existing masonry on the outside. Use caulking and flashing, if necessary, to provide weather-tight seal. Rather than caulking at the bottom, a pan with side flanges and a drip rail may be used to protect the wall opening. The pan should be sloped to the rear, and must also provide a weather-tight seal. Wood trim strips may be applied around the inside of the cabinet to complete the installation.

OUTSIDE SUPPORT BRACKET

If the air conditioner extends more than 14″ beyond the outside of the wall opening, the cabinet will require additional support from the outside. This support may be obtained by using the mounting legs and brackets, and the corresponding nuts, bolts, and washers, as supplied with the mounting kit for the standard window installation. Make sure that the mounting brackets rest firmly against the wall at the wall opening, as shown in Fig. 15.

CONSOLE TYPE INSTALLATION

It is extremely desirable that a survey of the room is made prior to the actual installation of the unit. Determine the most favorable location, taking into account the desirable location in the room, the exposure of the window, the width of the window, its height from the floor and the location of the electrical supply outlet. In this connection, it should be realized that since these types of units as a rule have a considerable larger cooling capacity than the window sill units, it will be necessary to install a

Fig. 15. Support bracket arrangement in typical window installation.

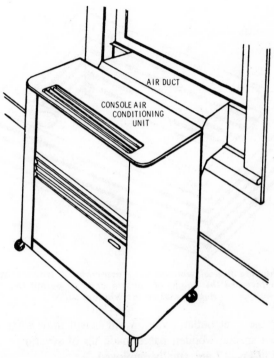

*Fig. 16. Console type air conditioning unit installation
in standard double hung window.*

special electrical connection from the meter or distribution panel
directly to the location of the unit.

The installation of a typical console room air conditioner in
double hung windows is illustrated in Fig. 16. A normal installation of this type will allow the window to be opened or closed
without interference from the duct or window filler panels. To
completely close the window the rain-hood must be retracted.
In order to adjust the height of the unit to obtain the necessary

405

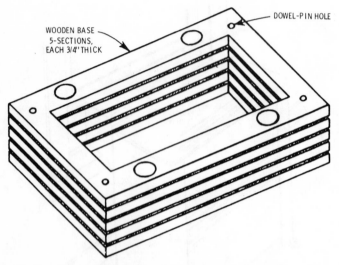

WOODEN BASE
5-SECTIONS,
EACH 3/4" THICK

DOWEL-PIN HOLE

Fig. 17. Showing typical wooden base assembly. A wooden base may be used to increase the height of console units to permit the standard duct to rest on the window sill.

height for the duct outlet (window sill height may differ by several inches) special wooden bases made up of several sections as illustrated in Fig. 17 are usually employed.

Installing Ducts

The standard duct (Fig. 18) usually furnished with the unit is approximately 8" deep. The unit end has a removable flange on it which slides on vertical tracks attached to the back of the unit. The window end of the duct has a rain-hood fitted in it. When the window is up the rain-hood is pushed out manually and secured in the open position by inserting a screw in each side of the duct after the holes in the duct and rain-hood are lined up.

The distance between the window and the nearest permissible

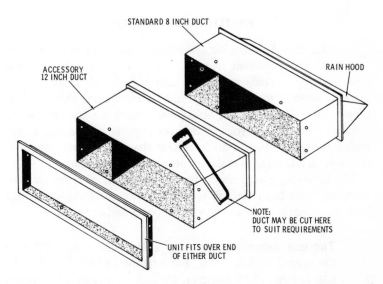

STANDARD 8 INCH DUCT

ACCESSORY
12 INCH DUCT

RAIN HOOD

NOTE:
DUCT MAY BE CUT HERE
TO SUIT REQUIREMENTS

UNIT FITS OVER END
OF EITHER DUCT

Fig. 18. Typical air duct units as employed in the installation of console type air conditioners.

location of the unit is measured direct and laid out on the duct measuring from the window end. Remove the screws holding the removable fitting to the duct; scribe and cut. File off all burrs and break the sharp edges. If the dimension is 8″ or less, the standard duct is used. If the dimension is greater than 8″ the standard and accessory ducts can be connected together to give a total distance of 20″. When cutting the accessory duct, be sure to take the measurement from the flared end to allow the extension piece to fit over the standard section. Use the unit fitting to locate new holes in cut end. Drill with a 1/8″ drill and reassemble. Installation of a console air conditioner in casement windows does not differ in any appreciable degree from that previously outlined in the case of the window sill mounted type.

THE ELECTRICAL SYSTEM

In order that the room air conditioning unit may operate properly it is very important that a check of the available electrical power supply is made before the unit is installed. If an existing branch circuit is to be used, it must be established that it is the proper rating and that the voltage is correct for the unit to be installed (110 or 220 volts, whichever appears on the unit nameplate). It should also be made certain that the electric supply at the outlet is adequate to maintain proper unit operation.

The following specifications for the operation of room air conditioning units from electric branch circuits are accepted by the National Electric Code and most local codes and ordinances:

1. The unit nameplate amperage should not exceed 80% of the branch circuit rating. For example, a No. 14 wire circuit is rated at 15 amperes; 80% of 15 equals 12 amperes, which is maximum loading.
2. If a unit nameplate amperage is greater than 50% of the circuit rating, then there should be no other outlet in that circuit available for additional loading by other electrical appliances, lights, etc.
3. If the unit amperage does not exceed 50% of the circuit rating, then a multiple outlet circuit can be used providing the additional loading of the circuit combined with the unit amperage does not exceed the circuit rating.

It should also be noted that the determination of a circuit's adequate rating does not necessarily establish that there is adequate voltage available for satisfactory operation of the unit. It is suggested (particularly on 110 volt circuits) that a voltage check be made with the circuit loaded by a current draw comparable to that of the unit nameplate amperage. The voltage under this loading should not drop lower than 10% below the unit nameplate voltage. If the voltage drops too low at the outlet, but remains satisfactory at the meter, this would indicate a new branch circuit is necessary.

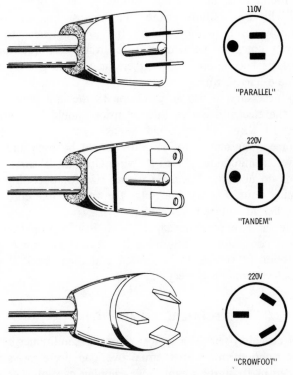

Fig. 19. Line cords and plug arrangement for various voltages as employed on air conditioning units.

Electrical load testers are available with selectable wattage which permits simulating a unit current draw. These instruments have a power cord with a wall plug that can be installed directly in the electrical outlet that is to be used for the unit. If the voltage does not drop below 90% of the unit nameplate voltage with this loading, the circuit should be satisfactory. It may be necessary however, to install a new circuit for the unit. In some instances, it may be found that there is not enough power supplied to the building. This may require changes in the fuse box and/or the power supply wiring to the building. It is recommended that the local power company be contacted regarding any questions or any problems encountered with either the electric power supply or with the electrical wiring.

If it is necessary to use an extension to the unit power cable to reach the electrical outlet, this extension should be connected with No. 14 wire and it should be as short as possible. On 2-1/2 horsepower units, No. 12 wire should be used and on 3 horsepower, a minimum of No. 10 wire. Ordinary electric extension cords do not have adequate wiring size for operating room conditioning units. Fig. 19 illustrates the various line cord plugs used for different voltage requirements.

Because the size (cooling capacity) in Btu is proportional to the current consumption, determine the correct cooling capacity for the room, or rooms, to be cooled and then check that the electric power supply is correct and adequate.

ELECTRICAL COMPONENTS

The electrical system of a typical room air conditioner consists of a motor-compressor with thermal overload protector, starting relay (when used) starting capacitors, running capacitor, fan motor, fan capacitor (on some models) main thermostat, unit control switch (on-off switch and fan speed switch combined) reactor (choke coil) on some models and connecting wires, which are shown in Fig. 20.

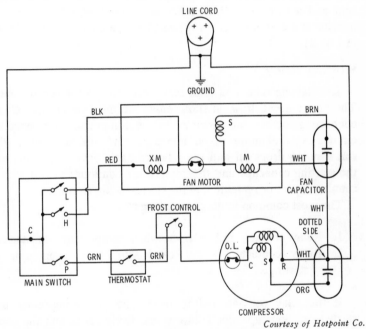

Fig. 20. Schematic diagram showing electrical connection for typical room air conditioning unit.

Courtesy of Hotpoint Co.

Compressors

Motor-compressors used on room air conditioners are similar to those used in household refrigeration. In operation, the compressor action necessary for the circulation of the refrigerant is obtained by a piston reciprocating inside a cylinder similar to

411

that of an automobile engine. Half of the shaft rotation is used to draw gas into the cylinder and the other half for compression and discharge. Reciprocating compressors are usually furnished in two styles, a single cylinder (pancake type) with a speed of 3,500 rpm and a twin-cylinder type having a speed of 1,750 rpm. An interior and exterior view of a pancake type compressor is shown in Fig. 21.

Starting Relay

The starting relay coil is in series with the motor run winding. The high current draw on start causes the relay contacts to close, connecting the starting capacitor to the compressor start winding circuit. As the motor speed increases, the current through the run winding drops off and the relay contacts open. This cuts out the starting capacitor and the compressor continues to run with a running capacitor remaining in the start winding circuit.

The most common faults of a starting relay are:

1. Relay contacts fail to open when compressor has started.
2. Relay contacts do not close while the compressor is starting.

If the relay contacts fail to open when the compressor has started, starting capacitor failure would likely result and the compressor would draw high amperage. If the relay contacts were not closed when the compressor was starting, difficulty could be encountered.

Overload Protector

The overload protector protects the motor against excessive overload and is usually located inside the compressor terminal cover. It opens the circuit to the compressor motor on abnormally

412

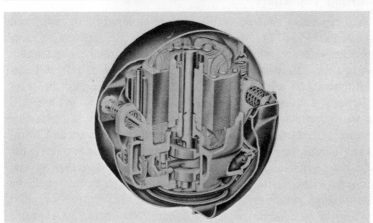

Fig. 21. View of single cylinder pancake type compressor; (A) Exterior view; (B) Cutaway view.

413

high amperage or objectionally high motor temperature. The overload protector on most models consists of a snap-action, bi-metal disc with contacts. The motor current passes through this disc. In the case of overload (failure of the compressor to start or unusual voltage conditions) the current through the disc will be high, thereby increasing its temperature causing it to automatically open and stop the motor. Due to its direct contact with the compressor body, as the motor temperature rises the heat of the compressor body will increase the overload disc temperature, this lessens the required current to open the circuit.

On some models a heater is combined with the bi-metal disc. Excessive current through this heater causes the temperature to rise and heat the disc. When the overload protector trips for any reason, the motor circuit remains open until the compressor cools sufficiently to cause the disc to snap closed, closing the circuit.

Starting Capacitors

All capacitors have two ratings, the microfarad (mfd) rating and a voltage rating. The mfd, rating identifies the capacitor's electrical capacitance, while the voltage rating identifies the maximum voltage. A 220 volt capacitor may be used on a 110 volt circuit, but a 110 volt capacitor cannot be directly connected across 220 volts. Starting capacitors are the electrolytic type and are used in the motor start winding circuit to affect an increase in starting torque. All starting capacitors are intended for short and infrequent compressor starts. Any operating fault that would cause a starting capacitor to remain in the circuit for more than several seconds could be the cause of its failure. Such causes could be low voltage, faulty relay, some fault of the compressor short cycling or a compressor motor failure. The cause of repeated capacitor failure should be investigated as being one of those mentioned above.

If a starting capacitor becomes shorted internally, starting trouble and possible blown fuses would result. If a capacitor should have a broken internal connection to either terminal, or any internal open circuit to its terminals, the compressor may not start. If a replacement is available, the simplest way to check a capacitor is to install a new one. If the trouble is corrected, discard the old capacitor.

Running Capacitors

Running capacitors differ from starting capacitors in that they are a heavy duty, oil-filled type capacitor that can remain in the circuit continuously. Running capacitors are much lower in microfarad (mfd) rating than starting capacitors of comparable size. The running capacitor remains in the motor start winding circuit at all times during compressor operation. This capacitor also increases starting torque and improves the motor's running abilities. The running capacitor also reduces the running amperage by increasing the power factor.

FAN MOTORS

There are usually two types of fan motors. Some air conditioners use a permanent split phase capacitor motor and others use a shaded pole type. The capacitor type is more efficient electrically, and it is used where there are current limitations. It can be readily identified as it requires a fan capacitor. The number of fan motor leads will vary from two to four, depending on the type of motor used and its application. Shaded pole motors will have either two or three leads, depending on whether the speed winding is incorporated in the motor or if a reactor is used to reduce the fan speed. Similarly, the capacitor type motors will either have three leads or four leads for the same reason.

It is very important that the fan motor leads be connected correctly to prevent damage to the motor. Reversal of the run lead and phase lead will result in motor rotation reversal on the capacitor type motors. All fan motors have a thermal overload protector embedded in the windings to protect the motor from damage in case of overheating. Certain types of air conditioners employ a reactor, sometimes called a choke coil, which is used to reduce the speed of the fan motor externally. The reactor, when connected in the fan motor circuit, adds resistance, lowering the voltage to the fan motor, thereby reducing the motor speed.

THERMOSTATS

The thermostat or temperature control stops and starts the compressor in response to room temperature requirements. Each thermostat has a charged power element containing either a volatile liquid or an active vapor charge. The temperature-sensitive part of this element (thermostat feeler bulb) is located in the return air stream. As the return air temperature rises, the pressure of the liquid or vapor inside the bulb increases. This closes the electrical contacts and starts the compressor. As the return air temperature drops, the reduced temperature of the feeler bulb causes the contacts to open and stops the compressor.

UNIT CONTROL SWITCH

The unit control switch may be located on top of the cabinet or one of the sides, depending upon the particular design. The control switch is usually of the knob or rotary control dial type and normally has four positions, marked *off, fan, cool,* and *exhaust.* The damper controls are usually marked *shut, vent,* and *open.* To provide cooling, the switch dial is turned to the cool position, and the damper dial to *shut* or *vent* depending on whether or not outside air is desired.

To operate the unit as a ventilator, the switch dial is turned to *fan* and the damper dial is turned as far open as desired. In the *open* position, the unit passes in 100% of outside air. To exhaust room air, the switch is turned to *exhaust* position, and the damper dial is turned to the *vent* position. When a thermostat is installed for automatic cooling, the compressor and fans will cycle according to dial requirements.

SERVICE OPERATIONS

The servicing of room air conditioners is similar to that of servicing refrigerators. Basically, an air conditioner is a refrigerant system that removes heat from a room. (In a refrigerator, the heat is removed from the food). An evaporator is employed to remove the heat and a condenser is used to liquefy the refrigerant. Air movement over the evaporator and condenser surface is accomplished by a fan. Hot air usually contains a greater percentage of moisture than colder air. When the evaporator fan moves hot humid air over the cold surface of the evaporator, a quantity of the moisture in the air will condense (form water) in addition to the air itself being cooled. In this manner, the relative humidity of the recirculated air is also reduced. The condensate water is drained into the condenser section where it is dissipated.

Servicemen having a good knowledge of refrigeration and combining it with the understanding that an air conditioner removes heat and humidity from a room by the process of refrigeration, will always be able to competently service air conditioners. Since most portable air-conditioning units of present design contain compressors of the hermetic or sealed type, the only parts that can be serviced in the field are the relay, control switch, fan, fan motor, starting and running capacitors, air filters, and cabinet parts. The refrigerating system, consisting of the cooling unit, condensers, compressors, and connecting lines, as a rule, cannot be serviced in the field.

DISMANTLING WINDOW AIR CONDITIONERS

The following discussion lists the procedure and the steps that are necessary to dismantle window air conditioners. The procedure can be used in its entirety or in part according to the service required. The procedure covers only those parts of the unit that can be serviced in the field and is not a complete disassembly. By presenting a dismantling procedure, it is possible to eliminate repetition of certain steps common to many service operations. Keep in mind that individual manufacturers may recommend a slightly different procedure. In all instances, follow the instructions of the manufacturer when dismantling an air conditioner. When reassembling the unit, the steps should be reversed. To dismantle the air conditioner proceed as follows:

1. Disconnect the air conditioner from the source of electrical supply, and remove the cabinet.
2. Remove the electrical control boxes. Remove the screws that secure each box to the partition. Remove the control-box covers, and disconnect the motor leads; remove the control box assemblies from the unit.
3. Remove the fan motor and fans. Loosen both fans and remove them from the shaft. Remove the access panel which fits down over the cooling unit fan shaft. Loosen and remove the motor cradle supports at each end of the motor and lift the motor up and out.

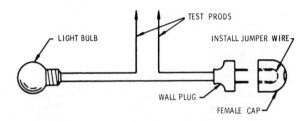

Fig. 22. Showing wiring of test lamp circuit.

ELECTRICAL TEST

In the event of operating trouble, a thorough check of the electrical system is often necessary. By checking the electrical system a great deal of time can be saved, since such a check usually reveals the more obvious troubles. To make a complete electrical test of the unit and its controls, a test-lamp circuit, such as shown in Fig. 22, can be used for both the voltage and continuity checks. When checking the electrical system, refer to the wiring diagrams, Figs. 23 and 24. It should be noted, however, that the wiring diagrams shown are only typical, and the arrangement and wiring of components may vary, depending on the manufacturer of the particular unit.

Testing for Current Supply

With cord plugged into the electrical outlet, place one prod of the test cord (Fig. 22) on terminal *N* and the other on terminal *L*. If the test bulb lights, current is being supplied to the relay.

Testing Fan Motors

Depending on the size of the unit, it may be equipped with one or two fan motors. In some smaller units, only one fan motor is used, in which case the shaft of the motor extends to operate

419

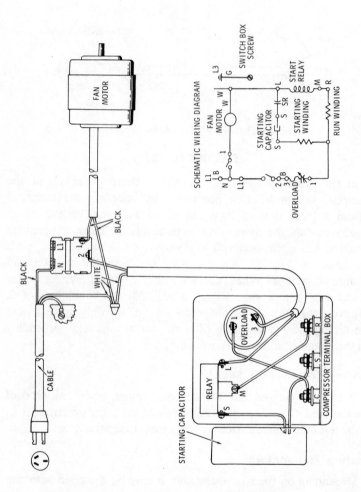

Fig. 23. Wiring diagram of a typical air conditioning unit having one fan motor and a sealed type compresor unit.

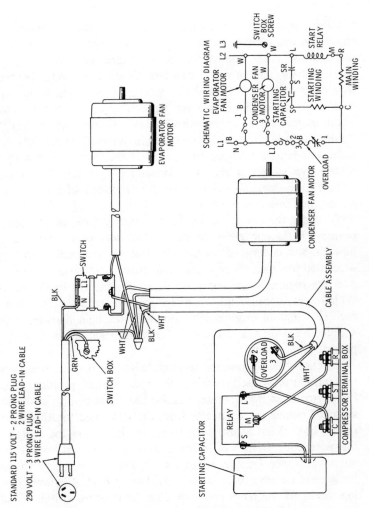

Fig. 24. **Wiring diagram of a typical air conditioning unit having two fan motors and a sealed type compressor unit.**

421

two fans, one for the evaporator and one for the condenser. To check the evaporator fan motor, turn the switch to the *running* junction-box cover and switch. Remove the connector from the wires tied together in the switch box. Place a test lamp between terminal *I* of the switch and the wire ends from which the connector was removed. If the lamp lights, the fault is in the motor. These motors are equipped with an internal overload protection. Permit the motor to cool for several minutes (with switch off) then recheck it before changing the motor. If the lamp does not light, a defective switch is indicated (assuming that there is voltage present at the switch), which should be replaced with a new unit having the same part number.

To check the condenser fan motor, turn the switch to *running position*. If the condenser fan motor does not operate, remove the junction-box cover and switch. Remove the connector from the wires tied together. Place a test lamp from these wires to terminal 3 of the switch. If the test lamp lights, the fault is in the motor. Wait several minutes for the motor to cool (with switch off) and recheck it before changing the motor. If the light does not light, a defective switch is indicated, (assuming that there is voltage present at the switch).

To check the evaporator and condenser fan motor, when only one fan motor is used, turn switch to the desired position. If the fan motor does not operate, remove the junction-box cover and switch. Remove the connector from the wires tied together in the switch box. Place a test lamp from terminal 1 on the switch to the wire ends from which the connector was removed. If the lamp lights, the fault is in the motor. Permit the motor to cool for several minutes (with switch off) then recheck it before changing motor. If the lamp does not light, a defective switch is indicated (assuming there is voltage at the switch) which should be replaced with a new unit.

Capacitor (Starting)

On most units an electrolytic starting capacitor is used in the starting winding circuit to increase the starting torque. If this capacitor developes a short internally, starting trouble and possible blown fuses will result. If the capacitor develops an open circuit, the compressor will not start. If a replacement is available, the simplest way to check the capacitor is to install a new one. If a replacement is not readily available, a check can be performed in the following manner.

To check a capacitor, disconnect the capacitor leads. Make certain that the capacitor has not retained a charge by placing the blade of an insulated screwdriver across the terminals. Touch the capacitor leads or terminals momentarily with the test probes of an ohmmeter, and observe the meter deflection. A satisfactory capacitor will show at least 100,000-ohms (100 K) resistance. It may take several seconds to arrive at this reading. A shorted capacitor causes the ohmmeter pointer to indicate a continuous low resistance. The pointer moves to the zero end of the scale and remains there as long as the probes are in contact with the terminals. An open capacitor causes no deflection of the pointer, which means there is no path or continuity thru the capacitor, which should be replaced. It is essential that the capacitor be replaced with an exact duplicate.

Compressor-motor Relay

The relay opens the circuit to the compressor-motor starting winding after the compressor has started. The duration of this start, or of the time that the starting winding is energized, is, under normal conditions, very short; it is usually 2 or 3 seconds. A defective relay may fail to close, which results in starting trouble; it may fail to open, which results in overload trip-outs, capacitor failure, or blown fuses.

Relay Check

Check the capacitor before making any relay operation checks, since a shorted capacitor will upset the accuracy of these checks. Remove the compressor junction-box cover. With the switch in the *off* position, attach a test lamp between terminal *S* of the relay and motor terminal *S* (see Fig. 24). With the switch in *cool*, position, the lamp should light for an instant only if the compressor starts. If the compressor does not start, the lamp should remain lit until the switch is turned *off* or until the overload trips out. Do not leave the switch in *on* position for more than several seconds, if the compressor does not start. If the lamp does not light, check for an opened overload. If the overload is not opened, change relay. To replace the relay, remove the screws securing it to the compressor shell bracket.

Compressor-motor Overload

The overload is a protective device used in conjunction with the relay, to open the compressor-motor circuit at abnormally high currents or dangerously high motor temperatures. The overload consists of a heater and a snap-action, bi-metal disc on which contacts are mounted. A heater is connected in series with the common terminal of the motor windings. In the case of overloads, the current through the heater is high, thereby increasing its temperature. This heats the bi-metal disc, thus causing it to automatically snap open and open the motor-winding circuit. Due to the direct contact of the overload to the compressor body, as the motor temperature rises the heat of the compressor body increases the overload-disc temperature, thereby reducing the current required to open the circuit.

If the overload trips for any reason, the circuit will remain open until the compressor body (or shell) cools sufficiently to cause the disc to snap closed. It will then close the circuit to the

424

motor. This protector is nonadjustable and must be replaced if it fails to function properly. To check overload, remove the compressor junction-box cover. Place the test lamp from terminal *L* of the relay to terminal 3 of the overload. (see Fig. 24). Turn the switch to the desired position. The lamp should light if voltage is available to the overload. Now, move the test lamp from terminal 3 of the overload to terminal 1. If the lamp lights from terminal *L* to 3 but does not light from terminal *L* to 1, this indicates that the overload is open. If it does not cut back in 10 to 15 minutes (time for motor to cool), the overload should be changed. If the overload does cut in, check for the cause of overloading or overheating. Low voltage, shorted capacitor, failure of the compressor to start, and excessive operating pressures or temperatures are some causes of overload trip-outs.

COMPRESSOR AND MOTOR

The compressor motor is a split-phase type motor that uses a capacitor when starting to increase the starting torque. Through the use of a capillary-tube method of refrigeration, the starting load is normally very low. After a certain specified speed has been attained the starting winding and capacitor are cut out of the circuit by the relay, and the full load is then carried by the running winding. To check the compressor motor, a continuity check for an open circuit within the motor can be performed by disconnecting the wires from the three motor leads *C, S,* and *R,* (Fig. 24). Plug the test cord, as shown in Fig. 22, in the electrical outlet. Place the test prods on terminals *C* and *S*. A glow of the lamp indicates a satisfactory continuity of the starting winding. Next, place the prods on terminals *R* and *C* and perform a similar test on the running winding. If the lamp glows, this indicates that there is continuity in the running windings.

No glow from the lamp on either check indicates an open circuit and necessitates changing the unit. A check for a burned out or grounded motor can be performed by checking the resistance of the motor windings to the compressor shell. Such a check can best be made with an ohmmeter capable of indicating sufficiently high resistance. A rough check can be performed with the test cord. With all wires removed from the motor terminals, place one prod on terminal *C*, and make a good electrical contact by touching the other prod to the compressor shell. Any glow in the test lamp indicates a grounded motor, which must be replaced.

It must be remembered that faults other than motor trouble may be the cause of compressor failure or of a motor drawing high current. A stuck compressor, high head pressure, low voltage, and a plugged capillary tube are some of the causes of compressor failure.

OILING OF MOTORS

The fan motors should be oiled at the start of each cooling season, or every six months if the unit is operated all year. Use a good grade of electric motor oil or SAE No. 20 automobile oil. A few drops in each oil hole is sufficient.

LEAKS IN SYSTEM

In the event that any part of the condensing unit should develop a leak, it will be necessary to repair the leak before the unit can be put into operation. A leak is usually discovered by the presence of oil around the point at which the leak developed. It must not be assumed, however, that the presence of oil on any part of the unit is a positive indication of a leak. Always check the suspected area with an approved leak detector.

FILTERS

The filters should be inspected at regular intervals. Refer to individual manufacturer's instructions for filter removal and cleaning. Periodic cleaning of filters assures maximum air delivery by the air conditioner at all times. Best results can be obtained if filters are replaced every year and cleaned often between replacements.

INTERIOR CLEANING

The interior of the unit should be cleaned periodically of all dust, grease, and foreign matter. Special attention should be given to the condenser and evaporator coils. Regular cleaning will assure continuous good service of the unit.

WINTER CARE

In many parts of the country, service of the cooling unit will not be required during the winter months. Such a unit can be conveniently removed from the window and stored in a convenient place. This prevents condensation of moisture in the unit and also makes available a greater window area. Before the unit is stored however, it should be checked for dirt in the evaporator and condenser and cleaned when necessary. Cleaning the evaporator once a year is recommended to avoid the development of objectionable odors.

The coils can be cleaned by the use of a stiff bristle brush and a strong solution of soap and water. All parts should be rinsed off after cleaning. It is also advisable to wash out the drain pan and retouch with an asphalt paint. When storing the unit, it should be put on blocks to take the weight off the sponge-rubber mounting. At the beginning of the cooling season when the unit is reinstalled, the fan motors should be oiled. After the unit has been reinstalled and started, it should be checked after a few minutes of operation to ascertain that the temperature drop across the evaporator is 10°F. or more.

REFRIGERANT SYSTEM SERVICE

When a unit operates but does not have its normal cooling capacity, the refrigerant system should be checked. Check for some obvious symptom such as partial icing of the evaporator, abnormally warm suction line or some such unusual condition. These could indicate a loss of refrigerant or a restricted capillary tube. The refrigerant system of most room air conditioning units is a sealed type circuit. Should trouble develop that requires opening the refrigerant circuit, the usual caution and requirements for repair of a capillary tube type system are necessary. This requires equipment and evacuating leak testing, and a means of accurate refrigerant charging.

Evaporator Temperature

Under average operating conditions of outdoor and indoor temperatures, all evaporator return bends should be cold and at the same approximate temperature. On most models, this check can be easily made by removing the front grille. If the first evaporator passes are iced over or if there is a noticeable temperature increase of the return bends of the last several passes, this could be an indication of either restriction or loss of refrigerant. It must, however, be remembered that with higher outdoor temperatures, the very last evaporator pass will not have as much refrigerant to affect cooling as it would at lower temperatures. It will therefore be at a slightly higher temperature if the outside temperature is high.

Frequently, servicemen check dry bulb temperature drop across the evaporator to determine if the unit is cooling satisfactorily. The temperature drop across the evaporator is not the same on all units. Also, higher outdoor dry bulb temperatures and high inside relative humidity tend to reduce the dry bulb temperature drop across the evaporator. On most units with an outdoor temperature between 80 and 90°, and with an indoor relative humidity between 40 and 50 percent, the temperature drop across the evaporator should be between 17 and 20 degrees. Where proper evaporator air flow is maintained, a 20° dry bulb temperature drop would normally indicate satisfactory cooling. When the room air relative humidity is considerably higher than 50% a smaller dry bulb temperature drop across the evaporator will be obtained. When the relative humidity is considerably below 40%, a higher temperature will result. It is therefore important that room air relative humidity be checked and considered when checking air temperature drop across the evaporator as a check for proper cooling.

Compressor Amperage

With normal evaporator loading and average outdoor temperatures, if proper cooling is being accomplished, the compressor motor will draw the approximate amperage shown on the unit nameplate. A unit drawing considerably below compressor nameplate amperage could be an indication of the refrigerant system not producing proper cooling. This is assuming that there is a normal flow of air over the evaporator and that the evaporator loading is not abnormally low.

Refrigerant Leaks

Whenever a shortage of refrigerant is suspected, this condition can be confirmed by identifying the source of leakage. A leak test operation can be performed with a Halide leak detector. The end of the exploring hose is passed around areas where a refrigerant leak is suspected. The air drawn into the hose passes through a copper reactor plate and through a small flame. If any refrigerant is contained in this air, the color of the flame turns slightly green. If a considerable quantity of refrigerant is leaking, the flame turns purple. When the location of leak has been determined, it is sometimes difficult to pinpoint the exact leak location; soapsuds can be used to pinpoint the exact source of leak.

Automatic Expansion Valves

Automatic expansion valves are used on some room air conditioners instead of the capillary tubes to control the flow of refrigerant into the evaporator. These valves are set to maintain a normal suction pressure. They are factory adjusted and sealed and no field adjustment is required. A small bleed port in the valve permits pressure equalization from high to low side on shut down. This is necessary for the starting of the unit's compressor. A small liquid line strainer is located in the liquid line ahead of the expansion valve.

TROUBLE CHARTS

The trouble charts shown on the following pages list the most common operating faults with possible causes and remedies suggested. This chart is intended to provide a quick reference to the cause and correction of a specific fault.

ROOM AIR CONDITIONER TROUBLE CHART

Unit Will Not Run

Possible Cause	*Possible Remedy*
Blown fuse	Check for an electrical short at wall receptacle.
Broken or loose wiring	Replace fuse.
Low voltage	Check voltage. Voltage should be within 10% of that shown on the unit nameplate.
Defective unit starting switch	Check voltage at switch. If there is proper voltage at switch, but no continuity through it, replace switch.

Fan Runs, But Compressor Will Not Operate

Possible Cause	*Possible Remedy*
Inoperative thermostat	If turning thermostat to its coldest setting does not start compressor (and room temperature is above 75°), but shorting across its terminals does, change thermostat.
Loose or broken wiring	Check unit wiring and wiring connections at the unit starting switch and at the compressor.
Starting capacitor faulty (if used)	Check starting capacitor (if used).
Running capacitor faulty	Check running capacitor.
Relay faulty (if used)	Check relay (if used).
Off on overload or overload fault	Check for overheated compressor or for defective overload.
Low voltage	Check voltage.

Unit Blows Fuses

Possible Cause	*Possible Remedy*
Shorted or incorrect unit wiring	Check unit wiring.
Shorted starting or running capacitor	Check capacitors
Shorted or stuck compressor	Check compressor.
Compressor starting difficulty	Check for low voltage. Check starting capacitor and relay.
Incorrect fuse	Check fuse size.

Compressor Cycles Off and On

Possible Cause	*Possible Remedy*
Low voltage	Check voltage and amperage with unit operating. If low, check other appliance loads.
Restricted air across the condenser	Check condenser fan and check for any restriction of condenser air.
Recycling of condenser discharge air back into unit	Check for inadequate clearance for proper discharging of condenser air. Check for any cause of hot discharge air reentering the unit.
Dirty or plugged condenser	Check and clean all dirt or line from condenser coil fins. Clean air filter.
Thermostat feeler bulb out of position	Check bulb for proper location in return air. Bulb should not touch the evaporator coil.
Faulty or incorrect overload	Check if overload has tripped. Refer to Capacitor, Overload and Relay Chart for correct overload. Check compressor temperatures. If compressor is not overheated and if amperage is not high, and overload trips out, change overload.

Unit Vibrates or Rattles

Possible Cause	*Possible Remedy*
Compressor shipping block not removed or shipping bolts not removed or properly loosened	Remove shipping bolt and shipping block on externally spring mounted compressors only.
Discharge or suction tube striking metal surface	Bend tube slightly for clearance where striking.
Loose compressor junction box cover or capacitor	Tighten.
Loose or bent fan blades	Replace fan.
Fan motor out of alignment or loose on mounting	Check alignment and tighten mounting.

Water Drips From Unit

Possible Cause	*Possible Remedy*
Unit not properly leveled	Level unit. Most models can be tipped slightly toward outside.
Condensate drain to condenser pan plugged	Clean condensate drain.

| Condenser fan slinger ring out of position | Check motor mounting and alignment for proper positioning of condenser fan slinger ring in water sump. |
| Evaporator drip pan, shroud or other source of water leaking requires sealing | Use Permagum or other sealing compound to seal leak. |

Noisy Fan Operation

Possible Cause	*Possible Remedy*
Fan striking	Check for proper positioning and clearance of fans.
Loose fan or fan motor	Check for fan tightness on shaft. Check for loose fan blade, fan loose at rubber hub and for loose fan motor mounting.
Bent fan blades	Check for bent fan blades.

Unit Not Cooling Properly

Possible Cause	*Possible Remedy*
Clogged air filter	Check air filter for dirt, cleaning or replacement.
Outside air entering the unit	Check for proper closing of outside air doors.
Air across condenser restricted	Check condenser air.
Dirty or blocked condenser	Check condenser for blocked dirt or lint.
Hot condenser discharge air re-entering unit	Check for restriction or obstruction to condenser discharge air that could cause it to re-enter unit.
Compressor or refrigerant system faulty	If compressor runs but the evaporator does not get cool, this would indicate either an inefficient compressor, restricted capillary tube or lost refrigerent charge.

Evaporator Ices Over

Possible Cause	*Possible Remedy*
Clogged or dirty air filter	Clean or replace air filter.
Evaporator fan motor tripping on overload	Check for overheated evaporator fan motor and tripping off on its internal overload.
Unit operating at too low room temperature	If room temperature drops below 70° the evaporator may ice over.
Too low outside temperature	Check for unit being operated when it is unusually cool outside.

Automobile Air Conditioning

The automobile air conditioner is basically no different from any other type of air-conditioning system. The major components, such as the compressor, condenser, and evaporator, are utilized in primarily the same manner as the common room air conditioner. Certain variations and differences are unique to automobile air conditioning systems, such as the power source, method and type of controls, and component design. A typical automobile air conditioner installation is shown in Fig. 1. Power is supplied to the compressor directly from the crankshaft of the engine by means of a V-belt assembly and a series of pulleys, as shown in Fig. 2. The idler pulley is a device that maintains the compressor at a constant speed independent of engine crankshaft speed. The compressor is able to operate at its specified rate even though the engine goes from idle, at several hundred rpm, to high speeds of several thousand rpm.

Two *temperature control* methods are most frequently used by automotive air-conditioning manufacturers. These are the magnetic (or electric) clutch, and the refrigerant-flow control. Normally, the *magnetic clutch* utilizes a stationary electromagnet which is attached to the compressor. The brushes and collector rings can be eliminated with this arrangement, since the electro-

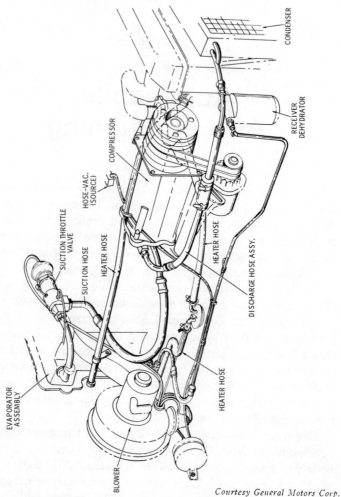

CONDENSER

RECEIVER
DEHYDRATOR

COMPRESSOR

HOSE-VAC.
(SOURCE)

SUCTION THROTTLE
VALVE

SUCTION HOSE

HEATER HOSE

HEATER HOSE

DISCHARGE HOSE ASSY.

EVAPORATOR
ASSEMBLY

HEATER HOSE

BLOWER

Courtesy General Motors Corp.

Fig. 1. Typical automobile air conditioning system showing location of main components.

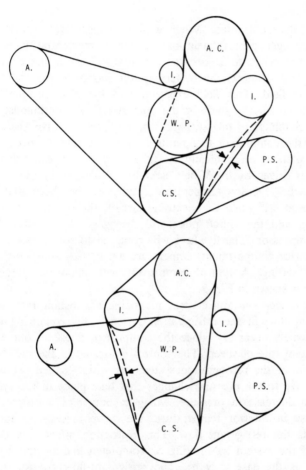

CS - CRANKSHAFT; A - ALTERNATOR; WP - WATER PUMP; PS - POWER STEERING;
AC - AIR COMPRESSOR; I - IDLER PULLEYS

Courtesy General Motors Corp.

Fig. 2. Typical belt arrangement in a modern automobile engine.

magnet does not rotate. When a high temperature is present in the passenger compartment of the car, a thermostat (which is set by the driver to a specified temperature) closes the electrical circuit that connects the battery power supply to the stationary magnetic field. This field exists around the electromagnet that is mounted on the shaft of the compressor. A continuously rotating clutch plate then engages the compressor drive shaft and causes the compressor to operate at a higher rate of speed. This clutch plate is mechanically attached to the compressor flywheel which is driven by the V-belt assembly. When the interior of the car reaches the low-temperature setting of the thermostat, the thermostat will open the electrical circuit; the current will cease flowing, and the clutch plate will disengage the flywheel from the compressor. The flywheel will continue to rotate freely until the interior compartment temperature again rises above the thermostat setting. A typical compressor with magnetic clutch assembly is shown in Fig. 3.

The *refrigerant-flow* control maintains a constant rate of refrigerant flow in the refrigeration system. This equalizing effect is extremely necessary, since the compressor does not operate at a constant rate of speed. The control is located in the suction, or low side of the refrigeration system; its spring-loaded bellows is responsive to the pressure changes that take place in the system. With a decrease in pressure, which accompanies a proportional decrease in interior temperature, the valve closes and thereby restricts the refrigerant flow. This restriction affects the operation of the system by limiting or completely halting the cooling effect, as the case may be. The refrigerant-flow control is also responsive to the flow rate of the refrigerant. The valve is closed by an increase in flow rate; this increase causes the refrigerant pressure surrounding the valve stem to decrease and thereby affect the control valve, independent of the low-side pressure.

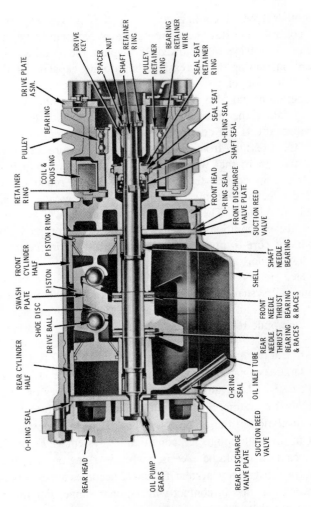

Fig. 3. Sectional view of an air compressor with double action piston design, and with magnetic clutch coil.

439

Another type of cooling control is the *hot-gas bypass valve*. This control regulates the temperature by constantly varying the amount of refrigerant allowed to bypass the cooling network, thereby increasing or decreasing the cooling capacity of the system. Utilization of this control valve permits constant compressor operation and also provides an evaporator antifreeze device. By regulating the internal pressure of the evaporator, the hot-gas valve affects the cooling capacity of the evaporator and prevents the pressure from decreasing to a pressure (29.5 pounds per square inch) that will cause the evaporator core to freeze. If this freeze-up occurs, the evaporator will not function, and the cooling effect of the air conditioner will be greatly lowered or halted completely. The reason the evaporator will not function under these conditions is because the air cannot pass thru the evaporator core to provide the necessary cooling in the interior of the automobile.

Sealed systems are highly improbable for use on an automobile, because all systems are, at present, powered by the engine crankshaft, which is an external source. The typical compressor used in the automobile refrigeration system has a large refrigerating capacity as compared to the average room air conditioner (15,000 to 20,000 Btu per hour as opposed to 6,000 to 10,000 Btu per hour). This large cooling capacity is due primarily to the large bore and stroke design of the automotive refrigerating compressor, and it is a necessity for automobiles because of the temperature range and poor insulation of the car interior. The refrigerant most commonly used in the automobile air conditioning system is *Freon-12*. Extreme caution should be exercised when working on or in the vicinity of the refrigeration system. *Freon-12* becomes a highly poisonous gas when it comes in contact with an open flame. For this reason, the system should be completely discharged when any repairs or replacements are made on the refrigeration unit.

AIR CONDITIONING SYSTEM OPERATION

Cool refrigerant gas is drawn into the compressor from the evaporator and pumped from the compressor to the condenser under high pressure (Fig. 4). This high-pressure gas will also have a high temperature as a result of being subjected to compression. As this gas passes through the condenser, the high-pressure, high-temperature gas rejects its heat to the outside air as the air passes over the surfaces of the condenser. The cooling of the gas causes it to condense into a liquid refrigerant. The liquid refrigerant, still under high pressure, passes from the bottom of the condenser into the receiver dehydrator. The receiver acts as a reservoir for the liquid. The liquid refrigerant flows from the receiver dehydrator to the thermostatic expansion valve. The thermostatic expansion valve meters the high-pressure refrigerant flow into the evaporator. Since the pressure in the evaporator is relatively low, the refrigerant immediately begins to boil. As the refrigerant passes through the evaporator, it continues to boil, drawing heat from the surface of the evaporator core warmed by air passing over the surfaces of the evaporator core.

In addition to the warm air passing over the evaporator rejecting its heat to the cooler surfaces of the evaporator core, any moisture in the air condenses on the cool surface of the core, resulting in cool dehydrated air passing into the inside of the car. By the time the gas leaves the evaporator, it has completely vaporized and is slightly superheated. Superheat is an increase in temperature of the gaseous refrigerant above the temperature at which the refrigerant vaporized. The pressure in the evaporator is controlled by the suction throttle valve. Refrigerant vapor passing through the evaporator flows through the suction throttle valve and is returned to the compressor where the refrigeration cycle is repeated.

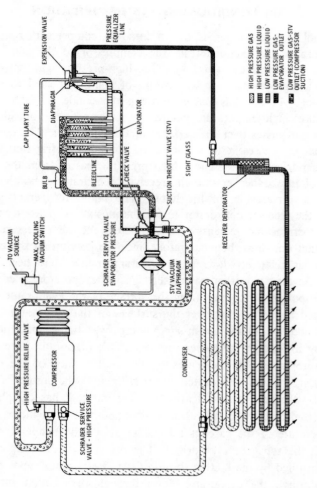

Fig. 4. Refrigerant circuit arrangement in a typical automobile air conditioning system.

COMPONENT DESCRIPTION

The problems encountered in automobile air conditioning will perhaps be understood by a thorough study of the basic components comprising the system. Fig. 4 illustrates typical components of an automobile air conditioning unit.

Compressors

In the early days of automobile air conditioning, modified commercial-type compressors were used. Because of the increase in engine speed, the design and development of precision high-speed compressors became necessary. All air conditioning system compressors are presently driven by belt take-off from the engine crankshaft. The compressor speed varies with the speed of the automobile engine, which is considerable. For example, at idling speeds, the compressor turns at a rate of about 400 rpm and develops a refrigerating effect in the area of three-quarters of a ton. In an automobile traveling 70 miles per hour, this same compressor may be turning as high as 5,000 rpm and developing capacities in the neighborhood of three and one-half to four tons. This varying capacity has dictated the design of the present automotive control systems.

To obtain a more favorable speed characteristic, a different solution to the problem could be utilized, such as a drive shaft take-off, or an electric motor drive through an alternator. Although some of these methods of operating the compressor might prove more desirable in forms of operating efficiency, the additional cost of application in addition to space requirement is, without doubt, an important consideration. The compressor has two functions:

1. To pump refrigerant through the system.
2. To raise the pressure of the refrigerant gas received from

the cooling coil so that it will condense more readily and give up heat as it passes through the condensing coil.

A typical automotive air conditioning compressor (six-cylinder rotary double-action piston type) is shown in Fig. 3. The reed-type suction and discharge valves are mounted in a valve plate between the cylinder assembly and the head at the end of the compressor. The ends are connected with each other by gas-tight passage ways which direct refrigerant gas to a common output. Each cylinder head contains suction and discharge cavities. In addition, the reed head contains an oil-pump cavity in the center of the suction cavity to house the oil-pump gears, which are driven by the compressor mainshaft. The suction cavity is in the center and indexes with the suction reeds. The discharge cavity is around the outside and indexes with the discharge reeds.

These cavities are separated from each other with a *teflon* seal molded to the cylinder head. The discharge cavity is sealed from the outside of the compressor by an O-ring seal which rests in a chamfered relief in the cylinder head and compresses against the compressor body. An oil pump mounted at the rear of the compressor picks up oil from the bottom of the compressor and pumps it to the internal parts. The inner gear fits over a matching "D" flat on the main shaft. The outer driven gear has internal teeth which mesh with the external teeth on the inner drive gear.

Condensers

Air conditioning condensers are similar to the ordinary automobile radiator but are designed to withstand much higher pressure. It is normally mounted in front of the car radiator so that it receives a high volume of air. Air passing over the condenser cools the hot high-pressure refrigerant gas causing it to condense into high-pressure liquid refrigerant.

Receiver-Driers

The purpose of the receiver-dehydrator assembly is to insure a solid column of liquid refrigerant to the thermostatic expansion valve at all times (provided the system is properly charged). The dehydrator (drier) part of the assembly is to absorb any moisture that might be present in the system after assembly. Also, it traps foreign material which may have entered the system during assembly. A liquid indicator or sight glass is a part of most systems, and is an integral part of the outlet pipe of the receiver dehydrator. The appearance of bubbles or foam in the sight glass when the ambient temperature is higher than 70° F.. indicates air or a shortage of refrigerant in the system.

Thermostatic Expansion Valves

The function of the thermostatic expansion valve is to automatically regulate the flow of liquid refrigerant into the evaporator in accordance with the requirements of the evaporator. The valve is located at the inlet to the evaporator core. It consists essentially of a capillary bulb and tube which are connected to an operating diaphragm (sealed within the valve itself) and an equalizer line which connects the valve and the low-pressure suction throttling valve outlet pressure. The thermo bulb is attached to the evaporator outlet pipe. The thermostatic expansion valve is the dividing line in the system between high-pressure liquid refrigerant supplied from the receiver and relatively low-pressure liquid and gaseous refrigerant in the evaporator. It is designed so that the temperature of the refrigerant at the evaporator outlet must have 4° F. of superheat before more refrigerant is allowed to enter the evaporator. Superheat is an increase in temperature of the gaseous refrigerant above the temperature at which the refrigerant vaporized.

A capillary tube filled with carbon dioxide, and the equalizer line provide the temperature regulation of the expansion valve. The capillary tube is fastened to the low-pressure refrigerant pipe coming out of the evaporator so that it samples the temperature of the refrigerant at this point to the expansion valve. If the temperature differential between the inlet and outlet decreases below 4° F., the expansion valve will automatically reduce the amount of refrigerant entering the evaporator. If the temperature differential increases, the expansion valve will automatically allow more refrigerant to enter the evaporator. A typical thermostatic expansion valve is shown in Fig. 5.

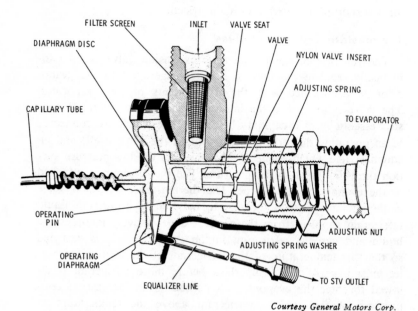

Courtesy General Motors Corp.

Fig. 5. Typical internally adjusted automobile air conditioning thermostatic expansion valve.

The temperature of the air passing over the evaporator core determines the amount of refrigerant that will enter and pass through the evaporator. When the air is very warm, the heat transfer from the air to the refrigerant is great and a greater quantity of refrigerant is required to cool the air and to achieve the proper superheat on the refrigerant gas leaving the evaporator. When the air passing over the evaporator is cool, the heat transfer is small and a smaller amount of refrigerant is required to cool the air and to achieve the proper superheat on the refrigerant gas leaving the evaporator.

A mechanical adjusting nut located within the valve is provided to regulate the amount of refrigerant flow through the valve. When adjusted, the spring seat moves to increase or decrease the tension on the needle-valve carriage spring. By varying the tension on this spring, it is possible to regulate the point at which the needle valve begins to open or close, thereby regulating refrigerant flow into the evaporator. Since this adjustment feature is inside the valve, *no external adjustment is possible.* All valves are preset at the time of manufacture.

When the air conditioning system has not been operating, all pressures within the thermostatic expansion-valve assembly will have equalized at the ambient (surrounding air) temperature, thus the pressure above and below the operating diaphragm and at the inlet and outlet side of the valve will be equal. Pressure under the diaphragm is evaporator pressure. It reaches this area by means of clearance around the operating pins which connect the area under the diaphragm with the evaporator pressure area. While pressures in the expansion valve are almost equal, the addition of the valve adjusting spring pressure behind the needle will hold the needle valve over to close the needle-valve orifice.

When the air conditioning system first begins to operate, the compressor will immediately begin to draw refrigerant from the

447

evaporator, lowering the pressure in the evaporator and in the area under the operating diaphragm. As the pressure in this area decreases, the pressure above the diaphragm exerted by the carbon dioxide in the capillary tube will overcome spring pressure and push the diaphragm against the operating pins, which in turn will force the needle off its seat. Refrigerant will then pass through the expansion valve into the evaporator where it will boil at a temperature corresponding to the pressure in the evaporator. This will begin cooling the air passing over the evaporator, and it will also begin to cool the evaporator outlet pipe. The valve adjusting spring is calibrated so that the pressure of the refrigerant in the evaporator outlet pipe and equalizer line to the valve, plus the spring force, will equal the force above the operating diaphragm when the temperature of the refrigerant in the evaporator outlet is 4° F. above the temperature of the refrigerant entering the evaporator. In other words, the refrigerant should remain in the evaporator long enough to completely vaporize, and then warm (superheat) to 4° F.

If the temperature differential begins to go below 4° F. (outlet pipe becoming too cold), carbon-dioxide pressure in the capillary tube and the area above the diaphragm will decrease, allowing the valve adjusting spring to move the needle valve toward its seat, closing off the flow of refrigerants past the needle valve. If the temperature differential begins to go above 4° F. (outlet pipe too warm), the pressure in the capillary tube and the area above the operating diaphragm will increase, pushing this diaphragm against the operating pins to open the needle valve further, admitting more refrigerant to the evaporator.

The equalizer line permits the suction throttle-valve outlet pressure to be imposed on the expansion-valve diaphragm, thus overriding its normal control of liquid refrigerant. As the compressor capacity becomes greater than the evaporator load, the drop in compressor suction-line pressure forces the expansion valve to flood liquid through the evaporator and the suction throttle valve, thus preventing the suction pressure from dropping below a predetermined pressure. The equalizer line is used primarily to prevent prolonged and constant operation of the compressor in vacuum conditions. This operation is considered undesirable, both from a noise angle and from the possibility of subjecting the compressor to reduced oil return. Second considerations for having the external equalized expansion valve is to maintain a full evaporator during throttling, and also guard against noncondensibles entering the system, especially through loosened fittings.

Evaporators

The purpose of the evaporator core is to cool and dehumidify the air that is flowing through it when the air conditioner is in operation. High-pressure liquid refrigerant flows through the orifice in the thermostatic expansion valve into the low-pressure area of the evaporator. This regulated flow of refrigerant boils immediately. Heat from the core surface is lost to the boiling and vaporizing refrigerant which is cooler than the core, thereby cooling the core. The air passing over the evaporator loses its heat to the cooler surface of the core. As the process of heat loss from the air to the evaporator core surface is taking place, moisture in the air condenses on the outside surface of the evaporator core and is drained off.

Since *Freon-12* will boil at 21.7° F. below zero at atmospheric pressure, and since water freezes at 32° F., it becomes obvious that the temperature in the evaporator must be controlled so that the water collecting on the core surface will not freeze in the fins of the core and block off the air passages. In order to control the temperature, it is necessary to control the amount of refrigerant entering the core, and to control the pressure inside the evaporator. To obtain maximum cooling, the refrigerant must remain in the core long enough to completely vaporize, and then to superheat to a minimum of 4° F. If too much or too little refrigerant is present in the core, then maximum cooling efficiency is lost. A thermostatic expansion valve in conjunction with the suction throttling valve is used to provide this necessary refrigerant volume control.

Solenoid Control

In early automobile air conditioning systems, a solenoid bypass arrangement (Fig. 6) was used for maintaining comfortable in-

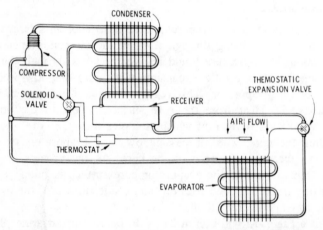

Fig. 6. Refrigerant circuit illustrating a solenoid hot gas bypass control system as used on early automobile air conditioning system.

terior temperatures. As noted in Fig. 6, this system consisted in connecting a solenoid valve into the system between the condenser and the suction line. When the valve is open, hot gas leaves the condenser and travels through the valve into the suction line, thus nullifying the compression effect of the compressor. The solenoid units were controlled initially by a manually operated toggle switch, but subsequently a thermostat was placed in the return air stream to provide automatic on-and-off control.

A later development brought about the installation of a bypass valve in the system. This application is the same as the solenoid valve with one exception, it is an automatic-type valve which provides a modulating control. As the suction pressure is lowered due to increased compressor speed, the bypass valve opens at its setting and bypasses a certain portion of the hot gas back into the suction line. The higher the speed of the compressor, the wider the valve opens in an attempt to maintain constant suction pressures. This bypass system is still used in many cars today. In a present refinement of this system, an operating cam has been installed on the valve and is connected with a wire so that the operator may adjust this valve to control the automobile interior temperature. The bypass system is based on constant compressor operation as long as the automobile engine is running. This situation has proven objectionable to car owners.

Magnetic Clutch Control

The pulley assembly contains an electrically controlled magnetic clutch, permitting the compressor to operate only when air conditioning is actually desired. When the compressor clutch is not engaged, the compressor shaft does not rotate, although the pulley is being rotated by the belt from the engine. The clutch armature plate, which is a movable member of the drive-plate assembly, is attached to the drive hub through driver springs and is riveted to both driver and armature plate. The hub of this assembly is pressed over the compressor shaft and is aligned with a square drive key located in the keyway on the compressor shaft. The pulley assembly consists of three units:

1. Pulley rim.
2. Power element ring.
3. Pulley hub.

A frictional material is molded between the hub and rim of the pulley which make up the magnetic-clutch assembly. A power-element rim is embedded in the forward face of the molded material which houses the electrical coils and components that make up the electromagnet circuit. When the air-conditioner controls are set for cooling, current flows through the coils, creating a magnetic force which draws the armature plate forward to make contact with the pulley. This action magnetically locks the armature plate and the pulley together as one unit to start compressor operation. An illustration of a typical magnetic clutch assembly is shown in Fig. 7. Application of a thermostat to the return air in the evaporator provides an off-on cycle. Under extreme conditions, the rapid heat gain of the average automobile interior causes the clutch to cycle quite often, occasionally several times a minute.

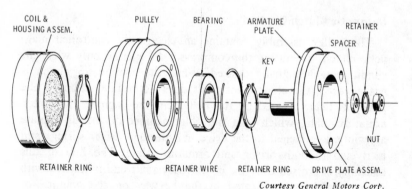

Courtesy General Motors Corp.

Fig. 7. A typical magnetic clutch assembly used on an automobile air conditioner compressor.

Suction Throttle Control

Some of the latest automobile air conditioning systems incorporate an evaporating regulating valve with the inlet connected to the evaporator outlet, and the outlet connected to the compressor suction port. A valve of this type, usually termed a *suction throttle valve*, is illustrated in Fig. 8, and consists essentially

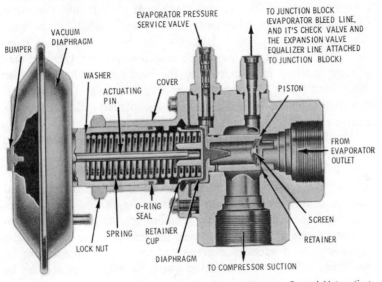

Fig. 8. Typical suction throttle valve.

of a valve body, piston, piston diaphragm, control spring, diaphragm cover, diaphragm cap, and vacuum diaphragm. The suction throttle valve controls the evaporator pressure and the evaporator outlet temperature. The inside of the piston is hollow and is open to the piston diaphragm through small holes in the end of the piston. Located in the lower extremity of the piston is a fine mesh screen held in place by a retainer. The purpose of this retainer is to prevent any foreign particles from entering the piston and lodging in the holes drilled in the piston walls.

The piston diaphragm is held in position by the piston on the front side, and by a retainer cup and spring on the rear side. The vacuum-diaphragm actuating pin fits in the end of the cup. The body of the vacuum diaphragm threads into the valve cover and determines the amount of spring tension on the cup. The vacuum diaphragm is locked to the cover after it has been set by a lock nut. A vacuum connection on the vacuum diaphragm housing is connected to the vacuum modulator on the instrument panel by a small hose. When vacuum is present on the diaphragm, it is pulled toward the piston and adds spring pressure to the piston diaphragm.

The flow of the low-pressure vapor from the evaporator to the compressor is determined and controlled by the position of the piston in the valve body of the suction throttle valve. The position of the piston in the body is determined by the balance of the forces that are applied to the piston diaphragm. These forces consist of the refrigerant vapor pressure returning from the evaporator on one side and the spring tension, plus the force of the actuating pin if vacuum is present at the vacuum diaphragm on the other side. Movement of the piston permits vapor to pass by scallops in the piston skirt and then on to the compressor inlet.

During the time that maximum cooling is being produced, the suction throttle-valve vacuum diaphragm does not have engine vacuum applied to it. The full flow of low-pressure refrigerant vapor is being returned to the compressor to permit it to exert its full capacity on the evaporator and produce maximum cooling. Under most all operating conditions, the suction throttle-valve inlet and outlet pressures will not be the same, as there will be some throttling to prevent evaporator icing. When the operator desires to raise the temperature within the car, the controls are changed to apply engine vacuum to the vacuum diaphragm. This checks or throttles the flow of the low-pressure vapor returning to the compressor. This results in a higher pressure to be maintained in the evaporator assembly. The suction throttle-valve outlet pressure will also increase, but the differential between inlet and outlet will be much greater than when the suction throttle valve is at maximum cooling.

Air Distribution

The air is introduced in the car by various outlets, depending upon the various types and models. The air-conditioner distribution system also varies, but is entirely separate from the car-heater distribution system. The air-conditioner distribution ducts are usually located forward of the car-heater ducts, with one end positioned against the evaporator housing.

Air Conditioner Control System

The operator controls the unit through switches located on the instrument panel or on the evaporator case, depending upon the installation procedure. Follow the manufacturer's instructions for proper operation.

SERVICE AND MAINTENANCE

Since automobile air conditioners do not differ in any important respect from those encountered in home air conditioners. as far as the refrigeration cycle is concerned, such common procedures as charging, leak detection, compressor testing, and other standard refrigeration service operations will not be discussed in this chapter. Only servicing and troubleshooting dealing with problems peculiar to automobile air conditioning will be treated.

Insufficient or No Cooling

In a system incorporating a magnetic clutch and thermostatic switch, the first check is to make certain that the compressor is running. The electrical system should also be checked. The condition and tension of the belt should be checked; in fact, correct tension on the belt is one of the most important service checks to be made. The tremendous load and high speed of these belts mean they must be kept very tight. Deflection of the belt between pulleys should not be over one-quarter of an inch. If a belt is replaced, this deflection should be checked after about one-half hour running period, and tightened again if necessary.

Air Output Not Normal

When it has been determined that the compressor is operating properly, blowers should be checked to make certain they are delivering air. The blower control should be set at high. The temperature control level (if there is one) should be set at maximum cooling. Insufficient discharge of air would indicate an obstruction in the evaporator, or electrical problems with the blower motor.

Air Output Normal

Assuming that actual air delivery at the discharge grill is about normal (around 300 cfm), the next check is the position of the bypass dampers. It is a well-known fact that the condensation of the refrigerant depends upon air passing over the condenser as the automobile travels on the road. To simulate this condition in the shop, a large fan should be placed in front of the car. Head-pressure readings will vary somewhat with the ambient air temperatures. A fast idle (about 1,500 rpm)and an ambient temperature of 75° F. should indicate head pressures from 100 to 130 psig. For every 10° F. increase in the ambient air temperature, an increase of about 20 psig will occur. Extreme ambient temperatures, such as 110° or higher, may send the pressure as high as 300 psig. Extreme head pressure could indicate the presence of dirt, air, or debris in the system.

Complete removal of air from the refrigerating system is essential for two reasons:

1. To prevent excessive head pressures when the air volume over the condenser is low.
2. To prevent decomposition of the oil which is accelerated by the normally higher operating temperatures encountered in these systems.

It is not too uncommon to find that an inexperienced person has serviced the air condition system and overcharged it, causing a high head pressure.

Checking Suction Pressures

Suction pressures normally run about 16 to 25 psig at 75° F. Any wide variation from these pressures indicates the usual service problems resulting from this condition. Abnormally high suction pressures indicate wide-open expansion valves, a loose feeler bulb, or leaky compressor valves. Valve plates usually can be replaced on these compressors. The normal refrigeration procedures for checking compressor operation are recommended.

Checking Control Systems

Systems equipped with either the evaporator regulator, the by-pass-valve type of controls, or the expansion valve, should present no difficult problems to qualified servicemen. Special features of these valves may dictate variations from normal refrigeration service practice.

Air Distribution

If an air-conditioner distribution system is not functioning properly, first check the vacuum hose connections, the control cable, and vacuum switch adjustments. If the controls and cables operate properly, check for vacuum at valve diaphragms, for proper functioning of the vacuum switches, and for the correct position of the air valves. If the air flow changes or shuts off when the car is accelerating, check for a faulty valve at the intake manifold. If there is no vacuum to the suction throttle valve when the cool switch is on, check for a disconnected vacuum hose at the vacuum modulator.

Defective Compressor

Compressor malfunctioning will appear in one of four ways:

1. Noise.
2. Seizure.
3. Leakage.
4. Low discharge pressures.

Resonant compressor noises are no cause for excessive alarm, but irregular noises or rattles are likely to indicate broken parts. Seizure will be indicated by the failure of the compressor to operate, if the clutch is in good operating condition and there is no break in the electrical system. (A wiring diagram of a typical automobile air conditioner is shown in Fig. 9.) Continued operation of a partially seized compressor will result in damage to the clutch. To check for seizure, de-energize the clutch and attempt to rotate the compressor by using a wrench on the compressor shaft. If the shaft will not turn, the compressor is seized. Leakage of compressor refrigerant may be detected through routine leak detection. Low discharge pressures may also be caused by

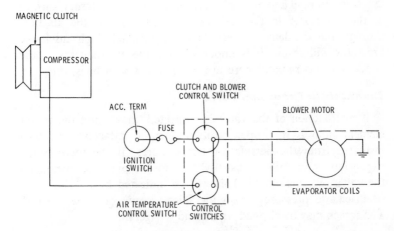

MAGNETIC CLUTCH

COMPRESSOR

CLUTCH AND BLOWER
CONTROL SWITCH

ACC. TERM

BLOWER MOTOR

FUSE

IGNITION
SWITCH

AIR TEMPERATURE
CONTROL SWITCH

CONTROL
SWITCHES

EVAPORATOR COILS

Fig. 9. Schematic wiring diagram of an electrical circuit in a typical automobile air conditioner.

insufficient refrigerant or a restriction elsewhere in the system. These should be checked out prior to compressor servicing.

Compressor Clutch

If the compressor is inoperative, the electrical lead to the clutch should be checked first. If there is current to the clutch and the compressor is not seized, the clutch is defective and should be repaired.

Condenser

There are two types of possible condenser malfunction. The condenser may leak, resulting in loss of refrigeration and a low system pressure. The condenser may also have a restriction, resulting in excessive compressor discharge pressures and inadequate cooling. If a restriction occurs and some refrigerant passes the restriction, icing or frost may occur on the external surface of the condenser in the area of the restriction. If the air flow through the condenser is restricted or blocked, high discharge pressures will result. It is important that the external fins of the condenser and radiator core are not plugged with bugs, dirt, etc.

Thermostatic Expansion Valve

If malfunction of the valve is suspected, make sure the power element bulb is in proper position, securely attached, and well insulated from the outside air temperatures. If the thermostatic expansion valve fails, it usually fails in the power element and the valve remains closed. This will be indicated by low high-side or discharge pressures. Also the inlet screen could be plugged. The screen may be cleaned with liquid refrigerant.

Evaporator

Dirt or other foreign matter on the core surface or in the evaporator housing will restrict the air flow. A cracked or broken housing can result in leakage of cold air and can result in insufficient air or warm air delivered to the passenger compartment.

Refrigerant Lines

Restrictions in the refrigerant lines may be indicated as follows:

1. High-pressure liquid line (low head pressure, no cooling).
2. Suction line (low suction pressure, low head pressure, little or no cooling).
3. Discharge line (compressor blow-off).
4. Received-drier (Leakage of refrigerant indicates a defective unit. This cannot easily be checked, but if the system has been exposed to outside air for a considerable length of time, the unit should be replaced).

Restrictions in the receiver-drier can also cause system malfunction. If the inlet tube is blocked, it is likely to result in high head pressure. If the outlet tube is blocked, head pressure is likely to be low and there will be little or no cooling.

Suction Throttle Valve

If the suction throttle valve is defective, it may cause evaporator pressure to be too high (air outlet temperature too warm) or it could cause the evaporator pressure to be too low (air outlet temperature too low which may cause icing of the evaporator core). If the vacuum diaphragm of the suction throttle valve is defective, there would be no means to change (increase) the air outlet temperature. Refrigerant leakage of the suction throttle valve may be detected through routine leak detection.

Before servicing the suction throttle valve, it should be determined that it is actually the cause of the complaint. If evaporator pressure remains too high when checking and adjusting the suction throttle valve, the low-pressure gauge line should be attached to the valve located on the compressor suction line. If the compressor suction pressure is also too high, the compressor or possibly the thermostatic expansion valve may be the cause of the trouble.

Use of Receiver Sight Glass for Diagnosis

A clear sight glass will indicate a properly charged refrigeration system. The occurrence of slow moving gas bubbles, or a broken column of refrigerant for momentary periods during normal operation, should not be considered an indication of refrigerent shortage if the sight glass is generally clear and performance is satisfactory. The tendency of the sight glass to indicate refrigerant shortage when the system is under light load should be considered.

461

If the sight glass consistently shows foaming or a broken liquid column, it should be observed after partially blocking the air to the condenser. If under this condition the sight glass clears, and the performance is otherwise satisfactory, the charge shall be considered adequate. In all instances where the indications of refrigerant shortage continues, additional refrigerant should be added in 1/4-lb. increments until the sight glass is clear. An additional charge of 1/2 lb. should be added as a reserve. In no case should the system be overcharged.

INSTALLATION PROCEDURE

There are two methods to acquire automobile air conditioning as:

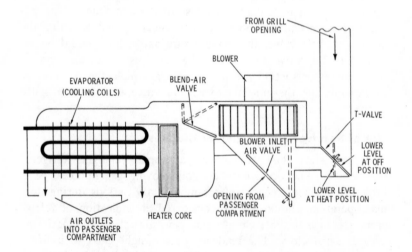

Fig. 10. Schematic diagram which shows the heating and cooling coil arrangements.

462

1. Factory installations.
2. Universal-type installations.

Factory installed air conditioners are furnished with the car, usually with instructions for its proper maintenance and operation. In such installations there are several methods used on the evaporator assemblies. Many such installations combine the heating system with the cooling system, as shown in Fig. 10, with the evaporator coil and heater core located in the same enclosure. One significant service problem that should be pointed out here is the function of the bypass dampers.

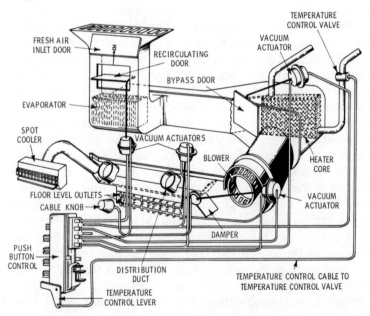

Fig. 11. Typical damper control assembly showing vacuum actuators with push button controls.

A common complaint of no cooling is corrected by proper adjustment of the bypass dampers. In many installations they are controlled by cables, which operate dampers to furnish outside or recirculated air. These control cables are connected to a control panel in such a way that the combined functions are accomplished or controlled through a single lever. A more recent refinement in damper controls is shown in Fig. 11. Here, vacuum actuators are used with push-button control. Installations of this type mean that servicemen must thoroughly acquaint themselves with the basic operating principle governing this type of control. They are similar in many respects to those controls used in pneumatic-controlled air conditioning systems.

The evaporator housings resemble the old-fashioned car heaters that were suspended under the dash. This construction, popular with independent automotive air conditioner manufacturers, simplifies installation. Its operating characteristics are the same as factory installed units. Fig. 12 illustrates a typical automotive air conditioning system condenser, which is usually located in front of the radiator. Circulation of air over the condenser depends upon either ram air, resulting from the forward movement of the car, or from air drawn across the unit by the engine fan.

It is interesting to note that head pressures vary on the highway when the car travels with or against the wind. When traveling "downwind", head pressure usually runs 10 to 15 lbs. higher than when traveling against the wind. Most road tests, however, have proven that the condenser does not materially affect temperature of the car engine. One major problem encountered is the head pressure increasing substantially when the engine is left idling, such as in slow moving or stalled traffic. Normally, air circulation over the condenser is supplied by the forward movement of the car; at high speeds, the ram effect of this air does an adequate job of cooling the condenser. At more moderate

speeds, the fan draws sufficient air over the condenser to keep
head pressures normal, but when the car is stalled or is traveling
very slowly, air volume is not sufficient to keep head pressures

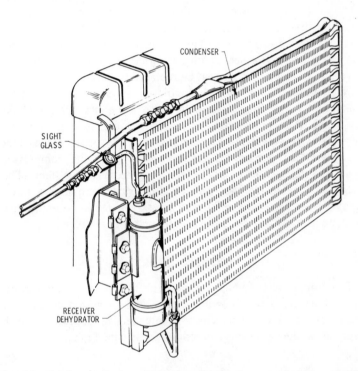

CONDENSER

SIGHT
GLASS

RECEIVER
DEHYDRATOR

**Fig. 12. Condenser and receiver installation in a typical automobile
air conditioner system.**

within operating limits. Some systems provide a *fast-idling* control, which increases the engine speed sufficiently to supply air
over the condenser.

465

Location of the condenser in front of the car contributes to accumulation of dirt and debris on the finned surface. Recently developed service tools for effectively cleaning finned surfaces are available. Also shown in Fig. 12 is the system receiver. An innovation is encountered here through the frequent practice of placing a drier core within the receiver, thus resulting in a combination receiver-drier unit. This construction may pose a question to some servicemen. With the drier located within the receiver, how can this component be replaced?

Since present automobile air conditioning systems make no provision to "pump down" the unit, there is no need for a liquid line valve. The only valves available are the suction and discharge service valves at the compressor. This simply means that if any service operation is required away from the compressor itself, the refrigerant must be removed from the system. The drier cartridge inside the receiver also usually provides a filter. Many times this is the only filter or screen in the system since the expansion valve is not always equipped with a screen.

TROUBLE CHART

The trouble chart which follows lists the most common operating faults along with possible causes and suggested checks and correction for each. This chart is intended to provide a quick reference to the cause and correction of a specific fault.

AUTOMOBILE AIR CONDITIONING TROUBLE CHART

Insufficient Cooling

Possible Cause	*Possible Remedy*
Low air flow	Check blower operation. Check for obstruction in air distribution system. Check for clogged evaporator. If iced, deice core and check adjustment and operation of suction throttle valve.
Defective heater temperature control valve	Check operation of valve. Adjust or replace as necessary.
Heater controls or ventilator control not in the "off" position.	Advise operator of correct operation of controls.

Compressor Discharge Pressure Too High

Possible Cause	*Possible Remedy*
Engine overheated	Check for possible cause.
Overcharge of refrigerant or air in system	Systems with excess discharge pressures should be slowly depressurized.

1. If discharge pressure drops rapidly, it indicates air (with possibility of moisture) in the system. When pressure drop levels but still indicates in excess of specifications, slowly bleed system until bubbles appear in the sight glass and stop. Add refrigerant until bubbles clear, then add one-half pound of refrigerant. Recheck operational pressures. If system pressures still remain above specifications, and the evaporator pressure is slightly above normal, then a restriction exists in the high-pressure side of the system.
2. If discharge pressure drops slowly, it indicates excessive refrigerant. If pressures drop to specifications and sight glass remains clear, stop depressurizing and recheck operational pressures. If pressures are satisfactory, depressurize until bubbles appear in the sight glass,

stop depressurizing, then add one-half pound refrigerant. Recheck operational pressures.

3. If discharge pressure remains high after depressurizing the system, continue depressurizing until bubbles appear in the sight glass. If evaporator pressures also remain high, there is a possibility of a restriction in the high-pressure side of the refrigeration system, or the suction throttle valve may require adjustment.

Possible Cause	Possible Remedy
Restriction in condenser or receiver liquid indicator.	Remove parts, inspect, and clean or replace.
Condenser air flow blocked	Clean condenser and radiator core surfaces as well as the space between the condenser and radiator.
Evaporator pressure too high	See *Evaporator Pressure too High*.

Compressor Discharge Pressure Too Low

Possible Cause	*Possible Remedy*
Insufficient refrigerant	Check for presence of bubbles or foam in liquid indicator. If bubbles or foam are noted (after five minutes of operation), check system for leaks. If no leaks are found, refrigerant should be added until sight glass clears, then add an additional ½ lb.
Low suction pressure	See *Evaporator Pressure too Low*.
Defective compressor and/or broken compressor reed valves.	Repair compressor.

Evaporator Pressure Too High

Possible Cause	*Possible Remedy*
Thermostatic expansion-valve capillary-tube bulb not tight to evaporator outlet tube	Check for tightness.

Thermostatic expansion valve improperly adjusted or inoperative.	Replace valve.
Suction throttle valve adjusted improperly or defective.	Check operation of suction throttle valve. Repair valve, if necessary.
Vacuum modulator defective.	There should be no vacuum to the suction throttle valve when "cool" level on instrument panel is at maximum "on" position. Replace vacuum modulator if defective. Note: If compressor suction line from suction throttle valve is extremely colder than suction throttle-valve inlet line from evaporator, this indicates that suction throttle-valve outlet pressure is much lower than inlet pressure, and suction throttle valve may be defective.

Evaporator Pressure Too Low

Possible Cause	*Possible Remedy*
Thermostatic expansion-valve capillary tube broken, inlet screen plugged, or valve otherwise failed.	Replace valve or clean inlet screen of valve.
Restriction in system tubes or hoses.	Replace kinked tube or restricted hose.
Suction throttle valve adjusted improperly or defective.	Check operation of suction throttle valve. Repair if necessary.

CHAPTER 18

Air Conditioning Control Devices

Air-conditioner control devices may vary, depending upon the size of the area under consideration, the number and size of the units involved, etc. There are generally three types of control used for air conditioning, dependent on the particular requirements. They are:

1. Manual.
2. Automatic.
3. Semiautomatic.

MANUALLY CONTROLLED INSTALLATION

This method requires personal attention and regulation at frequent intervals, especially when the load varies. Even if the plant is in operation only at certain times of the day, inside and outside conditions may vary so greatly that constant changes in adjustment are necessary. The manual control can be an ordinary knife switch which must be operated by hand when the actuating mechanism is started or stopped.

This type of control, while giving temperature and humidity regulation for a given set of conditions, does not provide the most desirable regulation because of fluctuating demands. Constant attention is required by the operator to maintain the predetermined conditions, and the cost of operation is usually found to be excessive. If a manual control is provided, the user may permit the unit to operate until the room is too cold, or else he may forget to start the machine until after the room has reached an uncomfortable warm temperature. In either case, the user will not be satisfied, and therefore it is usually wise to install an automatic control. An automatic control will protect the unit from excessive operation, and will eliminate costly utility bills.

Automatic Installation

The completely automatic installation usually meets the varying load almost constantly. This type of control involves the use of a large number of instruments, such as time clocks, thermostats, humidity controllers, and automatic dampers, operated either by electricity or compressed air. Automatically operated controls provide all the features that are considered most desirable for temperature and humidity regulation as well as economy of operation. The operator or owner is relieved of all responsibility for maintaining the predetermined conditions; operating costs are kept at a minimum, which satisfies the user.

Consider, as an example, an office being cooled by a unit air conditioner. The unit is specified to maintain comfortable conditions during the hottest days of the summer, and it also must furnish comfortable conditions on mild days in the spring and fall. Unless an automatic control is used, the office will become too cold on mild days and a complaint will be registered concerning unsatisfactory operation.

SEMIAUTOMATIC CONTROL SYSTEM

This method, containing a close-differential thermostat, is entirely satisfactory in most cases. Time clocks are also very desirable on installations where definite shut-down periods are required. The fresh-air intake from outdoors should be equipped with adjustable louvers, so that the maximum amount of air can be regulated for both summer cooling and winter heating.

It is desirable on any unit below 25-tons capacity to keep the control system as simple and free from service liabilities as possible. On large theatre- or office-building applications, the expenditure of a considerable amount of money for control equipment is warranted. For smaller installations, however, equipment for thermostatic or manual control should constitute the extent of the control system. This may include provisions for manually controlled ventilation and time-clock operation. If the additional expense is warranted, the unit can be equipped with automatic humidity controls. The control devices that may be encountered are briefly outlined as follows:

Thermostats

The device that operates by changes in room temperature is called a *thermostat*. Some thermostats depend on a bimetal strip to make and break a set of contacts. In another design, the bimetal strip is coiled into a loose helix, with the outer coil rigidly fixed to the case. The inner coil is free to move in accordance with temperature changes, and to this free end is secured a glass capsule containing an ample charge of mercury. (An illustration of this type of adjustable thermostat is shown in Fig. 1.) Two electric wires are sealed in one end of the capsule, their bare ends projecting into the capsule. When the capsule is tilted in one direction, the mercury flows to the lowest end; if this hap-

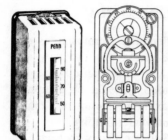

Fig. 1. Exterior and interior views of a typical two wire room thermostat. The single pole, single throw contacts open automatically on temperature rise and close on temperature drop.

pens to be the plain end, the circuit is broken. The electrical circuit is completed only when the capsule is tilted in the other direction, so that the mercury flows to the end containing the two wire ends. The mercury bridges the space between the two

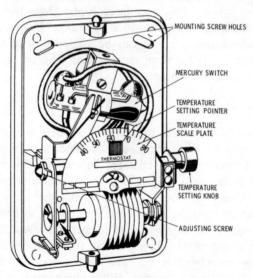

Fig. 2. Thermostat provided with a bellows type actuated mercury switch.

wires and acts as a metallic conductor. This type of mercury capsule is shown in Fig. 2.

Capsules are usually charged with an inert gas, so that no arcing occurs during the making or breaking of the electrical circuit. Such devices are made to handle currents up to and including that used by a one-horsepower motor. When larger motors must be started, the thermostat acts in conjunction with a relay and makes use of an automatic starting device.

A thermostat can be used to stop and start a system equipped with either an automatic constant-pressure expansion valve or a thermostatic expansion valve. Another variety of thermostat is one that depends on the pressure-temperature relationship of gases for its operation. In this type, a sealed bulb is provided with a charge of refrigerant. A small tube connects the charged bulb to an expanding diaphragm or drum. With an increase in temperature there is a corresponding increase in pressure, and, by means of levers, springs, and adjustments, the instrument can be set to cut in or out at any desired point.

There are many thermostats of varying quality on the market. If only cooling is desired, the simplest arrangement is to connect a single-pole, single-throw thermostat in series with the solenoid coil of a liquid-line magnetic stop valve in the liquid line of the evaporator-expansion valve. A thermostat with a two-degree differential should give satisfactory results, but it should be electrically connected in series with a snap switch, so that there is a means of making sure the thermostat will not operate the equipment during shut-down periods. The machine operation should be low-pressure controlled with this arrangement.

A separate thermostat should be used for controlling the fans and the steam-line solenoid (or damper control) when heating is desired. The single-pole, double-throw type should be avoided for combination summer and winter operation. A typical wiring

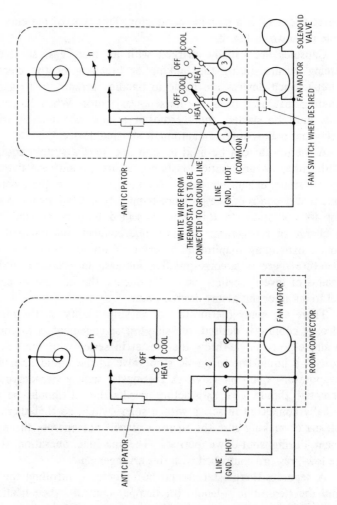

Fig. 3. Typical wiring diagram showing control arrangement when thermostat is used for automatic fan operation.

diagram showing control arrangement is illustrated in Fig. 3. For circulating cold water or brine systems, a thermostat can be connected in series with the solenoid coil of the starting switch of the circulating pump. Thus, one thermostat can be used to supply brine to a number of floor cabinets.

Automatic Humidity Control

The instrument supplied for automatic humidity control is known as a humidistat. The element in the instrument is some type of hygroscopic material, such as wood, human hair, paper, and similar materials. When the material absorbs water from the air, expansion takes place. It is this action that is used to make and break the circuit controlling humidifying or dehumidifying apparatus. A typical humidistat is shown in Fig. 4. The humidistat generally makes or breaks an electric circuit which controls the operation of an electric motor or valve and opens or closes a compressed-air circuit from which air is obtained to operate the air motor or valve. Both electric and air-actuated equipment are supplied for different types of duty but, as a rule, an electrical apparatus is used in most air-conditioning installations.

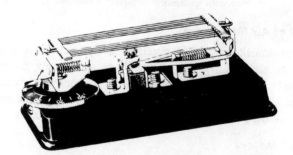

Courtesy Penn Controls Inc.

Fig. 4. Interior view of humidistat showing specially treated floating type human hair element.

477

Time Clocks

Timers are merely clock-operated switches that can be placed either with the thermostat or a manual switch, thus automatically preventing operation during certain periods. A typical timer circuit is shown in Fig. 5.

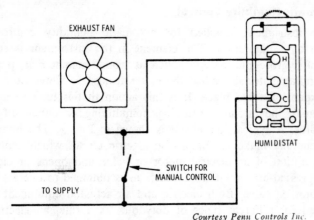

Courtesy Penn Controls Inc.

Fig. 5. Typical wiring diagram for exhaust fan operation with automatic humidistat control.

Control of Air Movement

Air movement is usually determined by such factors as the size of the blowers, the size of the ducts and supply grilles, and the speed of the blower motor. These factors are established when the system is installed and can only be varied by the manipulation of suitable dampers or by changing the motor speeds.

Damper Motors

Motors for operating dampers are provided when automatic regulation of air flow is required in heating systems, ventilating ducts, air-conditioning systems, and in air-conditioning supply duct for zone control. The motors are powered by electricity and controlled by action of a thermostatic element and compressed air. They can be connected directly to single or multiple dampers by a linkage. The dampers can be positioned by the motors as required and in accordance with an indication from the governing device. There are two general classes of electrically operated motors manufactured. These are known as *positive* and *reversing* motors. Each class is divided into several types the positive motor is known as the two-position positive, four-position positive, and five-position positive, all unidirectional in operation, with or without speed adjustments. A typical wiring circuit of a damper motor is shown in Fig. 6.

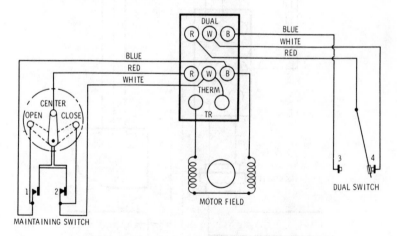

Fig. 6. Internal circuit of a damper motor control.

The reversing motor is known as the two-position, four-position, and five-position motor, which can be stopped, restarted in

479

the original position, or reversed at any point. These motors are supplied with or without speed adjustments. Standard three-wire thermostats, or proportioning thermostats are generally supplied to control the operation of the motors. Hygrostats and other control instruments can be used when other types of regulation are required. Dampers can also be operated by thermostatic ele-

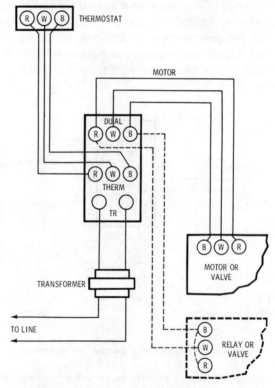

Fig. 7. External wiring diagram for damper motor.

ments (Fig. 7) in which the expansion and contraction of a liquid or gas supplies the power required to actuate the dampers.

Automatic Temperature Control

The thermostat is the automatic device that controls the temperature of the unit. It contains an element that is sensitive to changes in temperature. This element is usually a bimetal strip or a metal bellows filled with a volatile liquid. Either type of element gives good results, and both are found in general use. A typical thermostatic switch is shown in Fig. 8.

An automatic temperature-control system is generally operated by making and breaking an electric circuit or by opening and closing a compressed-air line. When using the electric thermostat,

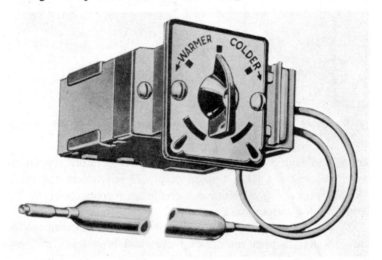

Courtesy Ranco Inc.

Fig. 8. Typical air conditioner thermostatic control switch. The control switch can be connected electrically to cycle for either condition of cooling only, or heating-cooling.

the temperature is regulated by controlling the operation of an electric motor or valve, and when using the compressed-air thermostat, temperature regulation is obtained by actuating an air-operated motor or valve.

Electrically operated temperature-control systems are used by manufacturers for practically all installations. However, compressed air temperature-control systems are used in extremely large

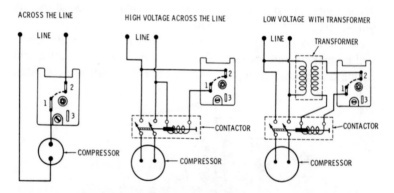

Fig. 9. **Wiring diagrams showing compressor connections for various voltages where the installation requirements are for cooling only.**

central and multiple installations, in close-temperature regulation work, and where a large amount of power is required for small control devices. Fig. 9 illustrates compressor connections to the thermostat for various voltages.

The proportioning thermostat is used in connection with modulating electric damper motors or valves and provides a partially or fully opened, as well as a closed, position for the damper or valve, depending on the demand made on the thermostat. With this type of operation, the correct amount of air can be furnished or the proper quantity of steam supplied, depending on the setting of the thermostat, which in turn, causes the apparatus to give the desired throttling action.

Contactors, Starters, and Relays

Most condensing units with motors above 1-1/2 hp have a starter or contactor, and, as a rule, these are furnished with the units when they are ordered. Relays are a necessary part of many control and pilot circuits. These automatic switches are similar in design to contactors, but are generally lighter in construction and carry a smaller amount of current.

Limit Switches

Limit switches are often used in heating installations to prevent the fan motor from circulating cold air when the heat is off. They are also used to prevent the humidifier from operating when the heat is off, or to cut off refrigeration when the heat is on.

AIR-CONDITIONING CONTROL SYSTEMS

Air-conditioning systems consist of several individual and distinctive units, each designed to perform a specific function. The degree of accuracy is determined by the efficiency and economy with which the system can be operated and maintained. The proper application of adequate, but not excessive, controls has proven to be the most satisfactory and least expensive means of accomplishing this purpose. No one type of control can be universally adaptable for use in every type of heating, cooling, and ventilating system. Therefore, the serviceman should have a fair knowledge of the various types of controls and their respective application. He should know the preparation of installations, adjustment and testing of controls, inspection, instruction for operators, and subsequent service when required. He does not need to know all of the component parts of the equipment, although he should know the proper control to use for each application.

For each air-conditioning system there is one control that will insure the proper program of operation. When designing control systems, it becomes necessary for the engineer to carefully analyze all types of controls available and select the particular type that will insure dependable service to the customer.

The principles of control systems can be classified into five groups:

1. Electrical.
2. Pneumatic.
3. Combination.
4. Hydraulic
5. Self-contained.

Electrical Control Systems

In an electrical control system, the prime mover utilized for operation is motivated by electricity. The units can be interconnected by line-voltage or low-voltage wiring. In the event low voltage is used, a low-capacity, step-down transformer must be used in the electrical circuit to reduce the voltage from the normal line voltage that enters the larger equipment to the desired voltage (usually 20 to 24 volts) for the control instruments. The basic function of this type of control consists of switching or adjusting electrical circuits to govern the operation of relays, starters, solenoids, or positioning motors. A typical wiring circuit of a heating-cooling system is shown in Fig. 10.

Pneumatic Control Systems

In pneumatic control systems, compressed air is used to actuate the controls. Usually, a small air compressor is provided with the

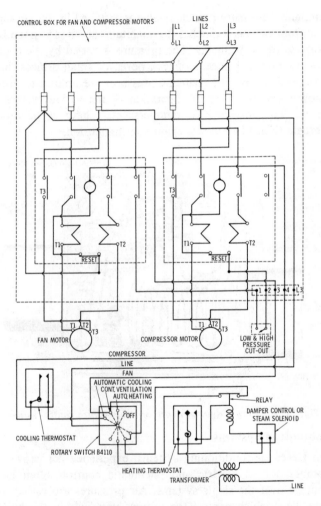

Fig. 10. Wiring diagram showing electrical connection for typical automatic summer and winter air conditioning system.

system, and a pressure reducing valve is installed in the air supply line to the various branches to maintain about 15 pounds of pressure to the instruments. The pressure is varied by the controlling devices through means of leak ports, or small orifices, in the control mechanism. The changing pressures are utilized to provide the power necessary for the operation of the various valves and dampers. The instruments, dampers, etc., have a bellows or diaphragm (Fig. 11) that acts against spring tension.

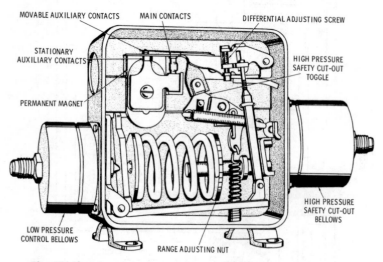

Fig. 11. Showing a dual pressure or temperature control switch.

Combination Systems

On larger air-conditioning systems, experience has proved that a combination of electric and pneumatic controls often has an advantage over the single systems. Air pressures are varied in the branch lines which control the various units within the building. Modulating electric controls actuate relays which operate motor starters for varying the compressor capacity as required for the necessary load.

Hydraulic System

This type of system is very seldom used. A liquid under pressure provides a controllable source of power to operate the various control devices in the system.

Self-Contained Systems

The self-contained systems have been more or less restricted in the past to a direct-connected power unit and controller. These applications consist of valves that are used to admit steam or hot water into heating coils which regulate the temperature as determined by the controller element. Usually, the control element and power unit are in very close proximity to each other in this type of application.

CONTROL OPERATION

This can be classified into three general types:

1. Two-position.
2. Floating.
3. Modulating.

Two-Position Control

This can be referred to as a positive-acting, "on-and-off" control. There are no intermediate positions between these two points. A valve is either completely open or closed; a switch mechanism is either in the open or closed position. This is the simplest type of control and is generally used to control a solenoid valve, a relay, a small damper (such as a volume damper), exhaust fan, etc.

487

Floating Control

This refers to a control valve or damper motor that operates to either extreme of its differential before making contact, and remains stationary only when the controlled apparatus has become stabilized between the two limits. Such a control can be classed as semimodulating, and can be used for static-pressure regulation or tank-level control. It is often used on suction-pressure variation, program-controlling compressor units, etc. However, it is often very difficult to obtain complete balance between the variation in suction pressure, weight, and spring pressure exerted on the differential mechanism. This type of control has its limitations.

Modulating Control

This can be described as a graduating or proportioning control, and is more widely used for the program control of compressors and for modulating or positioning dampers and valves. The method of controlling the volume handled in response to the change in conditions at the controller is briefly explained.

The modulating control causes motion to take place in the controller. This is done by very small degrees of variation in the medium to which the controller is responsive. Immediately upon completion of this small change at the controller, the controlled device assumes a new position and remains stationary until another change takes place in the controller. The whole cycle of operation is based on the potentiometer balancing of resistance in the controller and controlled devices.

The operating differential of a control can be defined as the change in a factor, such as a temperature, that will cause a change in the controller from one position to another, thereby causing a change to take place in the controlled device from one extreme to the other.

488

CHAPTER 19

Servicing Air-Conditioning Systems

A malfunctioning system may be caused by one portion of the system or a combination of several portions. For this reason, it is necessary and advisable to check the more obvious causes first. Each part of the system has a certain function to perform, and if any individual part does not function correctly and efficiently, the performance of the entire air conditioning system will be affected.

SERVICING COMPONENT PARTS

To simplify servicing a system, especially one with which he is unfamiliar, the serviceman should remember that the refrigerant, under proper operating conditions, travels through the system in one specified direction. Remembering this, the serviceman can trace the path of the refrigerant through any system. For instance, beginning at the receiver, the refrigerant will pass through the liquid shut-off valve. If this valve is partially closed, completely closed or clogged, no refrigeration is possible, despite the fact that the unit itself can and will operate.

Strainers and Filters

Most manufacturers place a strainer or filter in the liquid line. and, if this device becomes clogged or filled with dirt, the liquid refrigerant will be unable to pass. Filters are usually designed to hold a certain amount of dirt, scale, metallic particles, etc., but sometimes through carelessness, a little extraneous matter may be allowed to enter the system during assembling or servicing. The remedy is obvious; the dirt and foreign matter must be removed and the refrigerant allowed to pass through the filter.

Small Units

Many small units make use of copper tubing for the liquid and suction lines. Copper is not structurally as strong as iron or steel, and in many instances, a heavy moving object or a sharp blow will collapse the copper lines and prevent the circulation of refrigerant. In such a case, a new line or new section of line must be installed.

Expansion Valves

Expansion valves must be properly set and in perfect order to maintain proper pressure in the low side of the line. The following data will indicate the troubles pertaining to improper expansion-valve operation. In many cases, oil from the compressor crankcase enters and remains in the evaporator, occupying space intended for refrigerant. Naturally, the refrigerating effect is reduced, and service problems develop. The oil will have to be drained from the coil, and the compressor crankcase will have to be inspected to make sure that the oil level is correct.

Compressors

Compressors give trouble, especially after long use, as wear occurs and the pistons and rings become worn. Since some of the high-pressure gas leaks by the pistons and rings, proper compression cannot be obtained, and the compressor becomes inefficient and unable to take care of the load. New rings, pistons, and connecting rods usually are all that are required to bring the compressor back to its proper performance. Suction and discharge valves may stick, crack, or fail entirely. Sometimes, a slight warpage or piece of dirt under them results in improper operation. Seals around the crankshaft may leak and require repacking or replacement.

Condensers

The condenser may become dirty and inefficient, thereby resulting in high pressures, loss of efficiency, and an increase in the power requirement.

Ducts

Some ducts are provided with insulation on the inside; this may tear loose and flap, resulting in noise.

Water Jets

Water jets or spray heads may become clogged or worn. Automatic water valves may get out of adjustment, and the flow of water may become restricted through the clogging of the water strainer.

SERVICING DATA

The proper diagnosis of air-conditioning and refrigeration systems service problems can only be determined by intelligent thought, patience, and diligence. Each and every contributory factor must be considered and eliminated before going to some other cause.

The various important steps in checking a system are listed as follows:

1. Determine the refrigerant used in the system. This is an important factor, since each refrigerant has its own operating characteristics, such as pressure-temperature differences.

2. Install a gauge test set. If the unit is a large one, it will have a set of gauges as part of the equipment. The gauge test will indicate the condition of the refrigerant by checking pressure-temperature relations. Put the thermometer on the coil near the expansion valve and obtain a reading. This temperature reading and back-pressure reading will indicate the refrigerant condition. Then check for improper expansion-coil pressure.

3. A low-pressure reading may be caused by a shortage of refrigerant, the presence of ice or water in the adjustment side of the expansion valve, moisture in the refrigerant system, plugged screens, partly closed liquid shut-off or service valves, excessive charge, or air in the system. Improper valve settings, blocked air circulation over the condenser, cooled air passing over the condenser at too high a temperature, reversed rotation of the motor, bent fan blades, or a clogged condenser are indicated by high head pressures.

4. Frost or a sweat line on the coil should be noted. A coil is only active up to its frost or sweat line. All lengths of tubing beyond the frost or sweat line are inactive, since they do not receive liquid refrigerant. For greatest efficiency, the entire coil must have frost or sweat, and if the liquid line is obstructed, the screen plugged, or the expansion improperly set, the proper amount of liquid refrigerant will not enter the evaporator, and only a limited por-

tion of the coil will frost or sweat, depending on the type of liquid refrigerant supplied.

5. An increase or overabundance of refrigerant will cause the entire coil, and possibly the suction line, to frost or sweat. This may be caused by a leaky needle, improper adjustment, ice in the adjustment side of the expansion valve, or fused thermostat contacts. Most complaints with regard to excessive or insufficient frosting are due to weather conditions. During the winter, satisfactory operation may be maintained, but for summer operation, the expansion valve is usually opened a trifle more.

6. Improper operation will occur if refrigerant has escaped from the system. The first thing to do in the case where leakage has occurred is to detect and repair the leak. Indications of refrigerant shortage include hissing at the expansion valve, a warm or hot liquid line, little or no frost on the expansion valve or coil, continuous operation, low head pressure, and bubbles in the sight glass if it is inserted in the liquid line and used to test for refrigerant shortage.

7. With F-12 and methyl chloride, bubbles may form in the sight glass if the head pressure is under 120 lbs. with F-12, and under 100 lbs. with methyl chloride. An excellent indication of leakage is the presence of oil on a joint or fitting; methyl chloride and F-12 dissolve oils, and when a leak occurs, the escaped refrigerant evaporates in the atmosphere, leaving the oil behind. Refrigerant must be added to a system having a refrigerant shortage, until the bubbles in the sight glass cease, or until the hissing sound at the expansion valve is eliminated.

8. Check for improper installation. Compressor units and low sides must be level. Tubes and fittings forming the liquid

and suction lines must be the proper size. Baffles, ducts, and eliminators must be properly located and not obstructed. Ducts must be insulated properly, or short circuiting of air currents will take place and the ducts will sweat. Liquid and suction lines must be checked for pinches, sharp or flattened bends, and obstructions. Lines must not ber un along the ceiling in a hot room, and the lines should not run adjacent to hot-water or steam pipes.

9. The location and installation of the thermostat must be checked. The thermostatic switch bulb should be installed in a location where average temperature conditions exist. The thermostat bulb, or switch itself (if self-contained), should not be placed where an inrush of warm air, such as that caused by the opening of doors or windows, will cause the mechanism to cut in prematurely. Use thermostatic control switches with a minimum of tubing. Gas will condense in long runs of tubing and the condensate will produce erratic operation. If the thermostatic bulb is used to control a liquid bath or brine, the bulb should be housed in a dry well or cavity, the location of which should be where the average temperature conditions will be stable.

10. The condition of the thermostatic bulb should be checked. Apply heat gently by means of a cloth saturated with hot water, or else hold the bulb in the hand. If the contacts do not close after applying heat, the thermostatic element is discharged. Dirty or oxidized contacts can also cause defective operation.

11. Starter fuses should be checked, and if blown, replaced with the proper size. Determine the cause of the trouble—shortage of oil, air in the system, overcharge, misalignment, high back pressure, lack of air or water over the condenser

or motor—any of which may cause the fuses to blow. If the trouble is not corrected, serious damage can result in a short time.

12. Filters and/or screens must be checked. A clogged screen or filter, or a pinched or clogged liquid line will produce the same trouble as a leaky or stuck expansion valve, depending on the degree of the obstruction.

13. A leaky or stuck expansion-valve needle will be indicated by a low pressure in the evaporator side and continuous operation of the unit. Sometimes a low-pressure control is wired in series with the thermostatic control and motor. When this is done, the low-pressure control will cut out, and the unit will remain inoperative.

COMMON TROUBLES IN AUTOMATIC
EXPANSION-VALVE SYSTEMS WITH THERMOSTATIC CONTROL

Refrigerant Shortage

1. Warm or hot liquid line.
2. Hissing sound at valve.
3. Low head or condensing pressure.
4. Evaporator not entirely chilled.
5. Poor refrigeration.
6. Low-side pressure may be high if only gas is entering the evaporator.

Poor Refrigeration

1. Heavy coat of frost or ice on evaporator.
2. Refrigerant shortage.
3. Thermostat not adjusted properly.
4. Thermostat defective.
5. Thermostat shifted and not level.

6. Thermostat shielded by covering.
7. Thermostat in draft.
8. Stuck expansion valve.
9. Expansion valve set too low; allows only a portion of the evaporator to be effective.
10. Liquid line pinched or restricted.
11. Pinched or restricted suction line.
12. Compressor valves defective, broken, or sticking.
13. Strainer on liquid or suction line clogged.
14. Partially closed liquid- or suction-line valves.
15. Ice or moisture in adjustment side of expansion valve.
16. Ice freezing in seat of expansion valve.
17. High head pressure.
18. Compressor losing efficiency through water.
19. Compressor may be too small.

Compressor Discharge Valve Defective

1. Low head pressure.
2. Poor refrigeration.
3. Compressor excessively warm.
4. If compressor is stopped, pressure will equalize.

Expansion-Valve Needle Stuck Open

1. Poor refrigeration.
2. High head pressure if stuck partially open.
3. Low head pressure and high back pressure, if stuck wide open.
4. Frosted or sweating suction line.
5. Hissing sound at valve.
6. Impossible to adjust for higher or lower back pressures.
7. On methyl chloride and F-12 units, this may be caused by moisture freezing at seat.

8. Improper oil freezing at seat.
9. Improper oil and high compressor temperatures may result in carbonization which may build up at expansion valve, especially if filters are defective.

Expansion-Valve Needle Stuck Closed

1. No refrigeration if shut tight.
2. Little refrigeration if partially stuck shut.
3. Evaporater will be pumped down so that low side will show an unduly low pressure.
4. A pinched liquid line, plugged filter, or closed hand valve will give the same symptoms.
5. On methly chloride and F-12 units, this may be caused by moisture freezing in the expansion valves.

High Head Pressure

1. Air in system.
2. Excessive charge of refrigerant.
3. Air or water going through condenser at too high a temperature.
4. Air circulation over condenser blocked if air-cooled type.
5. If water-cooled, water may be turned off or restricted.
6. Rotation of motor reversed.
7. If a higher setting is used on the expansion valve, the head pressure will be higher, and vice versa.

Unable to Adjust Valve

1. Refrigeration shortage.
2. Compressor valve broken or defective.
3. Partially plugged screens or filters.
4. Liquid line pinched almost closed.
5. Stoppage in fitting or restriction in liquid line.

6. Needle or seat eroded and leaky.
7. Oil-logged coil.
8. Ice in adjustment side of expansion valve.

Low Head Pressure

1. Refrigerant shortage.
2. Worn pistons.
3. Head or clearance gasket too thick.
4. Suction valve worn, split, or stuck.
5. Low setting on expansion valve.
6. Gasket between cylinders split.

Suction Line and Drier Coil Frosted or Sweating

1. Expansion valve stuck open or leaky.
2. Needle seat eroded or corroded.
3. Valve set at too high a back pressure.
4. Ice or moisture in adjustment side of expansion valve.
5. Thermostat out of order or poorly located.
6. Fan not operating, so that air is not blown over coils.
7. No water, or water pump not operating to pass water over evaporator.

COMMON TROUBLES IN THERMOSTATIC EXPANSION-VALVE SYSTEMS WITH LOW-SIDE OR THERMOSTATIC CONTROL

Refrigerant Shortage

1. Continuous operation.
2. Low head pressure.
3. Poor refrigeration.
4. Warm or hot liquid line.

5. Evaporator coils not chilled throughout entire length.
6. Hissing at expansion valve.

Poor Refrigeration

1. Heavy coating of ice or frost on evaporator coils.
2. Valve set too high.
3. Refrigerant shortage.
4. Thermostat bulb placed where there is little change in coil temperature.
5. Thermostat bulb placed where it is in a cold pocket and not affected by average conditions.
6. Expansion valve set too low.
7. Pigtail of valve improperly placed, so that maximum coil surface is not used.
8. Compressor valves defective, broken, or sticking.
9. Liquid line pinched.
10. Suction line pinched.
11. Strainer clogged.
12. Suction line too small for job.
13. Partially closed liquid- or suction-line hand valves.
14. Compressor too small for job.
15. Moisture in methyl chloride or F-12 refrigerant.

Compressor Discharge Valve Defective

1. Low head pressure.
2. Poor refrigeration.
3. When compressor is stopped, pressures equalize.

Expansion-Valve Needle Stuck Open

1. Continuous operation.
2. Poor refrigeration.
3. High head pressure.

4. Hissing air-expansion valve.
5. Moisture in methyl chloride or F-12 refrigerant.

Low Head Pressure

1. Shortage of refrigerant.
2. Worn pistons in compressor.
3. Warped, split, or stuck discharge valve.
4. Suction valve warped, split, or stuck.
5. Needle stuck wide open.
6. Gasket between cylinders split.
7. Thermostatic bulb discharged.

Suction Line and Drier Coil Sweating or Frosted

1. Needle stuck open.
2. Needle or seat eroded and leaky.
3. Valve set too high above cut-out point.
4. Control-switch points fused together.
5. Low-side control switch locked in operating position.

Expansion-Valve Needle Stuck Partially Closed

1. Little or no refrigeration.
2. The high-pressure safety cut-out may trip.
3. Evaporator will be pumped down and show a low pressure at below cut-in pressure.
4. If the liquid line is plugged, the thermostatic bulb discharged, or the capillary tube pinched, the result will be the same as a needle stuck shut.

High Head Pressure

1. The high-pressure safety cut-out may cause system to be stopped.
2. Air in the system.

3. Overcharge of refrigerant.
4. Air or water passing over condenser at too high a temperature.
5. If unit is water cooled, flow may be restricted or turned off.
6. If a high setting is used on the expansion valve (resulting in high back pressure), the head pressure will be higher than if the suction pressure were low.
7. Rotation of fan for cooling condenser reversed.
8. Fan blades bent or the air passing over condenser restricted.

Unable to Adjust Valve

1. Oil-logged evaporator.
2. Shortage of refrigerant.
3. Compressor valve broken or stuck.
4. Partially plugged screen in filter.
5. Liquid line pinched.
6. Stoppage in fitting or restriction in liquid line.
7. Stop-valve seat dropped and sealing open.
8. Charge lost in valve bulb.
9. Valve bulb loosened in its cradle by frost action; not making proper contact.
10. Valve covered; not open to atmospheric conditions.
11. Valve in too cold a location.

An air-conditioning unit is dependent on the perfect operation of the refrigerating apparatus. Of course, water pumps, spray heads, nozzles, drains, eliminators, ducts, and distributing openings must be in proper order. Any trouble entailing individual parts should be easily detected, and only found through proper analysis. As a general rule, the customer should be questioned to obtain an idea of just how the unit performed when it was first

Table 1. Pressure in Pounds Per Square In. (Gauge) or Inches of Vacuum Corresponding to Temperature in Degrees F. for Various Common Refrigerants

Temp., °F.	Ammonia NH_3	Sulfur dioxide SO_2	Methyl chloride CH_3Cl	Ethane C_2H_6	Propane C_3H_8	Ethyl chloride C_2H_5Cl	Carbon dioxide CO_2	Butane C_4H_{10}	Iso-butane C_4H_{10}	Freon F-12 CCl_2F_2	Carrene CH_2Cl_2	Methyl formate $C_2H_4O_2$
− 40	8.7"	23.5"	15.7"	99.8#	1.5#		131.1#			11.0"		
− 35	5.4"	22.4"	14.4"	109.8#	3.4#		156.3#			8.4"		
− 30	1.6"	21.1"	11.6"	120.3#	5.6#		163.1#			5.5"		
− 25	1.3#	19.6"	9.2"	132.0#	8.0#		176.3#			2.3"		
− 20	3.6#	17.9"	6.1"	144.8#	10.7#	25.3"	205.8#		14.6"	0.5#		
− 15	6.2#	16.1"	2.3"	157 #	13.6#	24.5"	225.8#		13.0"	2.4#		
− 10	9.0#	13.9"	0.2#	172 #	16.7#	23.6"	247.0#		11.0"	4.5#	28.1"	
− 5	12.2#	11.5"	2.0#	187 #	20.0#	22.6"	269.7"		8.8"	6.8#	27.8"	
0	15.7#	8.8"	3.8#	204 #	23.5#	21.5"	293.9#	15.0"	6.3"	9.2#	27.5"	26.5"
+ 5	19.6#	5.8"	6.2#	221 #	27.4#	20.3"	319.7#	12.2"	3.3"	11.9#	27.1"	25.9"
+ 10	23.8#	2.6"	8.6#	239 #	31.4#	18.9"	347.1#	11.1"	0.2"	14.7#	26.7"	25.4"
+ 15	28.4#	0.5#	11.2#	257 #	35.9#	17.4"	376.3#	8.8"	1.6#	17.7#	26.2"	24.7"
+ 20	33.5#	2.4#	13.6#	227 #	40.8#	15.8"	407.3#	6.3"	3.5#	21.1#	25.6"	24.0"
+ 25	39.0#	4.6#	17.2#	292 #	46.2#	14.0"	440.1#	3.6"	5.5#	24.6#	24.9"	23.1"
+ 30	45.0#	7.0#	20.3#	320 #	51.6#	12.2"	474.9#	0.6"	7.6#	28.5#	24.3"	22.3"
+ 35	51.6#	9.6#	24.0#	343 #	57.3#	10.1"	511.7#	1.3#	9.9#	32.6#	23.5"	21.1"

+ 40	58.6#	12.4#	28.1#	368 #	63.3#	8.0"	550.7#	3.0#	12.2#	37.0#	22.6"	20.0"
+ 45	66.3#	15.5#	32.2#	390 #	69.9#	5.4"	591.8#	4.9#	14.8#	41.7#	21.7"	18.7"
+ 50	74.5#	18.8#	36.3#	413 #	77.1#	2.3"	635.3#	6.9#	17.8#	46.7#	20.7"	17.3"
+ 55	83.4#	22.4#	41.7#	438 #	84.6#	0.3#	681.2#	9.1#	20.8#	52.0#	19.5"	15.7"
+ 60	92.9#	26.2#	46.3#	466 #	92.4#	1.9#	729.5#	11.6#	24.0#	57.7#	18.2"	14.0"
+ 65	103.1#	30.4#	53.6#	496 #	100.7#	3.3#	780.4#	14.2#	27.5#	63.7#	16.7"	11.9"
+ 70	114.1#	34.9#	57.8#	528 #	109.3#	6.2#	834.0#	16.9#	31.1#	70.1#	15.1"	9.8"
+ 75	125.8#	39.8#	64.4#	569 #	118.5#	8.3#	890.4#	19.8#	35.0#	76.9#	13.4"	7.3"
+ 80	138.3#	45.0#	72.3#	610 #	128.1#	10.5#	949.6#	22.9#	39.2#	84.1#	11.5"	4.9"
+ 85	151.7#	50.9#	79.4#	657 #	138.4#	12.9#	1011.3#	26.2#	43.9#	91.7#	8.4"	2.4"
+ 90	165.9#	56.5#	87.3#	693 #	149 #	15.4#		29.8#	48.6#	99.6#	7.3"	0.5#
+ 95	181.1#	62.9#	95.6#		160 #	18.2#		33.2#	53.7#	108.1#	5.0"	2.1#
+100	197.2#	69.8#	102.3#		172 #	21.0#		37.5#	59.0#	116.9#	2.4"	3.8#
+105	214.2#	77.1#	113.4#		185 #	24.3#		41.7#	64.6#	126.2#	0.19#	5.8#
+110	232.2#	85.1#	118.3#		197 #	27.3#		46.1#	70.4#	136.0#	1.6#	7.7#
+115	251.5#	93.5#	128.6#		207.6#	31.6#			76.7#	146.5#	3.1#	10.4#
+120	271.7#	106.4#	139.3#		218.3#	35.5#			84.3#	157.1#	4.7#	13.1#
+125	293.1#	111.9#	150.3#		232.3#	39.5#			90.1#	168.6#	6.6#	15.7#
+130	315.6#	121.9#	161.3#		246.3#	44.0#			97.3#	180.2#	8.4#	18.2#

Note " inches of mercury
Note # PSIG

installed. First, check the fuses, electric lines, automatic starting devices, and the motor or motors when a self-contained unit is encountered.

Remember that the fuses, if blown, blew because of some extra-heavy load. Something out of the ordinary caused the overload. Therefore, check to determine the cause of this overload, and correct the fault before placing the machine in operation. If the defect is not corrected, further attempts to operate the compressor or motor may result in damage. When the motor and compressor are operating, the pressure of both high and low sides should be determined. The refrigerant should be determined and the pressures checked against the temperatures, as shown in Table 1.

REFRIGERANT PRESSURES

Table 1 lists 12 of the most common refrigerants which can be encountered in almost any unit. The column at the left in the table is temperature in degrees Fahrenheit. Each refrigerant is listed in a column, and the pressures given in these columns are listed in *pounds of pressure per square inch (gauge)*, or in inches of mercury if the pressures are below zero pounds gauge pressure. The temperatures are given in five-degree increments within the range of normal practice. The very low temperatures are seldom employed, but have been included for convenience. If the desired temperature lies between any two of the given temperatures, a little arithmetic can be used and the corresponding pressure can be obtained with sufficient accuracy to set valves or controls. To determine the vaporization pressure in the evaporator, the temperature of the liquid must be decided on.

For convenience, let us select ammonia as the refrigerant and decide to have the ammonia boil at 10° above zero F. With an ammonia system, the refrigerating plant will probably be located in the basement or on the roof and will be used to cool brine. The cooled brine will be pumped to the cooling coils at about 25° F. First, run down the temperature column until the 10-degree line is found, then follow the line horizontally to the right, and under the heading of Ammonia, read the pressure 23.8 lbs. The head or condensing pressures can then be checked. This

Table 2. Factors to be Added to the Initial Temperatures of the Coolant In Order That Condenser Temperatures May Be Determined

Evap. °F.	Initial Coolant Temp. °F.				
	60°	70°	80°	90°	100°
−30	15	15	15	10	10
−25	15	15	15	15	10
−20	20	20	15	15	15
−15	20	20	20	15	15
−10	20	20	20	15	15
− 5	20	20	20	15	15
0	25	25	20	20	15
+ 5	30	30	30	25	20
+10	35	35	30	25	20
15	40	35	30	25	20
20	40	35	30	25	25
25	45	40	35	30	30
30	50	45	40	35	35
35	50	50	45	45	40

is done by taking the temperature of the outlet water if the refrigerating unit is water-cooled, as is the case with ammonia apparatus. When we assume that the water is leaving the condenser at a temperature of 90° F., a reference to the table indicates that the head pressure should be in the vicinity of 166 lbs. Usual pressures will be a few pounds higher in actual practice.

If air-cooled apparatus is encountered, the temperature of the air passing over the condenser must first be determined. Let us assume that the air passing over the condenser is 70° F. In Table 2, it will be observed that a temperature column is also given which is the temperature of the liquid in the evaporator. In our particular case, the ammonia is evaporating at a temperature of 10° F. Therefore, find this specific temperature in the left-hand column and then continue horizontally from that point to the column headed 70° F. At this intersection, the figure 35 is given. This figure (35) is added to the temperature of the air (70), which gives a total of 105° F. Turn to Table 1 and find the 105° F. line, which is the pressure corresponding to the pressure that exists in the condenser. Table 1 gives the temperature at which boiling or vaporization of each particular refrigerant takes place; the pressure at which this occurs is listed under the refrigerant type.

If the refrigerant is ammonia at 15.7 *psig.*, the liquid will boil at 0° F. If it is desired to have a somewhat colder liquid, alter the pressure. This is accomplished in the refrigerating apparatus by adjusting the temperature control, if a thermostat is the control feature (such as with a low-side float), or by adjusting the thermostat or pressurestat in either a high-side or low-side float system. The continued operation will lower the evaporator temperature and the temperature of the room in which the evaporator is located. With an expansion-valve system, if a thermostat is employed to stop and start the system, the thermostat can be adjusted for a higher or lower temperature. Before and after the adjustment, it is important that the serviceman check the frost line on the evaporator.

If the expansion valve is opened to admit more refrigerant so that the pressure is raised and its boiling temperature increased, the suction line may frost back. Also, if the expansion valve is closed so that less refrigerant enters the evaporator, the compressor will be able to hold the evaporator at a lower pressure and a lower temperature. When this is done, only a portion of the coil may be effective. A coil must contain liquid refrigerant to be able to refrigerate. Therefore, if only half the coil is frosted, the other dry half might just as well be taken out, since it is doing no work. The best plan is to maintain the highest pressure possible so that the compressor will work on the densest vapor without having the suction line frost back.

It may be desirable, however, to make a change in the suction pressure so that the temperature of the coils can be altered. Thus, with ammonia, if it is desired that the coil temperature be 20° F., the expansion valve must be adjusted to maintain a constant pressure of 33.5 *psig.* in the evaporator. If a 40° temperature is desired, a 58.6 *psig.* reading on the low side would have to be maintained. If a 40° temperature were required in the evaporator of a methyl-chloride system, the expansion valve would have to be adjusted to hold a constant pressure of 28.1 *psig.*

Table 1 lists the temperature of the liquid refrigerant boiling at the constant pressure given. One factor cannot be varied without varying the other. The only way to obtain another boiling temperature is to adjust the expansion valve to maintain the pressure that corresponds to the temperature desired. If the liquid is contained in a vessel or cylinder, and the vessel is closed (such as in a supply drum), it will be observed that the pressure in such a vessel will be from one to five pounds greater than the temperature of the drum. This is due to the fact that pressure has built up and prohibits further evaporation. If a system contains an unknown refrigerant, such as one without an odor, the serviceman can determine which one it is if he will take a pressure reading of the refrigerant at rest; that is, while not in operation. That pressure which corresponds nearest to the reading will be that of the particular refrigerant tested.

If an attempt is made to make a combined low-side and high-side table, the pressures existing in the high side of the apparatus are known to vary with the condenser design, condition of its surfaces, amount of oil or oil film, amount of water or air passing over the condenser, the density of the gas being evaporated, super-heating effect due to long lines, and other equally important factors. There are many variable factors that affect the accuracy of such a table of refrigerants. Oil films, restrictions, superheating of gas, coating of frost and moisture on the evaporator, variation in pressure, change in cooling temperature, condition of the condenser, etc., all serve to bring about some change in the final pressure. In the majority of cases, Table 1 will provide adequate accuracy. Size, condition of the condenser, and the presence of air will bring about changes, increasing the head pressure considerably. Table 1 is based on determining, from a pressure reading of the low side or evaporator, just what the temperature of the boiling liquid may be. With a methyl-chloride system, if the low-pressure gauge reads 2 *psig.*, the temperature corresponding to this pressure is given as −5° F. in the table.

With the temperature of the evaporator known (−5° F.), refer to Table 2. The first column in the table on the left-hand side is the evaporator temperature. The other columns refer to the temperature of the water or air that is passed over the condenser. Assume for instance, that the room temperature is 70° F. and that the air is passing over the condenser at this temperature.

Since the evaporator temperature is known, find this temperature in the first column and then find the proper column for the coolant temperature (70° F.). At the intersection or box under these conditions, the figure 20 is given. This is added to the initial temperature, thus: 20° plus 70° = 90°. Take this figure (90°) and refer back to Table 1. Run down the temperature column to 90° and then across to the methyl-chloride column. It is found that a head or condensing pressure of about 87.3 lbs. can be expected. If the actual pressure reading varies from this, check the condition of the apparatus.

It is essential to obtain a pressure reading on the low or evaporator side, so that the temperature of the refrigerant can be determined. If the reading indicates too high a temperature, the expansion valve will have to be adjusted to maintain the proper pressure, and, of course, the proper evaporating temperature. Head pressures are important; excessive pressures indicate something out of the ordinary.

STARTING A SYSTEM

Whether the system is large or small, it is best to check it by starting with the refrigerating apparatus. This should be done before a new or strange unit is operated. The serviceman will usually save time by also checking for a faulty system at this point. First, turn the compressor over by hand, and see that it is absolutely free of obstructions. Examine the belt to be sure that it is in good condition. If the belt has begun to show signs of wear, or has stretched to a point at which there is no longer any take-up, a new belt should be installed.

Be sure that the belt is clean and flexible. If it is covered with dust, wipe it off with a piece of coarse cloth, otherwise slippage may occur. If the belt is covered with oil, it is best to clean it before putting it in operation. Never apply oil to leather or rubber belts; use the proper belt dressing. If the drive is of the multiple V-belt type, examine all the belts. If one or more belts are worn or stretched, the entire group should be changed. Never attempt to replace only one belt in a multiple V-belt drive, since the new belt will assume all of the load and will produce operating trouble. When a direct drive is used, check the coupling member. Some are driven by means of flexible leather or rubber discs. See that the discs are in their proper order and are not cracked or split. If the compressor is gear-driven, check the oil and its condition in the gear box.

MOTORS

Check the motor armature brushes and their holders. Make certain that the brush faces make proper contact with the commutator and that they are not worn too short. It is important that the brushes slide freely in their holders. Oil will occasionally gum up the holders and prevent the brushes from moving freely. If this condition is found, remove the brushes and scrape them clean. Wash the holders with carbon tetrachloride and remove the grease. On AC motors, slip the belt off and, after checking fuses and starting devices, allow the motor to start. Check the short-circuiting device by timing the throw-in. If it is delayed or too hasty, clean and readjust the device to its proper operating condition.

COMPRESSORS

If the compressor is driven by a V-belt, check the tension. When driven by a flat belt, be sure that the pulleys are in line and that the direction is proper. Check the idler, and make certain that the bearings are in proper working order. Idlers are neglected in most cases and soon show signs of wear. For this reason, check them carefully, and if signs of looseness are indicated, install new bearings. Be sure that the oil or grease cups are filled. It is best to unscrew the oil or grease cups and make sure that the channel is free and clear by running a wire through first and then washing it with carbon tetrachloride. The compressor shaft should turn over freely. Check the condition of the oil, and if it is dirty, change it; use the proper oil. The oil must be absolutely dry and kept in sealed cans. It must be of the proper viscosity and of the type intended for the refrigerant contained in the system. Fill the compressor crankcase to the proper level. In most cases, this will be a point just below the center of the crankshaft.

The suction and discharge valves should be pulled out of the compressor and examined for wear or corrosion. If they are worn, warped, cracked, or not properly seated, the valves should be changed or carefully ground to the correct size. Be sure to remove all traces of the grinding compound. See that the stuffing box is in proper order. If there is a puddle of oil outside or underneath it, investigate. It may need tightening or a new ring or packing, depending on the individual type and trouble. Check the packing around the stems of the suction and discharge shut-off valves. The packing may be dry and frayed. If so, remove and replace it with new asbestos-graphite packing. Make sure that both of these valves are open wide before any attempt is made to turn the compressor over by means of the motor. If the unit is water-cooled, check the scale trap, condenser, and compressor jacket to make sure that they are comparatively clean and not clogged with scale. Some units have a combination condenser-receiver arrangement. In this type of unit, remove one of the heads and check its internal condition.

When working on a system, make sure that it has the proper charge; have a gas mask handy in the event of a bad leak. Never remove a head or a flare nut until after the two faces are separated. If there is any gas pressure, it will blow out and pressure will be released. Merely loosen the nuts, thus permitting them to be tightened quickly if necessary to prevent a bad leak. Examine the filters and make sure that they are clean. If they are not, install new filters or wash the old ones, depending on the type. Check the water pump and its motor. Be sure that the packing is tight and in good condition. If the packing nut is tight, pull out the old packing and replace it. Check the bearings to be sure that they are oiled or greased. The water-pump motor must be examined; oil, brushes, alignment, and direction of rotation must be carefully checked and corrected if faulty.

AIR CONDITIONING SYSTEM TROUBLE CHART

Compressor Will Not Start

Possible Cause	Possible Remedy
Thermostat setting too high	Reset thermostat below room temperature.
High head pressure.	Reset starter overload and determine cause of high head pressure.
Defective pressure switch.	Repair or replace pressure switch.
Loss of refrigerant charge.	Check system for leaks.
Compressor frozen.	Replace compressor.

Compressor Short Cycles

Possible Cause	Possible Remedy
Defective thermostat.	Replace thermostat.
Incorrect setting on low side of pressure switch.	Reset low-pressure switch differential.
Low refrigerant charge.	Check system for leaks; repair and add refrigerant.
Defective overload.	Replace overload.
Dirty or iced evaporator.	Clean or defrost evaporator.

Evaporator blower and motor belts slipping.	Tighten or replace belts.
Dirty or plugged filters.	Clean or replace air filters.

Compressor Runs Continuously

Possible Cause	*Possible Remedy*
Excessive load.	Check for excessive outside air infiltration and excessive source of moisture.
Air or noncondensable gases in the system.	Purge system.
Dirty condenser.	Clean condenser.
Condenser blower and motor belts slipping.	Tighten or replace belts.
Thermostat setting too low.	Reset thermostat.
Low refrigerant charge.	Check system for leaks; repair and add refrigerant.
Overcharge of refrigerant.	Purge and remove excess refrigerant.
Compressor valves leaking.	Replace compressor.
Expansion valve or strainer plugged.	Clean expansion valve or strainer.

System Short of Capacity

Possible Cause	*Possible Remedy*
Low refrigerant charge.	Check system for leaks; repair and add refrigerant.
Incorrect superheat setting of expansion valve.	Adjust superheat to 10° F.
Defective expansion valve.	Repair or replace valve.
Air or noncondensable gases in the system.	Purge system.
Condenser blower and motor belts slipping.	Tighten or replace belts.
Overcharge of refrigerant.	Purge excess refrigerant.
Compressor valves leaking.	Replace compressor valves.
Expansion valve or strainer plugged.	Clean valve or strainer.
Condenser air short-circuiting.	Remove obstructions or causes of short.

Head Pressure Too High

Possible Cause	*Possible Remedy*
Overcharge of refrigerant.	Purge excess refrigerant.

Air or noncondensable gases in system.	Purge system.
Dirty condenser.	Clean condenser.
Condenser blower and motor belts slipping.	Tighten or replace belts.
Condenser air short-circuiting.	Remove obstructions or causes of short-circuiting air.

Head Pressure Too Low

Possible Cause	Possible Remedy
Low refrigerant charge.	Check system for leaks; repair and add refrigerant.
Compressor valves leaking.	Replace compressor valves.

Suction Pressure Too High

Possible Cause	Possible Remedy
Excessive load on system.	Remvoe conditions causing excessive load.
Expansion valve is struck in "Open" position.	Repair or replace expansion valve.
Incorrect superheat setting of expansion valve.	Adjust superheat setting to 10° F.

Suction Pressure Too Low

Possible Cause	Possible Remedy
Low refrigerant charge.	Check system for leaks; repair and add refrigerant.
Expansion valve or strainer plugged.	Clean expansion valve or strainer.
Incorrect superheat setting of expansion valve.	Adjust superheat setting to 10° F.
Evaporator air volume low.	Increase air over evaporator.
Stratification of cool air in conditioned area.	Increase air velocity through grilles.

Compressor Is Noisy

Possible Cause	Possible Remedy
Worn or scored compressor bearings.	Replace compressor.
Expansion valve is stuck in "Open" position or defective.	Repair or replace expansion valve.

Overcharge of refrigerant or air in system.	Purge system.
Liquid refrigerant flooding back to compressor.	Repair or replace expansion valve.
Shipping or hold-down bolts not loosened.	Loosen compressor hold-down bolts so compressor is freely floating in mountings.

Compressor and Condenser Fan Motor Will Not Start

Possible Cause	Possible Remedy
Power failure.	Check electrical wiring back to fuse box.
Fuse blown.	Replace blown or defective fuse.
Thermostat setting too high.	Reduce temperature setting of room thermostat.
Defective thermostat.	Replace or repair thermostat.
Faulty wiring.	Check wiring and make necessary repairs.
Defective controls.	Check and replace defective controls.
Low voltage.	Reset and check for cause of tripping.
Defective dual pressure control.	Replace the control.

Compressor Will Not Start, but the Condenser Fan Motor Runs

Possible Cause	Possible Remedy
Faulty wiring to compressor.	Check compressor wiring and repair.
Defective compressor motor.	Replace the compressor.
Defective compressor overload. (Single phase only).	Replace overload.
Defective starting capacitor (Single phase only).	Replace capacitor.

Condenser Fan Motor Will Not Start, but Compressor Runs

Possible Cause	Possible Remedy
Faulty wiring to fan motor.	Check fan-motor wiring and repair.
Defective fan motor.	Replace fan motor.

Condenser Fan Motor Runs, but the Compressor Hums and Will Not Start

Possible Cause	Possible Remedy
Low voltage.	Check line voltage. Determine the location of the voltage drop.
Faulty wiring.	Check wiring and make necessary repairs.

515

Defective compressor.	Replace compressor.
High head pressure.	Check head pressure and complete operation of system to remove the cause of the high pressure condition.
Failure of one phase. (Three-phase units only).	Check fuses and wiring.
Defective start capacitor. (Single phase only).	Replace capacitor.
Defective potential relay. (Single phase only).	Replace relay.

Compressor Starts, but Cycles On Overload

Possible Cause	*Possible Remedy*
Low voltage.	Check line voltage. Determine the location of the voltage drop.
Faulty wiring.	Check wiring and make necessary repairs.
Defective running capacitor. (Single phase only).	Replace capacitor.
Defective overload.	Replace overload.
Unbalanced line (Three phase only).	Check wiring; call power company.

Evaporator Fan Motor Will Not Start

Possible Cause	*Possible Remedy*
Power failure.	Check electrical wiring back to fuse box.

CHAPTER 20

Electric Motors and Their Control

It is of the utmost importance that a refrigeration serviceman know the fundamental laws of electricity as well as the principles upon which electric motors operate, since practically all condensing units are electrically operated, being driven by an electric motor. In order for the cooling unit to operate automatically, the motor must connect and disconnect itself as the temperature conditions of the chilling unit require.

Numerous electrical devices are necessary to provide this essential control, and while it is impossible to describe all such devices which might be used, a good practical knowledge of the characteristics of a particular device is important. Before an attempt is made to describe the customary electrical devices used in an automatic refrigeration system and their control, the following electrical definitions will be of value.

UNITS OF ELECTRICITY

In a direct current system, the products of *volts* multiplied by *amperes* equals watts. Thus one watt is produced when one ampere flows under a pressure of one volt. This relationship is written:

$$\text{Ampere} \times \text{volts} = \text{watts, or}$$
$$IE = W$$

The relations between current flow, resistance and pressure is written:

$$\text{Amperes} \times \text{resistance} = \text{volts, or}$$
$$IR = E$$

where

I = current in *amperes*
R = resistance in *ohms*
E = pressure in *volts*

The unit of power is usually expressed in kilowatts or horsepower. The relationship between horsepower, kilowatt, and watt is:

$$1 \text{ kilowatt} = 1,000 \text{ watts}$$

One horsepower contains 746 watts. Therefore, to reduce *kilowatts* to *horsepower,* it is necessary to divide 1,000 by 746, or

$$1KW = \frac{1,000}{746} = 1.34 \, HP$$

From this we know that *kilowatts* may be converted into *horsepower* by multiplying by 1.34. The formulas given are fundamental only and may be rewritten to suit any particular condition or requirement, as shown in Table 1.

THE ELECTRIC CIRCUIT

A simple way to consider electricity is to use the example of water flowing through a pipe. In a manner similar to the flow of water in a pipe, electrical conductors are arranged to form a path for the flow of an electric current. The paths in which electric current flows is called *electric* circuits. Current, which is

Table 1. Variations of Ohms Law

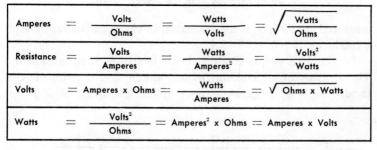

Amperes	$=$	$\dfrac{\text{Volts}}{\text{Ohms}}$	$=$	$\dfrac{\text{Watts}}{\text{Volts}}$	$=$	$\sqrt{\dfrac{\text{Watts}}{\text{Ohms}}}$
Resistance	$=$	$\dfrac{\text{Volts}}{\text{Amperes}}$	$=$	$\dfrac{\text{Watts}}{\text{Amperes}^2}$	$=$	$\dfrac{\text{Volts}^2}{\text{Watts}}$
Volts	$=$	Amperes x Ohms	$=$	$\dfrac{\text{Watts}}{\text{Amperes}}$	$=$	$\sqrt{\text{Ohms x Watts}}$
Watts	$=$	$\dfrac{\text{Volts}^2}{\text{Ohms}}$	$=$	Amperes^2 x Ohms	$=$	Amperes x Volts

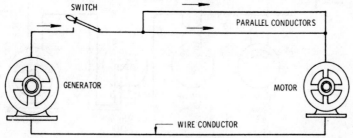

Fig. 1. A simple electric circuit consisting of a generator, motor, switch and a series of wire conductors.

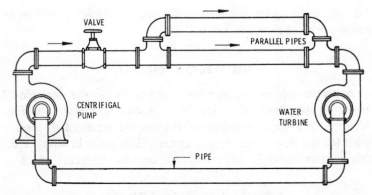

Fig. 2. A water system consisting of a pump, turbine, pipes and valves which correspond to the electric circuit.

measured in amperes, is the movement of electrons (water) through a conductor (pipe).

In Fig. 1, a simple electric circuit is shown diagrammatically. This consists of a generator, motor, switch, and a series of wire conductors. Fig. 2 shows a water system consisting of a pump,

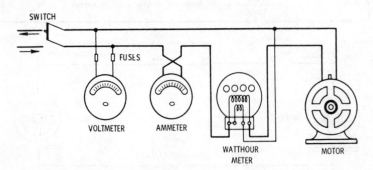

Fig. 3. Illustrating the method of connecting instruments in a circuit to measure voltage and current.

water turbine, pipes, and valve which corresponds to this electric circuit. The amount of water flowing through the pipe expressed in gallons per minute would correspond to the flow of current through the wire expressed in amperes. The pressure of water in the pipe expressed in pounds per square inch would correspond to the pressure of electricity, or the voltage of the circuit as it is usually expressed.

DIRECT CURRENT (DC)

The flow of electricity in a wire is often compared to the flow of water in a pipe. In a *direct current* circuit a voltmeter connected across the line and an ammeter connected in series with it (Fig. 3), will read the true voltage and current. The product of the two readings will be the power in *watts* used.

ALTERNATING CURRENT (AC)

This type of current, as its name implies, fluctuates in regular pulsations or cycles. It is a pulsating current but the flow analogy can be continued if we consider the movement of electricity in the wire comparable to the pulsating flow of refrigerant gas from the compressor in the discharge pipe. The difference in the analogy becomes evident when the flow of current or flow of pulsating gas is forced to perform useful work. The work it has to do dictates how the result is accomplished. With *DC*, the current and voltage work together because of the steady movement, as shown in Fig. 4. In *AC,* the current and voltage only work together (in phase) when a certain kind of load is connected to the line. This is illustrated in Fig. 5.

If the load is made up of resistance only, such as lights or heater elements, the voltage and current are in phase. If volts

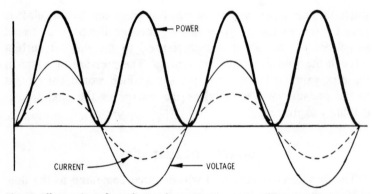

Fig. 4. *Illustrating the relation between current, voltage, and power in an alternating current circuit.*

are multiplied by amperes, the true watts of the circuit are ob-obtained, just like in a *DC* circuit. It is as though the open throttle valve (resistance) of the gas circuit does not disarrange the even balance between the surge of pressure and the quantity of gas going through the line. If an inductive load, like a motor,

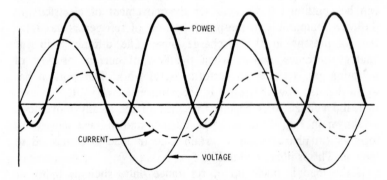

Fig. 5. *Illustrating the current and voltage out of phase.*

is connected to the line, there is an upset to the balance between the surge of voltage and current. A voltmeter and ammeter inserted in the line would give a product which is still watts (called *apparent power*), but the total is not the same as that which would be indicated by a wattmeter installed in the line (*truepower*). It is comparable to inserting a gas pump in the gas line. Before the gas can enter the cylinder of the pump, the pressure must first open the inlet valve. After the inlet valve is open, then the flow of fluid starts, but since the pressure surge must act first, there is an appreciable lag before the flow starts. Thus, for an inductive load like a motor, the current lags behind the action of the voltage. The two actions are out of phase and, therefore, the product of the two does not give the true value of power.

POWER FACTOR

The ratio of the power shown by a wattmeter to the power found from the product of volts and amperes, as indicated by a separate voltmeter and ammeter, is called the *power factor*. It is an indication of the out-of-phase relationship of voltage and current. For lights and resistance loads, the power factor is unity. For induction motors, it is a lagging power factor, meaning current is lagging voltage. The power factor of a motor varies for different designs. It is a common error for the uninformed to assume that some motors are more efficient than others because the name plate for one motor shows a lower current value than that of another motor of equal horsepower. Actually, the amount of power really drawn from the line in kilowatts can be the same. The motor having the higher current merely has a lower value of *power factor*. This will easily be found by the assistance of the following example:

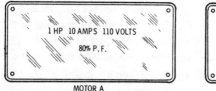 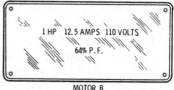

MOTOR A   MOTOR B

Fig. 6. Illustrating the typical data given on motor nameplate.

Two single-phase *AC* motors, *A* and *B* (Fig. 6), each having a capacity of one horsepower, has the data shown in the illustration on their respective nameplates.

The power taken from the line by the respective motor is:

Motor *A*—True Power = $110 \times 10 \times 0.80 = 880$ watts
Motor *B*—True Power = $110 \times 12.5 \times 0.64 = 880$ watts

The two motors using the same amount of power will cost the same to operate, even though motor *B* takes more current than motor *A*. There is one thing to notice, however. The motor with the lowest power factor will have more current flowing, which will require a change in size of thermal element in the starter to provide equal protection. Also, larger wiring has to be used to carry the heavier current.

FREQUENCY

The term *frequency* means the number of pulsations of the electric current which occurs during one second. The frequency of the current and the number of poles in the stator of a motor will determine the speed of the motor. The motor runs at an *in-phase* or *synchronous* speed, but there is usually a slip which causes it to run under this speed on full load.

To find the synchronous speed of any *AC* motor, use the equation below:

$$\text{Motor rpm} = \frac{120 \times \text{frequency}}{\text{number of motor poles}}$$

Thus, for example:

$$\text{Motor rpm} = \frac{120 \times 60}{4} = 1{,}800 \text{ rpm.}$$

Thus, all 4-pole 60-cycle motors that operate at a maximum of 1,800 rpm will usually be about 3% below this speed, due to slippage, or 1,750 rpm. A 4-pole 50-cycle motor that operates at a maximum of 1,500 rpm will usually be about 3% below this speed, due to slippage, or 1,450 rpm.

$$\text{Motor rpm} = \frac{120 \times 50}{4} = 1{,}500 \text{ rpm.}$$

Other examples at other frequencies can be worked out, remembering that the minimum number of poles is 2. An odd number of poles like 3, 5, 7, 9, etc., cannot be used. It must be an even number or any number that can be divided by 2.

ENERGY

Energy is the potential ability to do work. It is commonly expressed in terms of the rate at which the work is done and the time used in doing it. Since the rate of doing work is power, energy is equal to the product of power and time. For example, a five-horsepower motor requires two hours to pump the water to fill an elevated storage tank; the energy represented by this work is five times two hours, or ten horsepower-hours. Now, a ten-horsepower motor could do the same work in half the time, but the energy used would still be ten horsepower-hours. Mechanical energy is measured in horsepower-hours. Electrical energy is measured in *watts-hours,* or *kilowatt-hours.* A *kilowatt-hour* equals a *thousand watt-hours.*

If a power is known to remain constant on a circuit for a particular time interval, the energy can be determined by measuring the power with a wattmeter and multiplying this reading by the time in hours. For instance, if you measure the amount of energy consumed by one of our previously described motors during a period of 24 hours, assuming that the motors are running only 50% of the time mentioned, and assuming a constant current, we obtain:

$$\text{Energy consumed} = 880 \times 12 = 10{,}560 \text{ watt hours}$$

(or 10.56 kilowatt hours)

In power systems, however, it is an exception for both the load and voltage on a circuit to remain constant for any great length of time. Consequently, the method of measuring energy just described is not practical. To be practical, the measuring instrument must be sensitive to all changes in power and its recording element must sum up the power demand continuously for small intervals of time. An instrument that does this may be called an intergrating watt meter, but is generally known as a *watt-hour meter*, because its dials record the watt-hours (more commonly kilowatt hours) of energy passed through it. The *watt-hour meters* used in residences are smaller and, in most cases, have only one single-phase element.

MOTOR EFFICIENCY

The ratio of the actual power delivered at the pulley or shaft and the power input at the terminals of a motor (computed in the same units) is called the *motor efficiency*.

It is written:

$$\text{Efficiency} = \frac{\text{Output}}{\text{Input}}$$

An example in calculating the efficiency of a single-phase *AC* motor may be had by considering a motor whose nameplate has the following data:

1 HP. 10 *AMPS,* 110 *VOLTS, PF* 80%.

Since one horsepower equals 746 watts, a substitution in our equation gives:

$$\text{Efficiency} = \frac{746}{110 \times 10 \times 0.8} = 0.848 \text{ or } 85\% \text{ approx.}$$

It will readily be observed that the electrical power or the input to the motor may conveniently be measured at the motor terminals and reduced to horsepower by the usual method of calculation. The mechanical power developed by the motor is not readily available since the nameplate gives only the average power which the motor will deliver under normal conditions. The usual method adopted for calculating the mechanical power developed by a motor, and from which the efficiency may be obtained as previously described, is by the means of a *Prony brake test*.

As shown in Fig. 7, this brake consists of two blocks shaped to fit around the pulley of the motor. By means of two long bolts with handwheels at the top, the pressure of the blocks against the pulley can be varied. Two bars fastened to the top and bottom of the brake form an extension arm by which the torque of the motor is exerted upon the platform scale. The force factor,

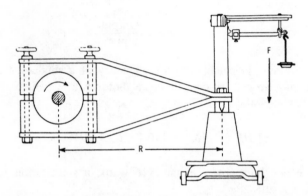

Fig. 7. Diagrammatic representation of arrangement for Prony brake test applied to the pulley of an electric motor.

F, of the torque is measured as the net reading on the scale in pounds; the radius factor, *R,* is measured in feet from the center of the shaft perpendicular to the bearing point on the scale.

The mechanical power of the motor equals its torque times the distance through which it operates per minute, or:

$$P = \frac{T \times 2 \times rpm}{33,000}$$

from which

$$T = \frac{P \times 5,250}{rpm}$$

where

P = power in terms of horsepower.

T = torque (= F × R) in pound feet.

2π = 6.2832 (the ratio of the circumference of a circle to the radius).

rpm = speed in revolutions per minute.

33,000 = number of foot pounds per minute equivalent to one horsepower.

As an example, we may make a test of a 4-horsepower motor which has a force of 5.5 pounds, the radius 2.5 feet, and the speed 1,440 rpm. The power delivered will be:

$$P = \frac{5.5 \times 2.5 \times 6.2832 \times 1,440}{33,000} = 3.77 \text{ horsepower}$$

To find the efficiency, we must measure (by means of a watt-meter or other suitable method) the input to the motor at the same time that the output is determined. Both output and input are then converted to the same units, preferably watts, and the efficiency found by the formula.

$$P = \frac{T \times 2 \times \text{rpm}}{33,000}$$

Other methods based upon the same principles, but somewhat more convenient in measuring the torque (or mechanical output of fractional-horsepower motors), are by means of a specially designed *Prony brake,* or by means of a *rope and weight.* The Prony and Rope method of testing torque for fractional horsepower motors is shown in Fig. 8.

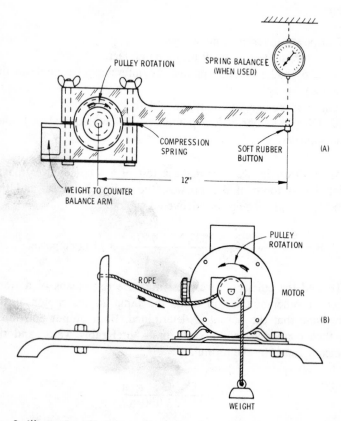

Fig. 8. Illustrating the Prony and Rope brake methods of testing torque for fractional horsepower motors.

The Prony brake, in this case, differs from that previously described only in construction. It requires a pulley, brake arm, and scale (may be either platform scale or spring balance). If a platform scale is used, be sure that the load is applied to the center of the platform. If a spring balance scale is used, the pull must always be at right angles to the brake arm, and in either case, the scale must have small enough variations to accurately read torque on smaller rated motors. The brake arm should be made up so that the distance between the center of the pulley and contact point where the load is measured is exactly 12 inches. The scale reading will then be in pound feet. Before starting the test, make sure that the direction of rotation is such that the brake arm will be moved *against* the balance.

In order to measure starting torque, clamp the arm to the pulley tight enough to allow the pulley to turn very slowly, then read the scale. To measure pull-in torque, release the clamp until the motor is just able to throw off the brushes and pull up to speed. Read the scale just as the brushes are leaving the commutator. The true pull-in torque is the highest scale reading at which time the motor brushes will throw-off and stay clear of the commutator.

ROPE-AND-WEIGHT METHOD

The rope-and-weight method gives equally staisfactory results and yet does not require the equipment of the *Prony brake* method. It requires a smooth faced flanged iron pulley, rope and weight. Tie one end of the rope to the projection from the test bench so that the rope will be at 90° to the shaft. Wrap the rope around the pulley opposite to the pulley rotation and hang a weight on the free end of the rope as shown in Fig. 8B. Wrap sufficient turns around the pulley so that the tie end of the rope will be slack when the weight is lifted and the pulley rotates. To prevent the rope from gripping the pulley, oil or paraffin the rope slightly. Be sure that the hanging weight does not touch the floor or test bench. Some protective measures should be taken to prevent the weight from injuring the operator in case the rope grips too tight. Increase the weight until the motor will just start, then calculate as follows:

For example, to test a ¼-*HP* 1,725-rpm motor, select a 4″ pulley, ⅛″ rope, and necessary weight. If an assortment of graduated weights are not handy, use a bucket and sand, adding weight so that the pulley is slowly turning.

$$\text{Brake arm} = \frac{\text{Pulley diameter in inches} + \text{rope diameter in inches}}{12 \times 2}$$

$$= \frac{4 + 0.125}{24} \text{ feet.}$$

Starting torque in lb. ft. = Brake arm × weight hung on rope

$$= \frac{4.125 \times W}{24}$$

$$\text{Full load torque in lb. ft.} = \frac{\text{Full load HP} \times 5250}{\text{Full load rpm}}$$

$$= \frac{0.25 \times 5{,}250}{1{,}725} = 0.76 \text{ lb. ft.}$$

$$\text{Starting torque in per cent of F.L. torque} = \frac{\text{Starting torque}}{\text{Full load torque}}$$

While both of these methods are widely used by small service organizations for checking test values on electric motors of all sizes, it should be specially noted that both methods do contain an element of danger to the operator, and should be used with extreme care from the standpoint of both safety to the operator and accuracy of the test results.

PULLEY SPEED AND SIZES

On a motor, the driving pulley is called the *driver,* and the driven compressor pulley or flywheel is called the *driven.* In some cases a gear drive is encountered in which the total number of teeth must be counted. For gears, therefore, the number of teeth should be substituted whenever diameter occurs. By the use of a formula, the unknown can be easily found if the other three factors are known. For instance, if one diameter and the two speeds are known, the other diameter can be ascertained. In order to illustrate the formula, the diagrammatic layout in Fig. 9 will be of assistance. The diameter and speed of both the driver and driven are given as a typical example.

CALCULATION OF DRIVER DIAMETER

Where the rpm of the driver, the rpm of the driven, and the diameter of the driven are known, the diameter of the driver

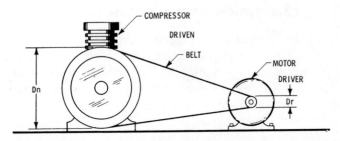

Fig. 9. Illustrating a typical belt arrangement for a motor and compressor drive.

may be found by multiplying the diameter of the driven by its rpm and dividing the product by the rpm of the driver. Thus, in accordance with the previous data, the problem may be written:

$$\text{dia. of driver} = \frac{\text{dia. of driven} \times \text{rpm of driven}}{\text{rpm of driver}} \text{ or}$$

$$Dr = \frac{Dn \times Rn}{Rr}$$

where
    Dn = Diameter of driven pulley.
    Dr = Diameter of drive pulley.
    Rn = Revolutions per minute of driven pulley.
    Rr = Revolutions per minute of driver pulley.

Example:

$$\frac{17 \times 200}{1,700} = 2'' \text{ diameter}$$

CALCULATION OF THE DRIVEN DIAMETER

Where the rpm of the driven, the rpm of the driver, and the diameter of the driver are known, the diameter of the driven can be determined by multiplying the diameter of the driver by its rpm and dividing the product by the rpm of the driven. In accordance with this, we may write:

$$\text{dia. of driven} = \frac{\text{dia. of driver} \times \text{rpm of driver,}}{\text{rpm of driven}} \text{ or}$$

$$Dn = \frac{Dr \times Rr}{Rn}$$

Example:

$$\frac{2 \times 1,700}{200} = 17'' \text{ diameter}$$

CALCULATION OF DRIVER RPM

Where the diameter of the driver, the diameter of the driven, and the rpm of the driven are known, the rpm of the driver can be found by multiplying the diameter of the driven by its rpm and dividing the product by the diameter of the driver. This may be written:

$$\text{rpm of driven} = \frac{\text{dia. of driven} \times \text{rpm of driver,}}{\text{dia. of driver}} \text{ or}$$

$$Rr = \frac{Dn \times Rn}{Dr}$$

Example:

$$\frac{17 \times 200}{2} = 1,700 \text{ rpm}$$

Where the diameter of the driven, the diameter of the driver and its rpm are known, the rpm of the driven can be found by multiplying the diameter of the driver by its rpm and dividing the product by the diameter of the driven. Therefore, we obtain:

$$\text{rpm of driven} = \frac{\text{dia. of driver} \times \text{rpm of driver}}{\text{dia. of driven}} \text{ or}$$

$$Rn = \frac{Dr \times Rr}{Dn}$$

Example:

$$\frac{2 \times 1,700}{17} = 200 \text{ rpm}$$

In the preceding calculations, no attention has been given to belt slip which may take place. Actual tests bear out that the slip factor may amount up to 3%, depending upon the size of pulleys, type of belt used, etc.

TYPE OF MOTORS USED

While there are many types of motors used in the various refrigerating units, the present trend is toward standarization within a few simple types. They are:

Where alternating current is available

1. The split-phase induction motor.
2. The repulsion-induction motor.
3. The capacitor (sometimes called condenser) motor.

Where direct current is available

1. The shunt-wound motor.
2. The compound-wound motor.

Induction motors operate on the principle of magnetic induction, in which the magnetic field in the rotor is induced by currents flowing in the stator, the rotor having no external connec-

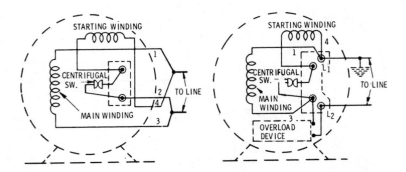

Fig. 10. Illustrating wiring diagrams of a split phase induction type motor.

tions. The magnetic action between the stator and rotor is similar to that of a transformer with its secondary short-circuited and current supplied to the primary. In the transformer, however, the energy would be given off as heat from the secondary, with the primary greatly overloaded. In the induction motor, the mechanical force produced between rotor and stator by the current is transformed into mechanical power.

Split-Phase Induction Motors

The split-phase motor is constructed with a separate starting and running winding. The purpose of the starting winding is to provide the extra torque needed to bring the motor up to its normal rate of speed, at which time it is automatically disconnected by means of an electrical relay device. This converts it into a simple single-phase induction motor. It should be noted that the wiring diagrams shown in Fig. 10 are of a representative type only. Since other connections are possible, each motor shall be connected according to the manufacturer's diagram.

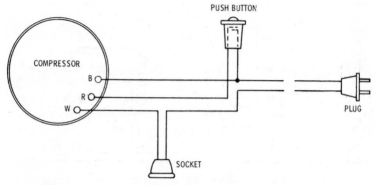

Fig. 11. A typical refrigerator test cord.

Reversal of rotation is obtained by reversing either the starting or running winding leads. This type of motor is commonly used in hermetic (sealed-in) units, but because of low starting torque, it will not start the compressor unless pressures and discharge are first equalized.

Method of Testing Sealed-in Units—Split-phase induction motors are supplied on numerous sealed-in domestic units. Testing a sealed unit to determine why it does not operate becomes a very simple process if the correct procedure is followed. Each test made should be one of a series of elimination tests to determine what part of the system is defective. By checking other parts of the wiring system before checking the unit itself, a great amount of time can be saved, as in most cases the trouble lies in the wiring or controls rather than in the unit.

In order to be able to make a complete electrical test on electrical outlets, and also on the unit itself, it is advisable to remodel the standard test cord by adding a weatherproof socket in the manner shown in Fig. 11. This is done by removing a small section of the rubber insulation from the cord between the push button and the terminal clips, thus exposing the three wires. Cut the white wire and connect the two wires from the socket at this point. This places the socket in series with the white wire and makes the standard test cord into a very useful tool in addition to its original purpose. By connecting the black and white terminal clips together and placing a light bulb in the socket, the cord may be used to check the wall outlet. By connecting the white and red terminal clips together, this same test may be made by depressing the push button. This will serve as a test to make certain the push button is in working order. When these tests have been completed, and it is known that current is being supplied to the unit, the next step is to check the three wires on the base of the compressor unit. Pull the plug from the wall receptacle and carefully examine the connecting nuts which hold the wires in position. Try each wire to be sure it is held firmly in place since a loose wire may keep the unit from operating.

Test the thermostatic switch to determine whether or not contact is being made at that point. Flip the *on* and *off* switch lever several times, and also check the position of the defroster button to be sure it is in the *off* position. If this fails to start the unit, then short out the thermostatic switch entirely. To do this, it is necessary to remove the cover from the motor protector relay, and short circuit the terminals of the red and black wires contained in the three-wire cord leading to the thermostatic switch. If the unit starts, it is an indication that the thermostatic switch is not operating properly and must be repaired or replaced. After the thermostatic switch has been checked, and if the trouble has not been located, it will be necessary to determine whether the trouble is in the motor or in the motor protector relay (motor operating relay).

The motor operating relay is used on most late-model household refrigerators. The function of this relay is to allow the com-

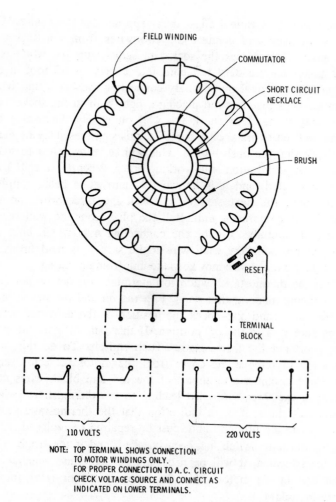

FIELD WINDING

COMMUTATOR

SHORT CIRCUIT
NECKLACE

BRUSH

RESET

TERMINAL
BLOCK

110 VOLTS

220 VOLTS

NOTE: TOP TERMINAL SHOWS CONNECTION
TO MOTOR WINDINGS ONLY.
FOR PROPER CONNECTION TO A.C. CIRCUIT
CHECK VOLTAGE SOURCE AND CONNECT AS
INDICATED ON LOWER TERMINALS.

Fig. 12. A typical wiring diagram of a single phase repulsion start
induction motor.

pressor motor to start on both starting and running windings and then disconnect the starting windings after the motor has reached a normal speed. The relay also has a thermal device which opens the circuit ahead of the motor when the circuit becomes overloaded. The thermal device resets automatically and will continue to cut-out and reset until the overload has passed.

Repulsion-Start Induction Motors

By definition, a repulsion-start induction motor is a form of repulsion motor which has a squirrel-cage winding in the rotor in addition to the repulsion winding. This type of motor (Fig. 12) has found application in household refrigeration compressor drives because it has a constant speed combined with a high starting torque and a low starting current. There are two types commonly used, namely:

1. The brush-lifting type.
2. The brush-riding type.

The *brush-lifting* type is so called because the brushes lift clear of the commutator when the motor reaches a certain speed. A clutch mechanism or governor device functions to lift the brushes from the commutator, and from then on the motor runs as an induction motor.

The *brush-riding* type is so called because the brushes ride on the commutator at all times, but carry current to the commutator only during the starting period. When the motor reaches a certain speed, a centrifugal short-circuiting device functions, and from then on the motor runs as an induction motor. This type of motor is designed to operate in either direction. Reversal of rotation is obtained by shifting the position of the brushes on the commutator.

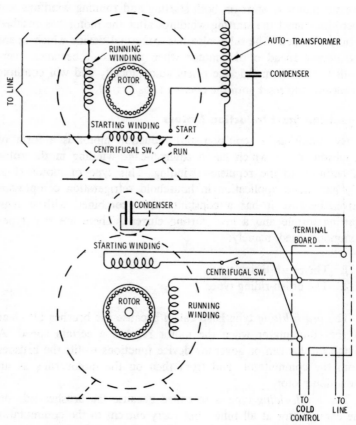

Fig. 13. A typical wiring diagram of a capacitor type motor.

Capacitor-Type Motor

This type of motor, alternately called *condenser motor* and *capacitor-start motor,* is a form of split-phase induction motor, having a capacitor connected in series with a transformer gen-

542

erally located outside of the motor housing. When the motor speed reaches a certain predetermined value, the governor device connects the motor to the running winding. Principally, the motor operates as follows:

> When the temperature-controlled switch actuates the motor circuit, a high potential is supplied through the transformer coil in order to produce the necessary starting torque. When the motor has reached approximately 75% of its normal speed, the governor device switches the motor from the starting to the running position, as shown in Fig. 13. The direction of rotation can be changed by reversing either the starting or running winding leads.

DIRECT-CURRENT MOTOR

Although alternating-current motors are the most common, some direct-current motors are still used for refrigerating service. There are three types of direct-current motors manufactured. They are, according to the method of winding employed:

1. The series motor.
2. The shunt motor.
3. The compound motor.

Because of their speed characteristics, however, only shunt and compound motors are used for condensing unit purposes. To reverse the direction of rotation in any direct current motor, the connections of the armature terminals alone, or the connections of the field windings alone must be reversed. If both (or all) windings are reversed, the direction will remain unchanged.

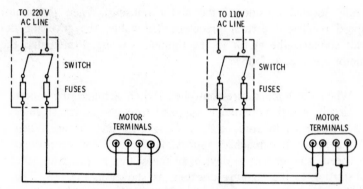

Fig. 14. Wiring diagram showing the method of connecting electric motors to 110/220 volt line.

STANDARD VOLTAGES

The voltage specified for single-phase motors is 110/220 volts meaning the leads are brought out of the motor so that they can be connected to either of these power-line voltages (Fig. 14).

FUSE SIZES

The function of a fuse is to remove the motor from the power source when the current exceeds the normal full-load or starting value. This removal is accomplished by a sudden melting of the fuse metal due to the high temperature caused by the excessive current, thus causing an opening of the circuit. The abnormal conditions may consist of a burned-out bearing, winding, etc., or an excessive overload due to a fault in the condenser unit. It cannot be too strongly emphasized that under no conditions shall a burned-out fuse of the correct size be allowed to be replaced by a fuse of a higher current rating. If this is done, damage to the motor or some other part of the unit may result.

Always keep in mind that the function of the fuse is to *protect the motor and its accessories*, and an incorrectly sized fuse immediately removes that protection. Table 2 lists the fuse sizes for motors having a rating within the power range employed in household refrigerating units. It should be used in connection with two-wire direct-current and single-phase alternating-current motors only.

Table 2. Fuse Size for Motor Protection

HP	110-Volt Single-Phase AC Repulsion-Induction or Capacitor motor	115-Volt DC compound-wound motors
$\frac{1}{8}$	4 Amp.	3 Amp.
$\frac{1}{6}$	4 "	3 "
$\frac{1}{4}$	6 "	4 "
$\frac{1}{3}$	8 "	6 "
$\frac{1}{2}$	10 "	8 "
$\frac{3}{4}$	15 "	10 "

WIRE SIZES

All wiring used in connection with household refrigerating units should be of a size and quality recommended by the *National Board of Fire Underwriters* or any local requirements. Number 14 wire is sufficient in size to use with motors up to 1/4-horse-power.

MOTOR INSTALLATION GUIDE

The following precautions should be observed before starting the motor for the first time:

1. Make certain that the line voltage and frequency agrees with the nameplate marking of the motor. If it is a dual-voltage motor, see that the leads are connected for the voltage on which it is to operate.

2. Check the ampere rating of the line fuses and see that the overload protective device in the starter, if any, is properly set. The ampere rating of the fuses should be approximately 10 to 25 per cent higher than the ampere rating of the motor.

3. Turn the driven equipment by hand to see that it does not bind, but turns readily, and that the motor armature moves freely.

4. Make sure that the bearings are lubricated in accordance with instructions on the tag furnished with the motor.

5. See that the motor is securely fastened to its base or foundation and that all connections have been made in accordance with the tag (and connection diagram, if any) furnished with the motor and the connection diagram furnished with the starter. *Do not throw these instructions away*. They might be useful some other time. Except on portable units, the motor frame should be grounded. On cushion-mounted motors, the frame is grounded to the base by a wire concealed in the rubber rings. Paint should be scraped away to make a good ground connection.

6. Run the motor for a short time without a load to check the starting and direction of rotation. If the direction of rotation must be changed, consult the tag attached to the motor. Rotation can usually be changed by interchanging the leads, except on dual-voltage motors with built-in overload devices.

7. The belt should be only tight enough to prevent slipping. Check the alignment of the driving and driven shafts, coup-

lings, or pulleys. Too much belt tension or misalignment may prevent the motor from starting on a load and cause rapid bearing wear. If the pulley ratio is such that it causes excessive belt tension, the ratio must be changed. If possible, the lower side of the belt should be the driving side. Do not drive or press the pulley or coupling on the shaft without providing a counter thrust at the opposite end; to do otherwise may injure the bearing and destroy the end-thrust washers or cause misalignment.

8. If the motor is equipped with a built-in overload device, such as *Fusetron* or *Microswitch,* see that the reset button, if any, has been depressed or the fuse plugs screwed in tight. The motor should be connected to the line in such a way that these devices are in the *hot* side of the line. The *hot* side of the line can be determined by connecting one lead from a test lamp to the ground, and the other alternately to each side of the line. The lamp will glow when it is connected to the *hot* side. Single-pole switches and control devices should be connected in the *hot* side.

9. If the motor has been exposed to dirt, grit, or moisture, as in a damp cellar or in new or unoccupied buildings, clean and dry thoroughly. If the windings have been exposed to moisture, remove to a competent service shop for drying. Never start a motor which has been wet without having it thoroughly dried, either by baking in an oven at not more than 85° C. (185° F.) or by passing low voltage through the windings until dry.

REFRIGERATOR MOTOR TROUBLE CHART

Because in most types of motors there is a direct relationship between troubles, causes, and their remedy, service instruction charts have been worked out which will be of great help in locating and repairing faults liable to be met with in day-to-day service work.

Failure to Start

Possible Cause	Possible Remedy
No Voltage	Check for voltage at motor terminals with a test lamp or voltmeter. Check for blown fuses or open overload device in starter. If motor is equipped with a *Fusetron*, see that the fuse plug is not open and that it is screwed down tight.
Low Voltage	Measure the voltage at the motor terminals with the switch closed. Voltage should read within 10% of the voltage stamped on motor nameplate. Overloaded transformers or circuits, or too light lead-in wire may cause low voltage. If this trouble occurs, check with the power company. Overloaded circuits in the building can be found by comparing the voltage at the meter with the voltage at the motor terminals with the switch closed.
Faulty cut-out switch operation	Cut-out switch operation may be observed by removing the inspection plate in the front end bracket. The mechanism consists of a cut-out switch mounted on the front end bracket and a rotating part called the governor-weight assembly, which consists of a bakelite disc supported so that it is moved back and forth along the shaft by the operation of the governor weights. At standstill, the disc holds the cut-out switch closed. If the disc does not hold the switch closed, the motor cannot start. This may call for an adjustment of the end-play washers. Dirty contact points may also keep the motor from starting. See that the contacts are clean. After the motor has accelerated to a predetermined speed, the disc is withdrawn from the switch, allowing it to open. With the load disconnected from the motor, close the starting switch. If the motor does not start, start it by hand and observe the operation of the governor

as the motor speeds up and also when the switch has been opened and the motor slows down. If the governor fails to operate, the governor weights may have become clogged. If it operates too soon or too late, the spring tension is incorrect. Remove the motor to a service shop for adjustment. Governor weights are set to operate at about 75% of synchronous speed. Place the rotor in balancing machine and, with a tachometer, determine if the governor operates at the correct speed.

Open overload device

If a motor is equipped with a built-in *Microswitch* or similar overload device, remove the cover plate in the end bracket on which the switch is mounted and see if the switch contact is closed. Do not attempt to adjust this switch or to test its operation with a match. Doing so may destroy it. If the switch is permanently open, remove the motor to a service shop for repairs.

Grounded field

If the motor gets very hot, produces shock when touched, or if idle watts are excessive, test for a field ground by connecting a test lamp across the field leads and frame. If grounded, remove the motor to a service shop for repairs.

Open field circuit

These motors have a main and a phase (starting) winding. Apply current to each winding separately with a test lamp. Do not leave the windings connected too long while the rotor is stationary. If either winding is open, remove the motor to a service shop for repairs.

Shorted field circuit

If the motor draws excessive watts and, at the same time, lacks torque, gets hot, or hums, a shorted field is indicated. Remove to a service shop for repairs.

Incorrect end play
(Adjustment necessary)

Certain type motors have steel enclosed cork washers at each end to cushion the end thrust. Too great an end thrust, hammering on the shaft, or excessive heat may destroy the cork washers and interfere with the operation of the cut-out switch mechanism. If necessary, install a new end thrust cushion bumper assembly. End play should not exceed 0.01 inches; if it does, install

Electric Motors and Their Control

additional steel end-play washers. End play should
be adjusted so that the cut-out switch is closed at
standstill and open when the motor is operating.

Excessive load

This may be approximately determined by checking the ampere input with the nameplate marking. Excessive load may prevent the motor from
accelerating to the speed at which the governor
acts and cause the phase winding to burn up.

Tight bearings

Test by turning the armature by hand. If adding
oil does not help, the bearing must be replaced.

Unsatisfactory Operation (General)

Possible Cause

Possible Remedy

Motor runs hot

Do not judge temperature by hand—use a thermometer. Motor insulation will successfully withstand a maximum observable temperature of 90°C.
(194°F.).

Check for—grounded field, short field circuit,
tight bearing, wrong voltage, faulty switch operation, or excessive load.

Excessive bearing wear

Check belt tension and alignment. Check for dirty,
incorrect, or insufficient oil (see tag furnished with
the motor). If the bearings have become clogged
with dirt, clean thoroughly. Replace worn bearings.

Excessive noise

Check for worn bearings. Check for excessive end
play. If necessary, add additional endplay washers. Check for loose parts on the motor, loose
hold-down bolts, loose pulley, bad alignment, bad
belts, sprung shafts, etc. Check for an unbalanced
rotor or burrs on the shaft shoulders.

Motor produces shock

Check for a grounded stator. Cushion-mounted
motors have a ground strip which carries static
electricity across the rubber mounting to ground.
If a static charge is retained, the strip may be
broken or connections may be poor. The frames
of all motors should be grounded.

Rotor rubs stator

Clean burrs or dirt from the rotor and stator, and
check for worn bearings.

Radio interference

Check for poor ground connections. Static electricity generated by the belts may cause radio
noises if the motor is not throughly grounded.
Check for loose contacts in switch, fuses, or starter.

REPULSION-START INDUCTION BRUSH-LIFTING MOTORS

Failure to Start

Possible Cause	*Possible Remedy*
Fuses blown	Check capacity of fuses. They should not be greater in ampere capacity than recommended by the appliance manufacturer, and in no case, smaller than the full-load ampere rating of the motor. They should also have a voltage capacity equal to or greater than the voltage of the supply circuit.
No voltage or low voltage	Measure the voltage at the motor terminals with the switch closed. See that it is within 10% of the voltage stamped on the nameplate of the motor.
Open field circuit or armature	Indicated by excessive sparking in starting, or refusal to start at certain positions of the rotor, or by a humming sound when the switch is closed. Examine for broken wires, loose connections, or burned segments in the commutator at the point of loose or broken connections. Inspect the commutator for any foreign metallic substance which might cause a short between the commutator segments.
Improper current supply—Incorrect voltage or frequency	Requires a new motor built for operation on the local power supply. DC motors will not operate on an AC circuit, or vice versa.
Worn brushes or sticking brushes	When the brushes are not making proper contact with the commutator, the motor will be weak in starting torque. This can be caused by worn brushes, brushes sticking in their holders, weak brush springs, or a dirty commutator. The commutator should be polished with fine sandpaper (never use emery). The commutator should never be oiled or greased.
Improper brush setting	Unless a new armature has been installed, the brush holder or rocker arm indicated should be opposite the index and locked in position. If a new armature has been installed, the position may be slightly off the original marking.

Improper line connection	Check to see that the correct wires have been properly connected to the right voltage points.
Excessive load	If the motor starts at idle, and if all the foregoing conditions are satisfactory, then failure to start is most likely due to excessive load.
Shorted rotor	Remove the brushes from the commutator and impress full voltage on the stator. If there is one or more points at which the rotor *hangs* or fails to revolve easily when turned, the rotor is shorted. By forcing the rotor to the position where it is most difficult to hold, the short can be located, as the shorted coil will become hot. Do not hold in position too long or the coil will burn out.

Motor Operates Without Releasing Brushes.
(Brushes should leave commutator in 5 to 10 seconds.
Troubles result from delayed operation.)

Possible Cause	*Possible Remedy*
Dirty commutator	Clean with a piece of fine sandpaper (do not use emery).
Governor mechanism or brushes sticking. Brushes worn too short for good contact.	See that the brushes move freely in their slots and that the governor mechanism operates freely by hand. Replace worn brushes with new.
Frequency of supply circuit incorrect	Run motor idle. After the brushes throw off, the speed should be slightly in excess of the full-load speed shown on the nameplate. An idle speed varying more than 10% from the nameplate speed indicates that the motor is being used on a supply frequency for which it is not designed, and a different motor will be required.
Low voltage	See that the voltage is within 10% of the nameplate voltage with the switch closed.
Line connection improperly or poorly made	See that contacts are good and that connections correspond with the motor diagram.
Incorrect brush setting	Check to see that the rocker-arm setting corresponds with the index mark.
Incorrect adjustment of governor spring	The governor should operate and throw off the brushes at approximately 75% of the speed stamped on the name plate. Below 65% or over 85% indicates incorrect spring tension.

Excessive load

An excessive load may be started and not be carried to and held at the full-load speed, which is beyond where the brushes throw off. Tight motor bearings may contribute to an overload. This is sometimes indicated by the brushes wearing off on the commutator.

Excessive Bearing Wear

Possible Cause	*Possible Remedy*
Belt tension too great, unbalanced line coupling	Correct mechanical condition.
Improper, unclean or insufficient oil	The lubrication system of most small motors provides for supplying the right amount of filtered oil to the bearings. It is only necessary for the user to keep the wool yarn saturated with a good grade of machine oil.
Dirty bearings	When bearings get clogged with dirt, the motor may need protection from excessive dust. Application may be such that a special constructed motor should be used.

Motor Runs Hot. (Don't judge motor temperature by feel of hand. Measure it with a thermometer and check with temperature rise stamped on nameplate.)

Possible Cause	*Possible Remedy*
Short-circuited coils in stator	Best check is a separate wattmeter reading on each of the two halves of the stator winding. Sometimes, a shorted coil may be located by the fact that one coil feels much hotter than the other. A very great increase over normal in magnetic noise may also indicate a shorted stator.
Rotor rubbing stator	Some extraneous matter may be between the rotor and stator, or the bearings may be badly worn.
Excessive loads	Be sure proper pulleys are on the motor and machine. Driving the load at a higher speed requires more horsepower. Take an ammeter reading. If the current draw exceeds the nameplate amperes for full load, the answer is evident.

Low voltage

Measure the voltage at the motor terminals with the switch closed. It should not vary more than 10% from value stamped on name plate.

Incorrect line connection to motor leads

Check with connection diagram supplied with motor.

Motor Burns Out

Possible Cause
Some condition of prolonged excessive overload

Possible Remedy
It is important that the load be examined carefully before the burned out motor is replaced so as to locate and remove the cause of the overload. Certain jobs such as refrigerators which represent heavy loads, will, under unusual operation, apply prolonged overloads which may destroy a motor and which may be difficult to locate unless examined carefully. On jobs where intermittent service will normally prevail, the load cycle should be especialy checked, as a change in this feature will easily produce excessive overload for the motor. Examine carefully to determine mechanical condition of the driven appliance.

Motor is Noisy

Possible Cause
Unbalanced rotor

Possible Remedy
When transportation handling has been so rough as to damage the heavy shipping case, it is well to test the motor for unbalanced conditions at once. It is even possible (though it rarely happens) that a shaft may be sprung. In any case, the rotor should be rebalanced dynamically.

Worn bearings
Rough commutator or brushes not *seating* well
Excessive end play

If unduly frequent, examine for cause.
This noise occurs only during starting period, but conditions should be corrected to avoid consequent trouble.
Proper end play is as follows: ⅓ HP and smaller—0.005 to 0.030 ½ to 1 HP—0.010 to 0.075. Washers supplied by factory should be used. Be sure to tell factory all figures involved. Remember, little end play is at least as bad as too much.

Motor not properly aligned with driven machine	Correct mechanical condition.
Motor not firmly fastened to mounting base	All small motors have steel bases so they can be firmly bolted to the mounting without fear of breaking. It is, of course, not to be expected that the base should be strained out of shape in order to make up for roughness in mounting base.
Loose accessories on motor	Such parts as oil covers, guards, if any, or endplate, etc., should especially be checked for security if they have been removed for investigation. The conduit box should be tightened when top is fitted after connections are made.
Air gap not uniform Amplified motor noises	This results from sprung shaft or unbalanced rotor. When this condition is suspected, set motor on a firm floor, and if motor is quiet, then the mounting is acting as an amplifier to bring about certain noises in the motor. This may occur even though mounting is quite firm in structure. Frequently correction of slight details in the mounting eliminates this, but a rubber-mounted type motor almost invariably eliminates noises.

Excessive Brush Wear

Possible Cause	*Possible Remedy*
Dirty commutator	Clean with piece of fine sandpaper (never use emery). Clean commutator grooves with the proper tools. (A hacksaw blade is sometimes used).
Poor contact with commutator	See that brushes are long enough to reach commutator, that they move freely in slots, and that brush spring tension gives firm but not excessive pressure.
Excessive load	If brush wear is due to overload, it can usually be checked by noting the time required for lifting the brushes from the commutator. Proper time is not in excess of 10 seconds.
High mica	Examination will show this condition and the remedy is to take a very light cut off commutator face and polish with fine sandpaper. Clean commutator grooves.

Brush Holder or Rocker Arm Wear

Possible Cause
Failure to throw off properly and stay off during the running period

Possible Remedy
No noticeable wear of this part should occur during life of motor. Troublesome wear indicates faulty-operation.

Radio Interference

Possible Cause
Ground static

Possible Remedy
Check for poor ground connections. Static electricity generated by the belts may cause radio noises if motor frame is not thoroughly grounded. Check for loose contacts in switch, fuses or starter.

Failure to Start

Possible Cause
Blowing of fuses or operation of overload device

Possible Remedy
Examine motor bearings. Be sure that they are in good condition and properly lubricated. Be sure motor and driven machine both turn freely. Check circuit voltage at motor terminals against voltage stamped on motor nameplate. Examine overload protection of motor. Overload relays operating on either magnetic or thermal principles, or a combination of the two, offer adequate protection to the motor. Ordinary fuses of sufficient size to permit motor to start do not protect motor against burnout. A combination fuse and thermal relay such as the *Buss Fusetron* protects the motor and is inexpensive. If motor does not have overload protection the fuses should be replaced with overload relays or *Buss Fusetrons*. After installing suitable fuses and resetting overload relays, allow the machine to go through its operating cycle and if protective devices again operate, check the load. If motor is excessively overloaded take it up with the appliance manufacturer.

No voltage or low voltage

Measure the voltage at the motor terminals with switch closed. See that it is within 10% of voltage stamped on nameplate of the motor.

Open field circuit

Indicated by humming sound when switch is closed. Examine for broken wires, connections.

Improper current
supply. Incorrect
voltage or frequency
Condenser circuit
short or open, or
cutout switch faulty

Requires motor built for operation on power supply available. AC motors will not operate on DC circuit or vice versa.

Cut-out switch operation. The cut-out switch mechanism consists of a normally open switch mounted on the front end bracket, and a rotating part called the governor weight assembly, which consists of a black bakelite disc so supported that it is moved back and forth along the shaft by the operation of the governor weights. At stand still the pressure of the disc against the switch holds it closed. When the motor has accelerated to a predetermined speed the disc is withdrawn from the switch, allowing it to open. The operation of the switch may be observed by removing the inspection plate in the end bracket. If the governor disc does not hold the switch closed the motor cannot start. This may call for additional end play washers between the shaft shoulder and the bearing. Dirty or corroded contact points may also keep the motor from starting. See that the contacts are clean. With the load disconnected from the motor, close the starting switch. If the motor does not start, start it by hand, and listen for the characteristic click of the governor as the motor speeds up and also when the switch has been opened and the motor slows down. Absence of this click may indicate that the governor weights have become clogged, or that the spring is too strong. Continued operation under this condition may cause the phase winding to burn up.

Open field circuit

These motors have a main and phase winding in the stator. With the leads disconnected from the capacitor, apply current to the motor. If the main winding is all right, motor will hum. If the main winding tests satisfactory, connect a test lamp between the phase lead (the black lead) from the capacitor and the other capacitor lead. Close the starting switch. If the phase winding is all right, the lamp will glow and the motor may attempt to start. If either winding is open, remove motor to the service shop for repairs.

Faulty capacitor

If the starting (electrolytic) capacitor is faulty the motor starting torque will be weak and the motor may not start at all but may run if started by hand. A capacitor can be tested for open circuit or short circuit as follows:

Charge it with a DC (if available) preferably through a resistance or test lamp. If no discharge is evident on immediate short circuit, an open or a short is indicated. If no DC is available, charge with AC. Try charging on AC several times to make certain that the capacitor has had a chance to become charged. If capacitor is open, short circuited or weak—replace. Replacement capacitors should not be of lower capacity or voltage, than the original. In soldering connections, do not use acid flux. Electrolytic capacitors if exposed to temperature 20°F. and lower may temporarily lose enough capacity so that the motor will not start, and may cause the windings to burn up, as the heat generated by the stalled motor will not heat the capacitor in time. Temperature of capacitor should be raised by running the motor idle or by other means. Capacitors should not be operated in temperatures exceeding 165°F. Frequency operation of electrolytic capacitors should not exceed two starts per minute of three seconds acceleration each, or three to four starts per minute at less than two seconds acceleration, provided the total accelerating time does not exceed one to two minutes per hour.

This may be approximately determined by checking the ampere input with the nameplate marking. Excessive load may prevent the motor from accelerating to the speed at which the governor acts and cause the phase winding to burn up.

Radio Interference

Possible Cause

Ground

Possible Remedy

Check for poor ground connections. Static electricity generated by the belts may cause radio noises if motor frame is not thoroughly grounded.

Static
Loose connections

Check for loose contacts in switch, fuses or starter. Capacitor motors ordinarily will not cause radio interference. Sometimes vibration may cause the capacitor to move so that it touches the metal container. This may cause radio interference. Open the container, remove the contact, and replace paper packing so capacitor cannot shift and touch metal container.

DIRECT CURRENT

Possible Cause	*Possible Remedy*
Seasoning	It requires some months of operation for a new commutator to become seasoned. During this period, segments may loosen, causing low or high bars or an eccentric commutator. Tighten the end ring while machine is hot. If eccentric, turn commutator in lathe at high speed. An eccentric commutator causes a distinct knocking action on the brushes.
Rough-Ridged-Grooved, High or low bars	Remove brushes. Use 60 to 90 grade cutting and 120 to 150 grade polishing stones on commutator. No. 1 and No. 00 sandpaper applied with a piece of hard wood can also be used. Reseat brushes— clean holders and commutator slots (if undercut).
Mica Not Undercut	If mica was originally undercut, it should be under as deep as the mica is *thick, but not over* $\frac{1}{16}$ in. Use a coarse hacksaw blade with set removed by grinding on stone.
Eccentric	Can be detected by measurements or distinct knocking when a finger is pressed on brushes. Tighten commutator end ring while hot. Turn commutator in lathe at high speed. Use sharp tool. Undercut mica between slots if originally undercut. Polish with very fine sandpaper before using it.
Poor Contact on Commutator. Caused by insufficient spring tension, brush sticking in holder.	Tighten the springs, oil brush, finger bearing (under spring) with thin oil. Renew spring if it has lost tension. Clean brush and holder. Use kerosene if necessary. Brush *must* move freely in holder.

Worn out brushes, not properly seated to commutator	Commutator should be smooth before installing new brushes. Use strips of sandpaper or a 150 grade commutator polishing stone until entire brush face fits commutator. Then clean parts thoroughly. If possible, allow machine to run at no load for several hours to polish commutator and brush faces after sanding in brushes.
Wrong brushes	Use only the make and grade of brushes recommended by the manufacturer of the machine. Trouble will likely result if other brushes are used.
Not properly seated	The brush must be properly seated. This is very important.
Incorrect face angle	Wrong angle is likely to cause chatter. This brush contact face should be at right angle for best operation. Raising or lowering the brush stud, will change the brush face angle. Reseat brushes. The proper height from end of brush holder to commutator is $\frac{1}{16}$ in. 0.063. in.).
Brushes not set on neutral point	The proper brush yoke position is marked on the yoke and hub of the end bracket and it should not be changed unless all other remedies fail. Then remove the yoke $\frac{1}{16}$ in. from factory mark. Measure accurately. Try both directions from factory mark.
Not correctly staggered	Brushes should be staggered. If the end play or armature is too great for proper staggering, use fiber washers on the shaft to reduce it. Top brushes go to the outside and bottom to inside end of the commutator. Be sure ends of brush holders are not more than $\frac{1}{16}$ in. (0.063 in.) from commutator.

Index

Index

AUDEL BOOKS *practical reading for profit*

Automobile Guide   (60015)

Practical reference for auto mechanics, servicemen, trainees & owners. Explains theory, construction and servicing of modern domestic motor cars. FEATURES: All parts of an automobile—engines—pistons—rings—connecting rods—crankshafts—valves—cams—timing—cooling systems—fuel-feed systems—carburetors—automatic choke—transmissions—clutches—universals—propeller shafts—differentials—rear axles—running gear—brakes—wheel alignment—steering gear—tires—lubrication—ignition systems—generators—starters—lighting systems—storage batteries.

Home Appliance Servicing   (60016)

A practical "How To Do It" book for electric & gas servicemen, mechanics & dealers. Covers principles, servicing and repairing of home appliances. Tells how to locate troubles, make repairs, reassemble and connect, wiring diagrams and testing methods. Tells how to fix electric refrigerators, washers, ranges, toasters, ironers, broilers, dryers, vacuums, fans, and other appliances.

Radiomans Guide   (60017)

A key to the practical understanding of radio. For radio engineers, servicemen, amateurs. FEATURES: Radio fundamentals and Ohm's law—physics of sound as related to radio—radio-wave transmission—electrical measuring instruments—power supply units—resistors, inductors and capacitors—radio transformers—vacuum tubes—radio receivers—speakers—antenna systems—radio testing.

Television Service Manual   (60018)

Now completely updated and revised to include the latest designs and information. Thoroughly covers television with transmitter theory, antenna designs, receiver circuit operation and the picture tube. Provides the practical information necessary for accurate diagnosis and repair of both black-and-white and color television receivers. A MUST BOOK FOR ANYONE IN TELEVISION.

Handy Book of Practical Electricity   (60019)

For maintenance engineers, electricians and all electrical workers. A ready reference book, giving complete instruction and practical information on the rules and laws of electricity—maintenance of electrical machinery—AC and DC motors—wiring diagrams—house lighting—power wiring—meter and instrument connections—bells and signal wiring—motor wiring—transformer connections—fractional-horsepower motors—circuit breakers—relay protection—switchgear—power stations—automatic substations. THE KEY TO A PRACTICAL UNDERSTANDING OF ELECTRICITY.

Truck & Tractor Guide   (60020)

A shop companion for truck mechanics and drivers—shop foremen—garagemen—maintenance men—helpers—owners—troubleshooters—fleet maintenance men—bus mechanics and drivers—farm tractor operators and mechanics. Covers gas and diesel motor principles—construction—operation—maintenance—repair—service operations—troubleshooting—engine tune-up—carburetor adjusting—ignition tuning—brakes—service of all parts.—1001 FACTS AT YOUR FINGER TIPS.

Plumbers and Pipe Fitters Library—3 Vols.   (60021)

New revised edition. A practical illustrated trade assistant and reference for master plumbers, journeyman and apprentice pipe fitters, gas fitters and helpers, builders, contractors, and engineers. Explains in simple language, illustrations, diagrams, charts, graphs and pictures, the principles of modern plumbing and pipe-fitting practices.
Vol. 1—(60064)—Materials, tools, calculations.
Vol. 2—(60065)—Drainage, fittings, fixtures.
Vol. 3—(60066)—Installation, heating, welding.

Painting & Decorating Manual   (60022)

A reliable guide for painters, journeymen, apprentices, contractors, home owners, and all paint users. The book is divided into two sections. Section I contains information on: basic tools and equipment; selection of paint; guide to color; techniques of applying paint with brush, roller and spray gun; wood and floor finishing. Section II provides information about: cost estimate; glossary of terms; a review of the mathematics and information about running a paint business. Profusely illustrated.

Carpenters & Builders Guides—4 Vols.   (60023)

A practical illustrated trade assistant on modern construction for carpenters, builders, and all woodworkers. Explains in practical, concise language and illustrations all the principles, advances and short cuts based on modern practice. How to calculate various jobs.
Vol. 1—(60068)—Tools, steel square, saw filing, joinery, cabinets.
Vol. 2—(60069)—Mathematics, plans, specifications, estimates.
Vol. 3—(60070)—House and roof framing, laying out, foundations.
Vol. 4—(60071)—Doors, windows, stairs, millwork, painting.

Diesel Engine Manual   (60024)

A practical treatise on the theory, operation and maintenance of modern Diesel engines. Explains Diesel principles—valves—timing—fuel pumps—pistons and rings—cylinders—lubrication—cooling system—fuel oil—engine indicator—governors—engine reversing—answers on operation—calculations. AN IMPORTANT GUIDE FOR ENGINEERS, OPERATORS, STUDENTS.

Welders Guide   (60025)

A concise, practical text on operation and maintenance of all welding machines, for all mechanics. Covers electric, oxyacetylene, thermit, unionmelt welding for sheet metal; spot and pipe welds; pressure vessels; aluminum, copper, brass, bronze and other metals; airplane work; surface hardening and hard facing; cutting; brazing; eye protection. EVERY WELDER SHOULD OWN THIS GUIDE.

Mathematics & Calculations for Mechanics   (60026)

Mathematics for home study or shop reference. This work has been arranged as a progressive study, starting with the first principles of arithmetic and advancing step-by-step, through the various phases of mathematics. Thousands of mathematical calculations and tables. New, easy, correct methods covering a complete review of practical arithmetic. Illustrated with examples. A REAL HELP TO ALL MECHANICS.

Wiring Diagrams for Light & Power   (60028)

Brand-new updated edition. Electricians, wiremen, linemen, plant superintendents, construction engineers, electrical contractors and students will find these diagrams a valuable source of practical help. Each diagram is complete and self-explaining. A PRACTICAL HANDY BOOK OF ELECTRICAL HOOK-UPS.

New Electric Library—10 Vols.   (60030)

For engineers, electricians, electrical workers, mechanics and students. Presenting in simple, concise form the fundamental principles, rules and applications of applied electricity. Fully illustrated with diagrams and sketches, also calculations and tables for ready reference. Based on the best knowledge and experience of applied electricity.
Vol. 1—(60031)—Electricity, magnetism, armature winding, repairs.
Vol. 2—(60032)—Dynamos, DC motors, construction, installation, maintenance, troubleshooting.
Vol. 3—(60033)—Electrical testing instruments, storage battery construction and repairs.
Vol. 4—(60034)—Alternating current principles and diagrams, power factor, alternators, transformers.
Vol. 5—(60035)—AC motors, converters, switches, fuses, circuit breakers.
Vol. 6—(60036)—Relays, capacitors, regulators, rectifiers, meters, switchboards, power-station practice.
Vol. 7—(60037)—Wiring, high-tension transmission, plans, calculations.
Vol. 8—(60038)—Railways, signals, elevators.
Vol. 9—(60039)—Radio, telephone, telegraph, television, motion pictures.
Vol. 10—(60040)—Refrigeration, illumination, welding, X-ray, modern electrical appliances.

Answers on Blueprint Reading (60041)

Covers all types of blueprint reading for mechanics and builders. The man who can read blueprints is in line for a better job. This book gives you this secret language, step by step in easy stages. NO OTHER TRADE BOOK LIKE IT.

Masons & Builders Guides—4 Vols. (60042)

A practical illustrated trade assistant on modern construction for bricklayers, stone masons, cement workers, plasterers, and tile setters. Explains in clear language and with detailed illustrations all the principles, advances and short cuts based on modern practice—including how to figure and calculate various jobs.
Vol. 1—(60072)—Brick work, bricklaying, bonding, designs.
Vol. 2—(60073)—Brick foundations, arches, tile setting, estimates.
Vol. 3—(60074)—Concrete mixing, placing forms, reinforced stucco.
Vol. 4—(60075)—Plastering, stone masonry, steel construction, blueprints.

Oil Burner Guide (60044)

A practical, concise treatise explaining in detail both domestic and industrial oil burners, including electrical hook-ups and wiring diagrams. Fully covering the theory, construction, installation, operation, testing, servicing and repair of all oil-burner equipment. Fully indexed for quick reference.

Sheet Metal Pattern Layouts (60045)

A practical illustrated encyclopedia covering all phases of sheet-metal work including pattern cutting, pattern development and shop procedure. Developed by experts for sheet-metal workers, layout men, mechanics and artisans, apprentices, and students. A MASTER BOOK FOR ALL THE SHEET METAL TRADES.

Sheet Metal Workers Handy Book (60046)

Containing practical information and important facts and figures. Easy to understand. Fundamentals of sheet metal layout work. Clearly written in everyday language. Ready reference index.

Questions & Answers for Electricians Examinations (60049)

A practical book to help you prepare for all grades of electricians' license examinations. A helpful review of all the fundamental principles underlying each question and answer needed to prepare you to solve any new or similar problem. Covers the National Electrical Code; questions and answers for license tests; Ohm's law with applied examples; hook-ups for motors; lighting and instruments. A COMPLETE REVIEW FOR ALL ELECTRICAL WORKERS.

Electrical Power Calculations (60050)

275 TYPICAL PROBLEMS WORKED OUT. Presents and explains the mathematical formulas and the fundamental electrical laws for all the everday, practical problems in both AC and DC electricity. EVERY ELECTRICAL WORKER AND STUDENT NEEDS THIS MODERN MATHE-MATICAL TOOL.

New Electric Science Dictionary (60051)

For every worker who has anything to do with electricity. The language of your profession in convenient, alphabetical order so you can instantly locate any word, phrase or term. To be an expert in any line you must talk the language. This new dictionary enables you to understand and explain electrical problems so you can be thoroughly understood. AN ABSOLUTE NECESSITY TO EVERY ELECTRICAL WORKER AND STUDENT.

Power Plant Engineers Guide (60052)

A complete steam-engineer's library in one book, with questions and answers. For all Engineers, Firemen, Water Tenders, Oilers, Operators, Repairmen and Applicants for Engineers' License Examinations. 1001 FACTS AND FIGURES AT YOUR FINGER TIPS.

Questions & Answers for Engineers and Firemans Examinations (60053)

An aid for stationary, marine, Diesel & hoisting engineers' examinations for all grades of licenses. A new concise review explaining in detail the principles, facts and figures of practical engineering. Questions & answers.

Pumps, Hydraulics, Air Compressors (60054)

A comprehensive guide for engineers, operators, mechanics, students. Question and answer form. Practical information covering: power & air pumps—condensers—calculations—cooling ponds and towers—water supply—hydraulic rams—dredges—hydraulic drives—machine-tool power—accumulators—elevators—airplane control—presses—turbines—compressor classification —inter and after coolers—regulating devices—installation—lubrication—operation—maintenance—pneumatic hand tools.

House Heating Guide (60055)

For heating, ventilating and air-conditioning engineers, plumbers, maintenance men, contractors, building superintendents and mechanics seeking practical, authentic information on heating, ventilating, air conditioning. This comprehensive reference book gives answers to 1001 questions.

Millwrights & Mechanics Guide (60056)

Practical information on plant installation, operation, and maintenance. For millwrights, mechanics, erecting maintenance men, riggers, shopmen, servicemen, foremen, inspectors, superintendents.

Do-It-Yourself Encyclopedia—2 Vols. (60057)

An all-in-one home repair and project guide for all do-it-yourselfers. Packed with step-by-step plans, thousands of photos, helpful charts. A really authentic, truly monumental, home-repair and home-project guide.

Water Supply & Sewage Disposal Guide (60059)

Fully illustrated with detailed data on every phase of rural water-supply, septic-tank, and sewage systems. A MUST BOOK for plumbers, well drillers, home owners and farmers located outside of municipal water and sanitary service areas.

Gas Engine Manual (60061)

A completely practical book covering the construction, operation and repair of all types of modern gas engines. Part I covers gas-engine principles; engine parts; auxiliaries; timing methods; ignition systems. Part II covers troubleshooting, adjustment and repairs.

Outboard Motor & Boating Guide (60062)

An essential tool for every outboard boating operator. Provides all the information needed to maintain, adjust and repair all types of outboard motors. Gives exploded views of the various parts assemblies, with relative position of each component.

Foreign Auto Repair Manual (60078)

Contains complete, service and repair data for the most popular imported makes, including Fiat, Hillman Minx, M.G., Opel, Peugot, Renault, SAAB, Simca, Volkswagen, and Volvo. Introductory chapters provide complete data on operation and maintenance of fuel and ignition systems.

Home Workshop & Tool Handy Book (60087)

The most modern, up-to-date manual ever designed for home craftsmen and do-it-yourselfers. Tells how to set up your own home workshop (basement, garage, or spare room), all about the various hand and power tools (when, where, and how to use them, etc.). Covers both wood-and metal-working principles and practices. An all-in-one workshop guide for handymen, professionals and students.

Home Modernizing & Repair Guide   (60097)

FOR THE "DO-IT-YOURSELFER" WHO LIKES TO DO MOST OF HIS HOME UPKEEP JOBS HIMSELF. Here is a practical guide that presents step-by-step instructions, photos, drawings, and other details for many typical home handyman jobs. Explains what tools are needed, how to use them, and includes tips for doing a really professional job.

Practical Guide to Mechanics   (60102)

A convenient reference book valuable for its practical and concise explanations of the applicable laws of physics. Presents all the basics of mechanics in everyday language, illustrated with practical examples of their applications in various fields.

Auto Engine Tune-Up   (60103)

A practical guide to the adjustment of modern autos. Comprehensive and fully illustrated instructions on how to keep your car in top-notch running condition. Covers ignition, valve, cooling, carburetion, and electrical systems on modern auto engines. Includes the use of tune-up test equipment.

Gas Appliances and Heating   (60104)

A reliable guide to acquaint repairmen and home owners with the construction, operation, and servicing of modern gas-fired appliances such as may be found in the average home.

Architects & Builders Guide   (60105)

A valuable reference for the architect, builder, and home owner. Explains the effects of natural phenomena such as wind, fire, sound, water, and lightning on all types of buildings. Tells how to minimize their destructive effects and take advantage of their beneficial effects.

Machinists Library   (60109)

Covers modern machine-shop practice. Tells how to set up and operate lathes, screw and milling machines, shapers, drill presses and all other machine tools. A complete reference library. A SHOP COMPANION THAT ANSWERS YOUR QUESTIONS.
Vol. 1—(60106)—Basic Machine Shop Practices.
Vol. 2—(60107)—Machine Shop.
Vol. 3—(60108)—Toolmakers Handy Book.

Practical Mathematics for Everyone— 2 Vols.   (60112)

A concise and reliable guide to the understanding of practical mathematics. People from all walks of life, young and old alike, will find the information contained in these two books just what they have been looking for. The mathematics discussed is for the everyday problems that arise in every household and business.
Vol. 1—(60110)—Basic Mathematics.
Vol. 2—(60111)—Financial Mathematics.

Handbook of Commercial Sound Installations   (60126)

A practical complete guide to planning commercial systems, selecting the most suitable equipment, and following through with the most proficient servicing methods. For technicians and the professional and businessman interested in installing a sound system.

Practical Guide to Tape Recorders   (60127)

Comprehensive guide to tape recorders, covering the history, operation, construction, and maintenance. Service technicians, hobbyists, and even professional recordists can perform their job or pursue their hobby better if they understand the principles of tape recorders.

Practical Guide to Citizens Band Radio   (60130)

Covers how to select, install, operate, maintain, and adjust all types of CB equipment. Also describes the latest equipment and FCC regulations. For everyone who now uses or plans to use a CB unit, as well as those who install and service such gear.

Practical Electronics Projects for the Beginner (60131)

This book can be your first venture in electronics. Clear, concise text plus hundreds of illustrations tell you all you need to know to build numerous functioning projects. HAVE FUN WHILE LEARNING ELECTRONICS FUNDAMENTALS—no previous knowledge necessary.

Practical Guide to Servicing Electronic Organs (60132)

Detailed, illustrated discussions of the operation and servicing of electronic organs. Including models by Allen, Baldwin, Conn, Hammond, Kinsman, Lowrey, Magnavox, Thomas, and Wurlitzer.

Home Refrigeration and Air Conditioning (60133)

NEW AND UP-TO-DATE. Covers basic principles, servicing, operation, and repair of modern household refrigerators and air conditioners. Automobile air conditioners are also included. Troubleshooting charts aid in trouble diagnosis. **A gold mine of essential facts for engineers, servicemen, and users.**

Practical Guide to Fluid Power (60136)

An essential book for the owner, operator, supervisor, or maintenance man concerned with hydraulic or pneumatic equipment. A complete coverage of modern design, application, and repair of fluid power devices. Fully illustrated.

Building Maintenance (60140)

A comprehensive book on the practical aspects of building maintenance. Chapters are included on: painting and decorating; plumbing and pipe fitting; carpentry; calking and glazing; concrete and masonry; roofing; sheet metal; electrical maintenance; air conditioning and refrigeration; insect and rodent control; heating; maintenance management; custodial practices: A MUST BOOK FOR BUILDING OWNERS, MANAGERS, AND MAINTENANCE PERSONNEL.

Practical Science Projects in Electricity/Electronics (60141)

An ideal collection of projects in electricity and electronics for the beginner. Practical projects constructed on pegboard with simple easily obtained parts make basic electronic principles fun to learn. Young and old alike will find this book the answer to their search for knowledge.

Carpentry and Building (60142)

Answers to the problems encountered in today's building trades. The actual questions asked of an architect by carpenters and builders are answered in this book. No apprentice or journeyman carpenter should be without the help this book can offer.

Commercial Refrigeration (60145)

Installation, operation, and repair of commercial refrigeration systems. Included are ice-making plants, locker plants, grocery and supermarket refrigerated display cases, etc. Trouble charts aid in the diagnosis and repair of defective systems.

Guide to the National Electrical Code (60149)

An interpretation and simplification of the rulings contained in the National Electrical Code. Electrical contractors, wiremen, and electricians will find this book invaluable for a more complete understanding of the National Electrical Code. Illustrated.

Electric Motors (60150)

New revised edition. Covers the construction, theory of operation, connection, control, maintenance, and troubleshooting of all types of electric motors. A handy guide for electricians and all electrical workers.

TO ORDER AUDEL BOOKS mail this handy form to
Theo. Audel & Co., 4300 W. 62nd
Indianapolis, Indiana 46206

Please send me for FREE EXAMINATION books marked (x) below. If I decide to keep them I agree to mail $3 in 7 days on each book or set ordered and further mail $3 monthly on each book or set until I have paid price plus shipping charges. Otherwise, I will return them.

☐ (60041) Answers on Blueprint Reading........$ 5.25
☐ (60105) Architects and Builders Guide........ 4.95
☐ (60103) Auto Engine Tune-Up................. 5.95
☐ (60015) Automobile Guide 7.95
☐ (60140) Building Maintenance................ 5.50
☐ (60023) Carpenters & Builders Guides (4 Vols.) 16.95
  ☐_____Single volumes sold separately..ea. 4.95
☐ (60142) Carpentry and Building.............. 5.95
☐ (60145) Commercial Refrigeration........... 5.95
☐ (60024) Diesel Engine Manual................ 6.95
☐ (60057) Do-It-Yourself Encyclopedia (2 Vols.).. 8.95
☐ (60077) Domestic Compact Auto Repair Manual 5.95
☐ (60050) Electrical Power Calculations........ 4.50
☐ (60150) Electric Motors..................... 5.95
☐ (60063) Encyclopedia of Space Science (4 Vols.) 19.95
☐ (60078) Foreign Auto Repair Manual.......... 5.95
☐ (60104) Gas Appliances and Heating.......... 4.25
☐ (60061) Gas Engine Manual................... 4.50
☐ (60126) Handbook of Commercial Sound
 Installations 5.95
☐ (60019) Handy Book of Practical Electricity.... 6.95
☐ (60016) Home Appliance Servicing............ 6.95
☐ (60097) Home Modernizing & Repair Guide..... 3.95
☐ (60133) Home Refrigeration and Air
 Conditioning 6.95
☐ (60087) Home Workshop & Tool Handy Book.... 5.00
☐ (60055) House Heating Guide................. 6.95
☐ (60019) Machinist Library (3 Vols.)........... 15.50
  ☐_____Volume 1 sold separately......ea. 5.50
  ☐_____Volume 2 sold separately......ea. 5.95
  ☐_____Volume 3 sold separately......ea. 5.50
☐ (60042) Masons & Builders Guides (4 Vols.).... 14.95
  ☐_____Single volumes sold separately..ea. 4.00
☐ (60026) Mathematics & Calculations for
 Mechanics 5.50
☐ (60056) Millwrights & Mechanics Guide....... 7.95

☐ (60030) New Electric Library (10 Vols.).......$35.00
  ☐_____Single volumes sold separately..ea. 4.00
☐ (60051) New Electric Science Dictionary....... 3.50
☐ (60044) Oil Burner Guide.................... 4.50
☐ (60062) Outboard Motor & Boating Guide...... 4.95
☐ (60022) Painting & Decorating Manual........ 5.50
☐ (60021) Plumbers & Pipe Fitters Library (3 Vols.) 12.50
  ☐_____Single volumes sold separately..ea. 4.50
☐ (60052) Power Plant Engineers Guide.......... 7.50
☐ (60098) Practical Chemistry for Everyone..... 5.95
☐ (60131) Practical Electronics Projects
 for the Beginner......................... 4.95
☐ (60130) Practical Guide to Citizens Band Radio. 4.95
☐ (60136) Practical Guide to Fluid Power........ 6.95
☐ (60102) Practical Guide to Mechanics........ 4.95
☐ (60132) Practical Guide to Servicing
 Electronic Organs 4.95
☐ (60127) Practical Guide to Tape Recorders.... 4.95
☐ (60112) Practical Mathematics for Everyone
 (2 Vols.) 8.95
  ☐_____Single volumes sold separately..ea. 4.95
☐ (60141) Practical Science Projects in
 Electricity/Electronics 4.95
☐ (60086) Programmed Basic Electricity Course... 4.95
☐ (60054) Pumps, Hydraulics, Air Compressors... 7.95
☐ (60049) Questions & Answers for Electricians
 Examinations 3.95
☐ (60053) Questions & Answers for Engineers &
 Firemans Examinations 4.95
☐ (60017) Radiomans Guide 5.50
☐ (60045) Sheet Metal Pattern Layouts.......... 11.95
☐ (60046) Sheet Metal Workers Handy Book...... 4.50
☐ (60018) Television Service Manual............ 5.95
☐ (60020) Truck & Tractor Guide............... 6.95
☐ (60059) Water Supply & Sewage Disposal Guide 4.50
☐ (60025) Welders Guide 5.50
☐ (60028) Wiring Diagrams for Light & Power.... 4.50

Name_____

Address_____

City_____State_____Zip_____

Occupation_____Employed by_____

☐ **SAVE SHIPPING CHARGES! Enclose Full Payment**
With Coupon and We Pay Shipping Charges. PRINTED IN USA
Prices Subject to Change Without Notice